Understanding Science 3

Teachers' Resource Book

Joe Boyd
Assistant Head, St David's High School, Dalkeith

Walter Whitelaw
Assistant Science Adviser, Lothian

and

Peter Warren
Co-ordinator of Science, Acton High School, London

$\frac{1}{10}$

URAL OWL.
SYRNIUM URALENSE.

Advisory panel
Peter Leckstein: *Inspector for Living Science, London Borough of Wandsworth*
Lesley Campbell: *Health Education Adviser*
Terry Allsop: *Lecturer in Education Studies, Oxford University*

The authors would like to thank their wives and families for their support and tolerance throughout the project.

First published 1991
by John Murray (Publishers) Ltd
50 Albemarle Street, London W1X 4BD

Designed by Impress International, 33540 France
Typeset by Blackpool Typesetting Services Ltd, Blackpool
Printed by Edmundsbury Press, Bury St Edmunds

British Library Cataloguing in Publication Data
Boyd, Joe
  Understanding science 3
  Teachers' resource book
  1. Science—for schools
  I. Title II. Whitelaw, Walter III. Warren, Peter
  500

  ISBN 0-7195-4825-X Teachers' resource book
  ISBN 0-7195-4824-1 Pupils' book

Contents

Acknowledgements

LINE DIAGRAMS: Art Construction; Technical Art Services;
John Townson/Creation
CARTOONS: Ainslie MacLeod
COVER PHOTO: ZEFA

Thanks are due to Dave Williams for the designs used on Resource Sheet 5.9, and to Jimmy Morrow and Noel Brown for preparing Resource Sheets E8.5A and B.

Thanks are due to copyright holders who have allowed the following extracts from, or reproductions of, their material to be used.

p.179 Consumers' Association, from *Handyman Which?* May 1981;
p.188 Consumers' Association, from *Which?* March 1983;
p.189 Consumers' Association, from *Handyman Which?* May 1981;
p.190 Consumers' Association, from *Which?* February 1984;
p.208 British Steel PLC, adapted from *Making Steel* (British Steel PLC 1990);
p.210 The Peters Fraser & Dunlop Group Ltd (agents for the Arthur Koestler estate), from *The Sleepwalkers* by Arthur Koestler (Hutchinson 1968);
p.211 Macdonald, from *Cosmos* by Carl Sagan (Macdonald Futura 1981);
p.214 Wayland (Publishers) Ltd, from *Famous Names in Medicine* by G. De Stevens (Wayland 1979);
p.215 Tim Radford, from *The Guardian* 20 September 1989;
p.216 BBC Enterprises Ltd, from *The Ascent of Man* by Dr J. Bronowski (BBC 1973);

Every effort has been made to contact copyright holders and obtain permissions: the publisher will be grateful for notification of any omissions for correction in subsequent printings.

Introduction

Using this course

Understanding Science has been written to support modern science education. Learning in science is an active process and the pupil is therefore encouraged to be involved in different types of activity, within a carefully structured and organised course. The approach is flexible and can be adapted to suit most teachers' methods while providing the hard scientific input which will be needed later in assessed and certificated work.

This course can be taught in any type of classroom, although it will work best in a science laboratory equipped with gas, water and electricity services. The wall space of the classroom should be used to display pupils' work, particularly the results of the Problems and Talkabouts.

If possible, keep all the practical equipment for the current unit in the room. This alleviates much of the need for technician and other auxiliary back-up. It is helpful to have much of the unit apparatus in a labelled tray, with one tray for each topic in the unit.

Practical activities occur throughout the course. Pupils usually work best with a partner or in a group of three. A basic set of laboratory equipment for each pupil group is:

    safety glasses for *each* pupil
    Bunsen burner
    heatproof mat
    tripod stand and gauze
    test-tube rack
    boiling tubes
    test tubes
    6 beakers of various sizes (plastic and glass)
    100 cm³ measuring cylinder
    test-tube holder
    gas lighter
    coloured pencils
    rulers

Written work has a key role in the course. Pupils write their own notes, mainly to express their ideas and to show the quality of their understanding. In addition, each pupil learns to present ideas, observations and descriptions in a form that other people can understand and react to positively. Each pupil will need a notebook or file and access, if possible, to a junior dictionary.

Organisation of the Pupils' Book

Within Book 3 there are 8 units, each broken down into topics. Each topic has three levels: core, reinforcement and extension.

- **Core work** (labelled **A**) provides work essential to all pupils.
- **Reinforcement** material (labelled **B**) consolidates the core work and is appropriate for pupils who find the core fairly demanding or difficult.

- **Extensions** are considerably more demanding and best suited to those pupils who find the core work straightforward. They may also be beneficial to highly motivated children. The extensions are grouped together at the end of the pupils' book.

Within a topic, pupils are guided to various activities.

Reading: Information is given at the beginning of a topic. Pupils should read this, and all instructions, before starting an activity. There may be instances when the teacher wishes the pupils to copy this information.

Doing (surrounded by red boxes): In these activity sections, pupils do the activity as well as they can, sometimes after guidance or a demonstration. The equipment required is listed in the yellow panels. It should be returned when the activity is finished.

Answering ✍ : The questions and written activities should be answered in a notebook or file. Pupils' writing skills will develop gradually. Points for the teacher to insist on are that:
- the heading is copied and the work dated
- all the questions are answered
- answers are (where appropriate) in sentences
- the notes make sense to the pupil
- the written work expresses the pupil's idea
- all written work is read through slowly by the pupil before bringing it forward for marking at a Checkpoint.

Checkpoints 🏁 : These are informal assessment points. The intention is that work is marked as soon as possible by the teacher and discussed where necessary. In this year of the course teachers are likely to be concerned mainly with the quality of the scientific thinking.

Each checkpoint requires a routing decision from the teacher. What does the pupil do next? There are several possibilities because the material lends itself to a flexible response. Obviously the routing decision will become more obvious as the teacher gets to know the pupils better.

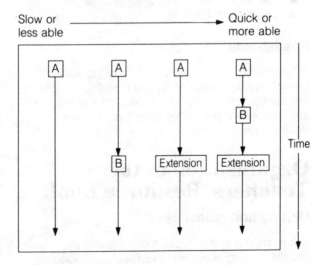

Fact-finders 📖 : It is important that pupils appreciate the relevance of their school science. There is an opportunity, at the end of each topic, for pupils to engage in a related informal research task, most of which could be set as homework. Each task attempts to link classwork to a local context. Pupils should be encouraged to maintain a file of their research findings. The results could also provide the basis of a constantly changing wall display.

Discussion: There are many opportunities for pupils to discuss work with their partner(s), particularly when investigating problems or developing concepts.

Problem pages

The open-ended problems in each unit can be tackled in a number of ways and could be used as assessment exercises. Pupils are encouraged by the text to consider possible solutions in groups. It is the group, not the teacher, who should then solve the problem.

Talkabouts

Talkabouts encourage pupils to express and develop their ideas about open-ended subjects. Discussion work is very difficult to initiate and organise. However, some points to consider for **group** discussions are:
- stress the focus of the discussion before the pupils begin and exemplify it with photographs or video material, if available
- self-selected groups of four work well
- give pupils a time limit
- arrange the seating so that each group is in a ring
- require that some modest report-back or summary activity be completed after the discussion.

For **whole class** discussion:
- take an active role in keeping order, but not an active role in discussing
- arrange the class as nearly as possible in a circle
- encourage debate between pupils
- encourage listening

Readabouts

A Readabout is included as a longer passage of unbroken text. These passages introduce pupils to the applications and social implications of science and encourage the development of reading and library skills.

Organisation of the Teachers' Resource Book

Unit by unit guidance

For each unit in the Pupils' book there is a corresponding chapter in the Teachers' resource book. Each chapter contains the following sections.

Contents and skills: The content of the unit is described and a list is given of the skills developed in each topic. The content of each topic is cross-referenced to the original Attainment Targets 2–17 of the National Curriculum. For example, topic 4.3 meets the second point, at level 6, of Attainment Target 9, and this is indicated by *AT 9–6b*. Attainment Target 1 is covered throughout the course.

Equipment: Detailed equipment lists are given for each topic as well as helpful hints on setting up and running the experiments.

Revision question sheet: These photocopiable sheets provide an introduction to the unit by highlighting key words and ideas that pupils should be familiar with. Pupils should be encouraged to complete the definitions before referring to an answer file or to **Understanding Science 1** and **2** (for which page references are given).

Assessment: There is a short photocopiable assessment test for the unit and answers.

True/false statements: These are to be completed by the pupils. They cover all the attainment targets introduced in the unit.

Summary: Photocopiable summary sheets cover the main points of the unit. They require pupils to fill in missing words in simple statements.

Resources: The photocopiable resources include extra instruction sheets, worksheets, diagrams etc. Their use is indicated in the equipment lists, and each is numbered; for example, R2.4 would be a resource sheet for unit 2, topic 4.

Skills sheets

The Skills sheets provide an extra tier of extension material (or homeworks). They build on the Skills sheets in books 1 and 2 and cover the skills of
- revision
- reading
- examination preparation
within a scientific context. The activities are suitable for all pupils and they can be used in any order.

It is suggested that Skills sheets 1–15 are photocopied and made into a booklet. Pupils then work, in order, through the sheets, either when asked, or when they have a few spare minutes at the end of a lesson. The activities are answered in the back of their notebooks or files and each one is self-corrected from the teacher's master set as soon as it is completed. Sheets 16–30 are designed to help the pupil revise for the examinations at the end of Key Stage 3. They will make a useful addition to homework materials.

Pupils will complete a widely varying number of Skills sheets, depending on their ability. Less able pupils could be encouraged to concentrate on selected sheets.

Photocopying: Individual departments can make their own selection from the wide range of resource material provided.

Meeting the demands of the National Curriculum

At the time of going to press, the proposed changes to the National Curriculum have not been agreed. The list here therefore matches **Understanding Science 3** to the original Statements of Attainment. The coverage is divided between the core activities and the extension activities. Some topics do not relate to specific statements but are used to prepare students for later topics or to cover the Exploration of Science. The letters *a, b, c* etc. denote the statement within a given level. PoS denotes coverage of Programme of Study material. Attainment Target 1 is covered throughout but is dependent on the teaching methods employed:

Topic	Core/Reinforcement	Extensions
1.0	AT2—5a; AT3—6a, b; AT5—3a, 4a, 5a, b; AT9—5c; AT13—6d	—
1.1	AT2—5b, 6a; AT3—3a	AT3—7a
1.2	AT2—6a	AT2—6a
1.3	AT2—5d, 7b; AT13—4a	AT3—6b, 7a
1.4	AT2—4b, 6b	AT2—6b, 7a
1.5	AT5—6a, b, 7a	AT5—6a, b; AT12—4b
1.6	AT2—5c	—
1.7	AT5—6c, 7a, b; AT12—3a; AT17—5b	—
1.8	AT5—6c, 7a, 7b	—
2.0	AT3—4b, 5a, 3, 6f	—
2.1	AT4—4a, 5a, 6a, b	AT4—7a
2.2	AT3—6c, d	AT3—6e
2.3	AT3—4b, 5c, 7b	AT3—7b
2.4	AT15—4a, 6b	AT3—7c
2.5	AT14—6b	—
2.7	AT3—6d	—
2.8	AT3—5d	—
3.1	AT15—3a, b, 5a, 7c	AT15—6c
3.2	AT15—3a, b, 4a, b, 6a	AT15—7a, b
3.3	AT14—3a, 5a	PoS
3.4	AT12—7c; AT14—3a, b, 4a, 6a	AT14—5b, 7a
3.5	AT14—5c	—
3.6	—	—
3.7	AT17—4a, 7b	—
4.0	AT2—4c; AT9—5a, b, 6a; AT16—4a	—
4.1	AT16—3a, 4b, c, 5a, b, 6a, b	AT16—7a
4.2	AT9—6a	AT9—6c, 7a
4.3	AT9—6b	AT9—7b
4.4	—	—
4.5	AT9—5a	—
4.6	AT6—6e; AT16—6b, 7b	—
5.0	AT10—3a, 5d, 6c; AT13—4a, c	—
5.1	AT13—4c, 6a, d	AT13—6a, b, 7b
5.2	AT13—7a	AT13—5a, 7a, c
5.3	AT13—4d, 7a	AT11—6d
5.4	AT10—4b, 5c, 7a	AT10—4a, 6a, 7a
5.5	AT10—3a, 4d, 5b, 6b, 7b	AT10—3a, 5a, 7a
5.6	AT10—6c, 7a; AT13—6c	AT10—7a; AT13—6c, 7b
5.7	AT5—7a; AT13—7a	—
5.8	AT6—5a; AT17—5b	—
6.0	AT6—3a, 5c, 6b, 7c; AT7—4a, 6b, c; AT8—5a, 6c, 7b, c	—
6.1	AT7—4a, 6c; AT8—6c	AT6—6d
6.2	AT7—7a	AT7—7a
6.3	AT7—7a, b	AT7—7b
6.4	AT6—6d, 7c	AT6—6d
6.5	AT6—6c; AT7—7b, c; AT8—7b; AT11—7b; AT17—5b, 6b	AT8—7b
6.6	AT7—4a, 6c	—
6.7	AT8—7d	—
6.8	AT8—7c; AT17—7a, b	—
7.0	AT11—6b, c; AT12—5a	—
7.1	AT11—6c, 7a	AT11—6c, 7a
7.2	AT11—6c, 7a; AT14—6c	AT11—7a; AT14—6c, 7a
7.3	AT12—6a, b, 7a; AT14—7a	AT12—7a; AT14—7a; AT15—7c
7.4	AT12—4b, 5b, 7b	AT12—7c
7.5	AT11—7c	AT11—7c
7.6	AT12—6b	—
7.7	AT13—5b	—
7.8	AT14—7a	—
8.0	AT6—3a, 4a, b, c, d, e, 5c; AT7—4a, b, 5a; AT8—4a	—
8.1	AT6—7a	AT6—6a, 7b
8.2	AT6—6a, 7b	AT6—6a, 7b
8.3	AT6—7b	AT7—5c, 7c
8.4	AT7—7d	AT6—7b
8.5	AT6—5b; AT7—6a	AT5—5a, 6a
8.6	AT6—6a, 7b	—
8.7	AT7—4b; AT13—5b	—
8.8	AT7—6b, 7c; AT11—7b	—

The following shows where specific statements of attainment are covered in **Book 3.**

AT2	4b	1.4
	c	4.0
	5a	1.0
	b	1.1
	c	1.6
	d	1.3
	6a	1.1, 1.2, 1.2E
	b	1.4, 1.4E, 1.5
	7a	1.4E
	b	1.3
AT3	3a	1.1
	4b	2.0, 2.3
	5a	2.0
	c	6.0, 8.0
	d	2.8
	e	2.0
	6a	1.0
	b	1.0, 1.3E

	c	2.2
	d	2.2, 2.7
	e	2.2E
	f	2.0
	7a	1.1E, 1.3E
	b	2.3, 2.3E
	c	2.4E
AT 4	*4a*	2.1
	5a	2.1
	6a	2.1
	b	2.1
	7a	2.1E
AT 5	*3a*	1.0
	4a	1.0
	5a	1.0, 7.5E
	b	1.0
	6a	1.5, 1.5E, 7.5E
	b	1.5E
	c	1.7, 1.8
	7a	1.5, 1.7, 1.8, 5.7
	b	1.7, 1.8
AT 6	*3a*	6.0, 8.0
	4a	8.0
	b	8.0
	c	6.0, 8.0
	d	8.0
	e	8.0
	5a	5.8
	b	8.5
	c	8.0
	6a	8.1E, 8.2, 8.2E, 8.6
	b	6.0
	c	6.5
	d	6.1E, 6.4, 6.4E
	e	4.6
	7a	8.1
	b	8.1E, 8.2, 8.2E, 8.3, 8.4, 8.6
	c	6.0, 6.4
AT 7	*4a*	6.0, 6.1, 6.6, 8.0
	b	8.0, 8.7
	5a	8.0
	c	8.3E
	6a	8.5
	b	6.0, 6.5, 8.8
	c	6.0, 6.1, 6.6
	7a	6.2, 6.2E, 6.3
	b	6.3, 6.3E
	c	8.3E, 8.8
	d	8.4
AT 8	*4a*	8.0
	5a	6.0
	6c	6.0, 6.1
	7b	6.0,6.5, 6.5E
	c	6.0, 6.8
	d	6.7
AT 9	*5a*	4.0, 4.5
	b	4.0
	c	1.0, 4.2E
	6a	4.0, 4.2
	b	4.3
	c	4.2E
	7a	4.2E
	b	4.3E
AT 10	*3a*	5.0, 5.5, 5.5E
	4a	5.4E
	b	5.4

	d	5.5
	5a	5.5E
	b	5.5
	c	5.4
	d	5.0
	6a	5.4E
	b	5.5
	c	5.0, 5.6
	7a	5.4, 5.4E, 5.5E, 5.6, 5.6E
	b	5.5
AT 11	*6b*	7.0
	c	7.0, 7.1, 7.1E, 7.2
	d	5.3E
	7a	7.1, 7.1E, 7.2, 7.2E
	b	6.5, 8.8
	c	7.5, 7.5E
AT 12	*3a*	1.7
	4a	
	4b	1.5E, 7.4
	5a	7.0
	b	7.4
	6a	7.3
	b	7.3, 7.6
	7a	7.3, 7.3E
	b	7.4
	c	3.4, 7.4E
AT 13	*4a*	1.3, 5.0
	c	5.0, 5.1
	d	5.3
	5a	5.2E
	b	7.7, 8.7
	6a	5.1, 5.1E
	b	5.1E
	c	5.6, 5.6E
	d	1.0, 5.1
	7a	5.2, 5.2E, 5.3, 5.7
	b	5.1E, 5.6E, 5.7
	c	5.2E
AT 14	*3a*	3.3, 3.4
	b	3.4
	4a	3.4
	5a	3.3
	b	3.4E
	c	3.5
	6a	3.4
	b	2.5
	c	7.2, 7.2E
	7a	3.4E, 7.2E, 7.3, 7.3E, 7.8
AT 15	*3a*	3.1, 3.2
	b	3.1, 3.2
	4a	2.4, 3.2
	b	3.2
	5a	3.1
	6a	3.2
	b	2.4
	c	3.1E
	7a	3.2E
	b	3.2E
	c	3.1, 7.3E
AT 16	*3a*	4.1
	4a	4.0
	b	4.1
	c	4.1
	5a	4.1
	b	4.1
	6a	4.1

	b	4.1, 4.6
	7a	4.1E
	b	4.6
AT 17	*4a*	3.7
	5b	1.7, 5.8, 6.5
	6b	6.5
	7a	6.8
	b	3.7, 6.8

Assessment in Book 3

The following shows which questions from the end-of-unit tests can be used to test specific Attainment Targets. 5—1 is used to indicate Test 5, Question 1. The end-of-unit tests have been designed to test the **new** material introduced in each topic and a matrix matching each question to the Attainment Targets and Core Extension work is provided in the teachers' notes for each unit. This analysis only covers the written tests and teachers may wish to add marks from the many other activities throughout the course including the True/False statements which are matched to the National Curriculum in the teachers' notes.

AT 2	*4b*	1—8
	5b	1—1, 1—2, 1—3
	c	1—13
	6a	1—4, 1—5, 1—17, 1—18, 1—19
	b	1—8, 1—9, 1—22, 1—23
	7a	1—22, 1—23
	b	1—6, 1—7
AT 3	*5d*	2—18
	6c	2—7
	d	2—6
	e	2—21, 2—22
	7a	1—15, 1—16, 1—20, 1—21
	b	2—8, 2—9, 2—10, 2—23, 2—24
	c	2—25, 2—26
AT 4	*4a*	2—1
	5a	2—2
	6a	2—3, 2—5
	b	2—4
	7a	2—19, 2—20
AT 5	*5a*	8—12, 8—13, 8—15
	6a	1—10, 1—11, 1—12, 8—14
	b	1—10, 1—11, 1—12
	c	1—14
	7a	1—10, 1—11, 1—12
	b	1—14
AT 6	*5b*	8—12
	6a	8—8
	c	6—12
	d	6—7, 6—16, 6—19, 6—20
	e	4—14
	7a	8—1
	b	8—3, 8—4, 8—5, 8—9, 8—10
	e	6—8, 6—9, 6—10, 6—11
AT 7	*6a*	8—7
	b	6—13, 6—14
	c	6—1
	7a	6—2, 6—3, 6—4, 6—5, 6—17
	b	6—6, 6—18
	c	8—11
	d	8—6
AT 8	*6c*	6—18

	7b	6—12, 6—13, 6—14
	d	6—15
AT 9	*6a*	4—8, 4—9, 4—10
	b	4—11, 4—12, 4—13
	c	4—16, 4—17
	7a	4—16, 4—17
	b	4—18, 4—19
AT 10	*3a*	5—9
	4b	5—8
	5a	5—19
	6a	5—18
	b	5—10, 5—11
	c	5—12
	7a	5—7
AT 11	*6c*	7—1, 7—2, 7—3
	d	5—17
	7a	7—1, 7—2, 7—3, 7—12, 7—13, 7—14
	b	6—13, 6—14
	c	7—10, 7—11, 7—18
AT 12	*4b*	7—7
	5b	7—8
	6a	7—5, 7—6
	7a	7—5
	b	7—9
	c	7—17
AT 13	*4c*	5—1
	6a	5—2
	b	5—15
	c	5—13
	d	5—2
	7a	5—3, 5—4, 5—5, 5—6
	b	5—20
	c	5—16
AT 14	*3a*	3—8
	b	3—12
	4a	3—11
	5a	3—9, 3—10
	b	3—17
	c	3—13
	6a	3—12
	b	2—14, 2—15, 2—16, 2—17
	c	7—4, 7—15
	7a	7—6
AT 15	*3a*	3—3
	b	3—3
	4a	3—5
	b	3—4
	5a	3—3
	6a	3—6, 3—7
	b	2—11, 2—12, 2—13
	c	3—14
	7a	3—16
	b	3—15
	c	3—2, 7—16
AT 16	*4b*	4—1, 4—2, 4—3
	c	4—1
	5a	4—4
	b	4—5, 4—6
	6a	4—1
	b	4—1, 4—7
	7a	4—15
	b	4—14

Record sheet KEY STAGE THREE

PUPIL NAME...

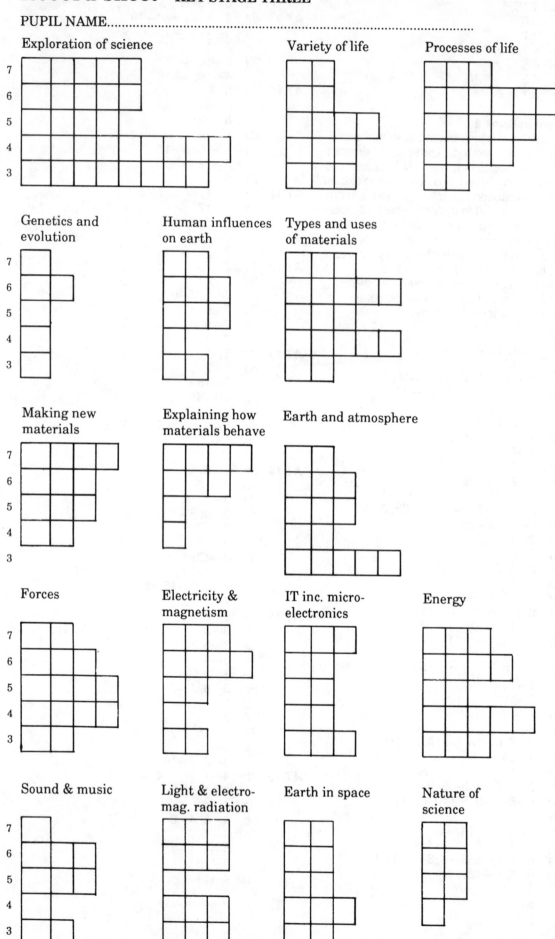

Unit 1 Spaceship Earth

Explaining ecology

This unit builds upon those aspects of unit 1 in Book 2 that introduced a scientific study of the environment. The revision work therefore refers to the water cycle, photosynthesis and respiration, and conservation and pollution. Each of the next five topics introduces an important ecological principle; the scientific naming of living organisms, animal and plant adaptations, energy flow in the ecosystem, the recycling of essential elements, and the need for management of the environment. The content of the unit could be reinforced by fieldwork, by viewing video material, and by actively seeking to introduce references to local environmental issues. Pupils are engaged in investigative work in their locality and encouraged to develop sound experimental design. The final three topics comprise an open-ended problem on the benefits of artificial fertilisers, a discussion based on the pupil's evaluation of environmental issues, and a short reading exercise. This unit deals with Attainment Targets 2 and 5 of the 1989 National Curriculum. In addition to meeting the general demands of Attainment Target 1, this unit deals specifically with AT1 levels 5a, 5b, 5c, 5d, and 7.

Core and Reinforcement

1.0 Revision—Beauty and the Beast

> Revise background work.
> Complete a revision question sheet.
> Write an imaginative short story or poem.
>
> *page 8*

Revise earlier work.
Apply knowledge in an imaginative way.

1.1 Life on Earth AT 2–5b, 6a

> Identify the invertebrate group to which given animals belong.
> Observe a living animal.
> Complete an animal classification table.
> Complete a blank plant kingdom key.
>
> *page 10*

Observe accurately and systematically.

1.2 Adaptations AT 2–6a

> Play 'adaptation dominoes', matching animals with adaptations for survival.
> Study *Daphnia* behaviour in response to various environmental conditions.
>
> *page 12*

Observe accurately and systematically.
Deduce relationships from given data.
Devise and carry out experiments for a given purpose.
Suggest a scientific explanation of unfamiliar observations.

1.3 The delicate balance AT 2–5d, 7b; AT13–4a

> Read a passage about pyramids of biomass and number.
> Estimate own energy needs.
> Identify predators and prey in a food web.
>
> *page 14*

Extract relevant information from a passage.
Use an equation to calculate energy needs.

Extension

AT 3–7a

> Identify variables in an experiment on plant mineral requirements.
> Deduce the importance of nitrogen, phosphorus, potassium and magnesium to plant growth.
>
> *page 136*

Observe accurately.
Draw conclusions from data.

AT 2–6a

> Investigate the distribution of *Pleurococcus*.
> Suggest, test and modify a hypothesis to explain the observed distribution.
>
> *page 137*

Observe, measure and record systematically.
Recognise patterns in experimental data.
Form and modify a hypothesis.

AT 3–6b, 7a

> Test seeds for starch.
> Prepare a wet-mount slide of plant stem material.
>
> *page 138*

Extract relevant information from text and diagrams.
Observe accurately.

Core and Reinforcement

1.4 Going round in circles   *AT 2–4b, 6b*

> Design an experiment to make grass rot
> quickly.
> Design an experiment to prevent the decay of
> grapes.
> Identify examples of decomposers from a food
> web.   *page 16*

Design and carry out investigations to solve a given
problem.
Communicate observations in written form.

1.5 Managing the environment   *AT 5–6a,b, 7a*

> Read about and carry out experiments on a
> given pollutant.
> Write a report on the activity.
> Carry out tests on polluted water, and devise
> methods to clean the water.   *page 18*

Extract information from available resources.
Carry out experiments for a given purpose.
Design and carry out experiments to solve a given
problem.
Communicate ideas in written form.

1.6 Problem—Grow more   *AT 2–5c*

> Investigate the most effective way to use an
> artificial fertiliser.
> Produce an 'advertisement' poster giving the
> results of the investigation.   *page 20*

Design and carry out experiments to solve a given
problem.
Draw conclusions from experimental data.
Evaluate environmental and economic implications
of experimental results.

1.7 Talkabout—Headline news   *AT 5–6c, 7a,b*

> Discuss environmental issues as described in
> newspaper headlines/articles.
> Discuss the validity and fairness of the
> evidence presented.
> Record opinions on the articles.   *page 21*

Make decisions based on the examination of
evidence and arguments.
Recognise that the study and practice of science
are subject to limitations and uncertainties.
Evaluate the social and environmental implications
of science.

1.8 Readabout—Times past, present and
future   *AT5–6c, 7a,b*

> Read a passage on the global impact of
> human activity and answer questions on it.
>   *page 22*

Extract relevant information from a passage.
Recognise the social, economic and environmental
impact of science.

Extension

AT2–6b, 7a

> Complete diagrams of the nitrogen and
> carbon cycles.
> Discuss the effect of human activities on the
> carbon and nitrogen cycles.
>   *page 139*

Extract relevant information from diagrams.
Evaluate the environmental implications of human
activity.

AT 5–6a,b; AT 12–4b

> Carry out water-pollution tests.
> Write a report on the tests.
>   *page 140*

Carry out experiments to research a given problem.
Communicate ideas in written form.

Equipment

1.0—Revision—Beauty and the Beast
- Revision question sheet

1.1—Life on Earth
- Invertebrate animal picture-card set **(R1.1A)**
- Petri dish
- Hand lens
- Live invertebrate, e.g. woodlouse, worm
- Animal kingdom table **(R1.1B)**
- Plant kingdom key **(R1.1C)**
- Variety of live plants

Extension
No equipment required

1.2—Adaptations
- Set of adaptation dominoes **(R1.2)**
- *Daphnia* (available from local pet shops)
- Glass U-tube
- Plasticine
- 2 corks to fit the U-tube
- Dropper bottle of vinegar
- Dropper bottle of sodium bicarbonate solution (1%)
- Bench lamp
- Black paper
- Coloured light filters

Extension
- Moisture meter
- Cobalt chloride paper
- Compass
- Thermometer
- Metre rule
- Plastic 10 cm-square quadrat
- Light meter

1.3—The delicate balance
- Bathroom scales
- Food web diagram **(R1.3)**
- Coloured pencils (red and green)
- Glue

Extension
- Seed collection, e.g. beans, peas, lentils
- Dropper bottle of iodine solution
- Plant stem material, e.g. celery, rhubarb or any soft-stemmed house plant
- Potato

Notes

Access to copies of *Understanding Science 1* and *2* will allow pupils to check their work and look for information they are unsure of.

Avoid using larval stages of invertebrates, e.g. mealworm larvae, which will not show features of the phylum.
The classification given is based on recommendations of the Institute of Biology.
Plants on display should include mosses and ferns as well as conifers and flowering plants.

The activity could be supported by plants with mineral deficiencies, e.g. oat seedlings. The exercise offers the chance to reinforce the concept of control experiments.

The topic introduces the concept of adaptation to the habitat.
Daphnia prefer light, acidic conditions. They move to the surface and may show a preference for red light. This behaviour is related to the need to find their food, green algae. The algae need red light for photosynthesis. They live at the surface so as to obtain light, and the CO_2 they produce during respiration makes the water acidic.
Pupils should transfer about 5 *Daphnia* into each arm of the U-tube and note their behaviour. The U-tube acts as a choice chamber.

This is an open-ended investigation.
Pupils should first be shown some *Pleurococcus*, then asked to search for it outside. From a description of the habitat, including as many detailed measurements as possible, a hypothesis can be formed to explain the distribution. This can be checked by looking for more *Pleurococcus* in predicted habitats.
Pleurococcus grows best on rough, wet, south-facing, vertical surfaces. The equipment could be on view to stimulate ideas.

The concept of energy flow through an ecosystem is very important in ecology. The rather abstract idea of pyramids of numbers and biomass can be difficult for pupils, but it does graphically illustrate the inefficiency of energy flow along a food chain.

The plant stem material should be soaked in hydrochloric acid for an hour, then rinsed. This can then be easily macerated on the slide and viewed. Long spirals of lignin from the plant vascular system can be clearly seen. Prepared slides can also be used.

Equipment

- Scalpel
- Glass microscope slides
- Microscope

1.4—Going round in circles

- Black polythene bag
- Grass cuttings
- 5 grapes or pieces of soft fruit
- 4 test tubes
- Petri dish
- Vinegar
- Salt
- Sugar

Extension

- Nitrogen and carbon cycle diagrams (RE1.4)
- Glue

1.5—Managing the environment

- Car pollution card (R1.5A)
- Textbooks, pamphlets on pollution

1 Carbon monoxide

- Carbon monoxide tester

2 Soot

- Spatula
- Glass microscope slide
- Vaseline
- Plastic gloves
- Microscope

3 Acid gases

- Sticky tape
- pH paper

4 Lead

- Plastic gloves
- Plastic bag
- Spatula
- Nitric acid (1 M)
- Bunsen burner, tripod and gauze, heatproof mat
- Sodium hydroxide solution (1 M)
- Dropper bottle of lead indicator solution
- Safety glasses

- Water test cards (R1.5B)

1 pH test

- Samples of 'river water'
- pH colour chart
- Spotting tile
- pH paper

Notes

Large starch grains can be seen in the potato even without staining the tissue.

The cuttings will rot fastest if they are shredded, compacted together, warm and moist.
Pupils can usually recall methods of food preservation from their domestic experience. The equipment list anticipates the most frequently requested preservatives. Access to a fridge is commonly requested.
Pupils should be encouraged to consider controls and how the results of both experiments can be evaluated. The experiments should be allowed to run until the end of the unit.

The car engine should only be turned over in the open air, and pupils should avoid breathing the exhaust. A breathing mask could be employed in Experiments 1 and 2.

A lead indicator solution can be made by dissolving 2 mg of dithizone (diphenylthiocarbazone) in 100 cm³ of 1,1,1-trichloroethane.

The lesson can be handled in a number of ways depending on available time and resources. For example, each group could carry out one of the tests before and after cleaning, and the class results collated.
The sample could be real or 'doctored'.
Experiment 4 should be carried out after filtering out the suspended solids.

Equipment	Notes

Equipment

2 Turbidity test
- Turbidity tube
- Scrap paper
- Ruler

3 Suspended solids
- Filter paper
- 100 cm^3 measuring cylinder
- Beaker

4 Dissolved solids
- Beaker or evaporating basin
- Bunsen burner, tripod and gauze, heatproof mat
- Safety glasses
- 100 cm^3 measuring cylinder
- Filter-bed equipment (see Book 1 topic 3.6)

Extension
- Stream-water sample
- Rain-water sample
- Microscope slide
- Microscope
- Oxygen meter
- pH paper
- pH colour chart
- pH meter
- Dropper bottle of silver nitrate solution (0.05 M)
- Dropper bottle of barium hydroxide solution (0.1 M)
- Access to chemistry textbook (with analytical tests)

1.6—Problem—Grow more
- Liquid fertiliser
- Measuring cylinder
- Petri dishes or seed boxes
- Filter paper or vermiculite
- Peas
- Poster paper
- Stencils
- Coloured pencils
- Rulers

1.7—Talkabout—Headline news
- Information sheets (R1.7)
- Audio tape
- Tape recorder
- Headlines from current papers

1.8—Readabout—Times past, present and future
No equipment required

Notes

A long piece of rigid plastic tubing can be used. Mark the outside with a scale in millimetres.

The samples can be real or 'doctored'.
The range of tests can be increased.
The exercise can be extended to produce an in-depth survey of local water sources.

This is an open-ended investigation. Peas will germinate within a few days.
It is best to grow them on filter paper or in vermiculite since compost will provide a source of plant minerals.

The activity offers the opportunity to use real headlines from the national and local press to raise awareness of current issues.

Assessment 1

The questions are designed to assess the skills and knowledge developed in the unit, as shown in the table. The Attainment Target assessed by each question is also shown. A selection of questions would be appropriate for a unit test.

Topic	Core	Attainment Target
1.1	1, 2, 3	AT 2–5b
1.2	4, 5	AT 2–6a
1.3	6, 7	AT 2–7b
1.4	8	AT 2–4b, 6b
	9	AT 2–6b
1.5	10, 11, 12	AT 5–6a,b, 7a
1.6	13	AT 2–5c
1.7	14	AT 5–6c, 7b
	Extension	
1.1	15, 16	AT 3–7a
1.2	17,18,19	AT 2–6a
1.3	20,21	AT 3–7a
1.4	22, 23	AT 2–6b, 7a

Answers

1 a A—earthworm, B—jellyfish, C—liver fluke.
b A—segmented worms, B—coelenterates, C—flatworms.
c A—backbone, B—jointed limbs, C—soft body, usually with shell.
d A—vertebrates, B—arthropods, C—molluscs.
2 1—mosses (and liverworts), 2—no roots/tiny leaves, 3—I, 4—scale-like leaves, spores in cones, 5—F, 6—tiny, divided, leaves, 7—B, 8—conifer, 9—E, 10—seeds/flowers, 11—A/C/H.
3 a A—5, B—1, C—2, D—4, E—3.
b 1—seeds, 2—spores/no seeds, 3—flowers, 4—divided leaves/spores in clusters, 5—scale-like leaves, spores in cones, 6—spores in cones, 7—no true transport/tiny leaves and stem/ spores in capsules, 8—flowering plants, 9—conifers, 10—club mosses.
4 a C, D, F.
b A—to attract a mate/guard territory, B—protect stems/prevent grazing, C—camouflage.
5 a A—fur/blubber, B—streamlined shape/ sharp claws/webbed feet, C—large eyes, D—stores water in hump/large feet for soft sand.
b Desert. No need to drink water, excretes very little water so retains lots, burrows to avoid sun/heat.
c A—2, B—1, C—4, D—3.
6 a Pyramid shape—oak tree at base, cat at apex.
b Mass of biological/living material.
c Movement, heat, excretion, uneaten parts.
d Predator—thrush or cat; prey—thrush or caterpillar.
7 a Sun→grass→insects→moles→foxes.
b (i) More moles; **(ii)** damage to crops.
8 a (i) Draw and label a pile of compost that is

compact, not covered/moist, shredded. Addition of microbes may also be labelled.
(ii) Higher temperature/more decomposers active/alive.
b (i) Aphids increase **(ii)** Plants ruined
(iii) Earthworm, fungus/mushroom; recycle essential elements/material.
9 a C, D, F, G.
b Bacteria, fungi, invertebrates, for example.
c Removes habitat/removes food sources/ upsets food web/allows erosion.
10 a A—produces acid rain, B—introduces bacterial pollution, C—introduces chemical pollution, D—introduces chemical pollution.
b Description of water-cleaning system—filtering and chlorination.
11 a B, C, F.
b Any three from tests for pH, turbidity, suspended solids, dissolved solids.
12 a Tabulate information—table headers, correct units, data transferred accurately.
b Fines, recycling, treatment, anything else sensible.
13 a Use ground not previously suitable for farming, produce larger crops.
b More expensive, water pollution.
14 a Any sensible answer balancing usefulness/ necessity of activity with harmful effects on environment.
b Reference to industrial, social and economic demands.
15 a Nitrogen, phosphorus, potassium.
b Nitrogen—normal all-round growth; phosphorus—developing fruit, leaves; potassium— leaf growth, fruit growth (*any two*).
16 a A—magnesium, B—potassium, C—phosphorus.
b Through the roots/dissolved in soil water.
17 a Any sensible hypothesis—observed growth pattern is over the food-carrying tissue (phloem) of the plant.
b Tests on composition of wood; idea of growing fungi in a range of different conditions.
18 Bird droppings act as a fertiliser. Rainwater spreads this to create the observed growth pattern. Test effect of bird droppings on algal growth.
19 Features to show adaptation to cold (e.g. fur), soft terrain (e.g. large flat feet), inaccessible food (e.g. long mouthparts).
20 a Photosynthesis.
b Cellulose—cell wall material; lignin—strengthens cell walls; pectin—holds cells together; starch—food reserve (*any two*).
21 A—5, B—4, C—1, D—3, E—2.
22 a (i) X—photosynthesis, Y—respiration;
(ii) green plants.
b Photosynthesis and respiration rates same.
c Burning fossil fuels (e.g. in car engines)/ destroying forests.
23 a X—lightning creates nitrates, Y—N-fixing bacteria, Z—de-nitrifying bacteria.
b Adding artificial fertilisers *or* removing organic matter (e.g. harvesting).
c Microbes/bacteria.

True/false 1

Each statement is marked as either true or false by the pupil. This gives a rapid assessment of a pupil's grasp of the Attainment Targets covered in the unit. This list gives the Attainment Targets covered by each set of statements.

1 AT 2–4b	8 AT 5–6b
2 AT 2–5b	9 AT 5–6c
3 AT 2–5c	10 AT5–7a
4 AT 2–6a	11 AT 5–7b
5 AT 2–6b	12 AT 2–7a
6 AT 2–7b	13 AT 3–7a
7 AT 5–6a	

Unit 1 Spaceship Earth

Name _____

1 Write the meaning of each word or phrase in the space provided. The figures in brackets are references to *Understanding Science*, Books 1 and 2 (**book number**, page number). Use the references to *check* your answers.

- habitat (**1**, 30)

- the water cycle (**1**, 41)

- photosynthesis (**2**, 16)

- respiration (**2**, 141)

- a herbivore (**1**, 125)

- a carnivore (**1**, 125)

- a food chain (**2**, 16)

- conservation (**2**, 18)

- pollution (**2**, 18).

2 The spider diagram shows some connections between these terms. Complete the diagram with the correct words.

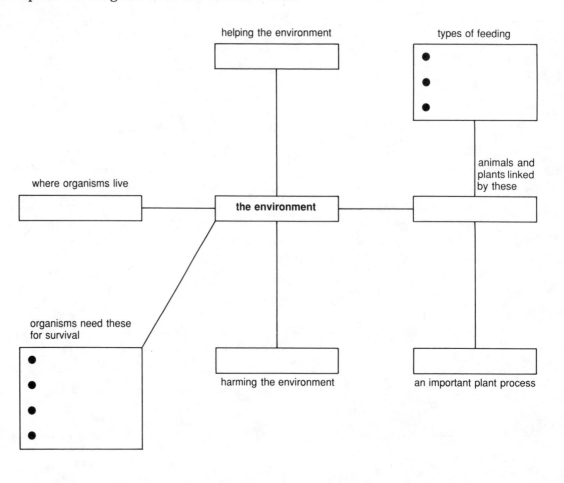

1 Study the animals in each of the three sets below.

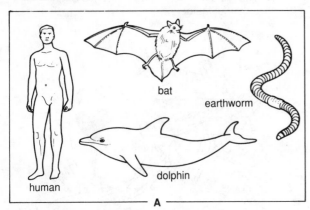

A

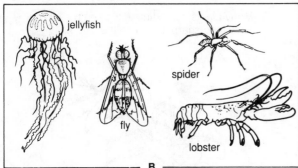

B

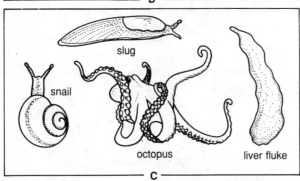

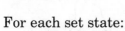

C

For each set state:
a which is the odd one out;
b what animal group it belongs to;
c what feature is common to the other three animals in the set;
d what animal group these three animals belong to.

2 Study the plants A–I below.

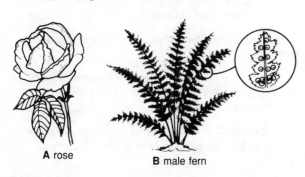

A rose

B male fern

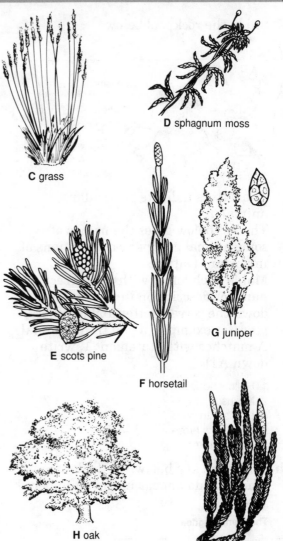

D sphagnum moss

C grass

E scots pine

F horsetail

G juniper

H oak

I club moss

Copy and complete spaces 1–11 in the table.

Plant group	Important features	Example
1	2	D sphagnum moss
club mosses	transport system, spores in cones	3
horsetails	4	5
ferns	6	7
8	needle-like leaves, seeds produced in cones	9
flowering plants	10	11

continued ▶

3 a Study the rockpool below.

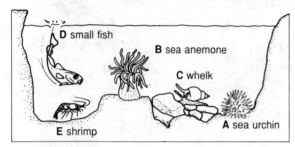

The letters indicate particular animals.

The list below gives the names of some animal groups or descriptions of important features.

Match each letter with the correct name or description in the list. Write down the correct letter and number pair (for example, if you think animal A matches with statement 1, write down A1).

1 Hollow body
2 Mollusc
3 Limbs with joints
4 Backbone present
5 Echinoderm

b Study the key below. Write down what should appear in each numbered box.

The plant kingdom

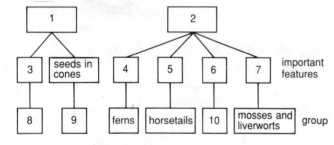

4 a Read the list of statements below. Write down the letters of the statements that describe adaptations for survival.

A My cat prefers fish to rabbit meat.
B All mammals have backbones.
C Brown bears hibernate in winter.
D Polar bears have thick white fur.
E Tadpoles live in water.
F Some types of birds migrate in winter.
G The grass goes yellow in dry weather.

b Explain the adaptation for survival in each example A to C following.

A The male of most types of bird has bright colourful feathers.

B Many plants, for example the sea buckthorn, have long sharp thorns on their stems.

C The coat of the arctic hare goes white in winter.

5 a Suggest one physical feature that allows each of the animals below to survive in its habitat.

A Leopard seals live in the freezing waters of the Antarctic.
B Otters catch fish for food.
C Owls hunt by night.
D Camels live in deserts.

b Read this description of an animal.

Dipodomys gets all its water when digested food is respired in its body cells. Its kidneys produce very concentrated urine, containing little water. It burrows underground during the day.

Suggest what type of habitat it lives in. Explain how *two* of its features help it to survive.

continued ▶

c The beak of a bird gives a good indication of the food it eats. Match the beak to the correct food. Write down the letter and number pair. Explain how each beak is well adapted.

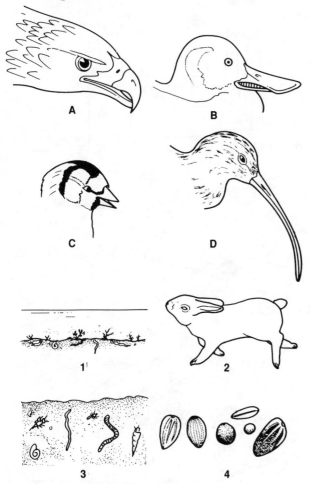

A   B

C   D

1   2

3   4

6 a Draw a pyramid of biomass for this food chain.

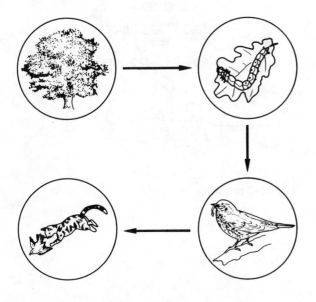

b What does *biomass* mean?
c Give three ways in which energy is lost between links in a food chain.
d Write down the name of one predator and one prey from the food chain shown.
e What is the difference between a food chain and a food web?

7 A pyramid of numbers is shown below.

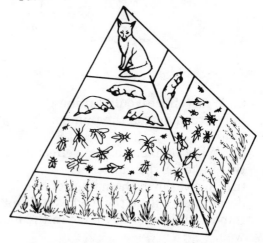

a Write down the food chain that this pyramid represents. Include the source of energy for the food chain.
b Imagine that all the foxes were killed by a farmer.
(i) What effect would this have on the food chain?
(ii) Why might the farmer regret what he had done?

8 a (i) Three neighbours were trying to make compost from their garden rubbish. The diagrams show their compost heaps.

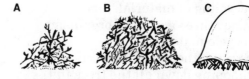

A   B   C

Imagine you were the fourth neighbour. Draw and *label* your compost heap to show the best conditions for decaying plant material.
(ii) The compost should form most quickly in the summer. Why should this be?

continued ▶

b A garden food web is shown below.

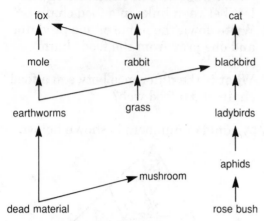

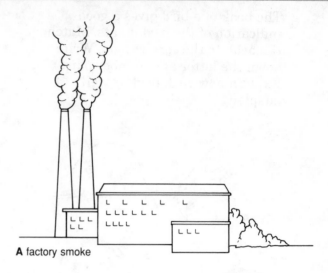

A factory smoke

(i) What effect would killing the ladybirds have on the number of aphids?

(ii) What unexpected side effect could this have for the gardener?

(iii) Write down the names of two decomposers from the food web. What important job do they have in the food web?

B sewage pipe

9 In natural habitats materials are kept in balance by recycling. The list below describes some human activities in a wood.

A Having a tidy picnic
B Birdwatching
C Chopping wood for campfires
D Picking all the mushrooms
E Pitching a tent
F Adding fertilisers to the soil
G Draining the ground
H Building a badger hide

a Write down the letters of the activities that would affect the recycling of materials.

b What three groups of organisms recycle material?

c Explain the harmful effects of chopping down all the trees in the woodland.

C too much fertiliser

10 Study the drawings A to D.

a Explain how each of the processes affects water purity.

b Describe how water can be made safe to drink.

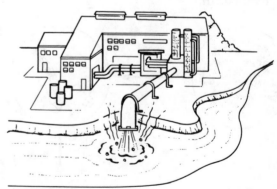

D industrial chemicals

continued ▶

11 The list below describes how humans use water.

A Watering the garden and crops
B Cooling industrial processes
C Cleaning industrial machinery/removing industrial waste
D Cooking
E Recreation – swimming, boating etc.
F Flushing away human waste
G Generating electricity.

a Which three activities are most likely to cause pollution?

b Describe any three tests you would carry out to test if water was fit to drink.

12 The bar chart below shows the number of tonnes of metals passed into the North Sea in the early 1980s from London alone in the form of industrial liquid waste.

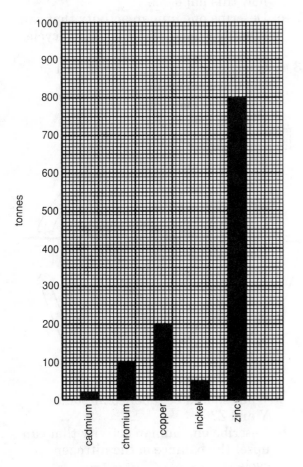

a Record this information in the form of a table.

b These metals are dangerous pollutants. Suggest ways in which the dumping of such waste could be controlled.

13 a Give two reasons for using artificial fertilisers in agriculture and horticulture.

b Give two problems caused by using artificial fertilisers.

14 Three examples of ways in which humans extract raw materials from the environment are given below.

A Mining for coal
B Quarrying for limestone, granite, sand
C Felling trees

a Choose one example. Explain why the activity is useful or important. Describe possible dangers to the environment.

b 'The bigger the human world population, the bigger the impact of human activity on the Earth.' Suggest why this is true.

Extension questions

15 a What are the three most important elements in an artificial fertiliser?

b Explain why any two of these are important for the growth of the plant.

16 Read the descriptions of three unhealthy plants below.

A The leaves are pale green or yellow
B A small, withered plant with brown marks on the leaves
C A very small plant whose leaves have a purple shading

a What essential element does each plant lack?

b How do plants normally get these elements?

17 a Suggest a reason for the following observation.

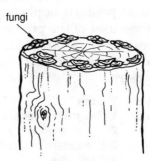

Small fungi were growing in a ring near the bark on the stumps of trees.

b How could you test your hypothesis?

continued ▶

18 Suggest a reason for the following observation.

More green algae grow on the roof under the TV aerial.

How could you test your hypothesis?

19 This is a description of a habitat on an alien planet.

Very cold and windy, but very dry. The surface is covered in a deep, soft layer of very find sand. Tiny plant-like organisms live at the bottom of the sand layer.

Describe the features of an animal that could survive in this climate, move on this land and feed on the plant-like creatures.

20 This is the word equation for an important plant process.

water + carbon dioxide → glucose + oxygen

a Name the process.
b Glucose can be converted into a range of products. List any two products and explain why they are important to the plant.

21 List X below gives the names of direct and indirect products of photosynthesis. List Y gives uses of the products. Match each product with its correct use. Write down the correct letter and number pairs.

X–products	Y–uses
A Cellulose	1 Raw material for all other products
B Starch	2 Holds cell walls together
C Glucose	3 Strengthens cell walls
D Lignin	4 Food store
E Pectin	5 Cell wall material

22 a The diagram below shows part of the carbon cycle.

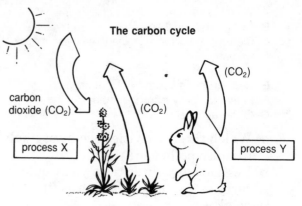

The carbon cycle

(i) What processes should be labelled at X and Y?
(ii) What group of organisms carry out process X?
b In the diagram the amount of carbon dioxide remains the same. Explain how this happens.
c Describe one human activity that can upset the balance of the carbon cycle.

23 a Study the diagram below of part of the nitrogen cycle.

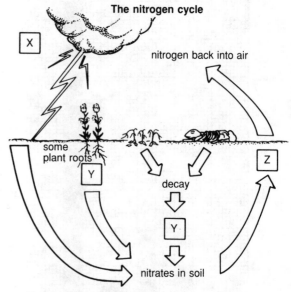

The nitrogen cycle

What should be labelled at points X, Y and Z?
b Describe one human activity that can upset the balance of the nitrogen cycle.
c What type of organism is mostly responsible for keeping the balance in the nitrogen cycle?

Name_____

Put a tick after the statements that are true. Put a cross after the statements that are false.

1 a Material heated to kill all microbes will decay very quickly. ☐
b Dry newspaper will decay more quickly than wet newspaper. ☐
c Decayed material can be recycled. ☐
d Dead leaves do not decay quickly in cold weather. ☐

2 a Living organisms can be divided into large groups called kingdoms. ☐
b Animals in the same group have similar behaviour. ☐
c Plants in the same group have similar structures. ☐
d All vertebrate animals have fur. ☐
e Plants can only reproduce by seeds. ☐
f Mosses are flowering plants. ☐

3 a The more fertiliser used the better a crop grows. ☐
b Fertilisers are used to make food taste better. ☐
c Some fertilisers will be washed from the soil before the plant can use it. ☐
d Fertilisers are only safe to use on plants used for food production. ☐
e Fertilisers must be used carefully to avoid causing water pollution. ☐

4 a All animals can adapt quickly to a different habitat. ☐
b Animals show adaptations in their behaviour. ☐
c A rose bush covered with greenfly is an example of a well-adapted rose bush. ☐
d Adaptations help plants and animals to survive. ☐
e Webbed feet on birds are an adaptation for swimming. ☐

5 a Recycling means using spaterial to make tyres. ☐
b The level of elements in the environment is kept steady by recycling. ☐

c Decomposers are dead animals and plants. ☐
d Fungi and worms are examples of decomposers. ☐
e Human activities can affect recycling. ☐
f Adding fertilisers to the soil is an example of natural recycling. ☐

6 a Energy is passed very efficiently along a food chain. ☐
b Some energy is lost from a food chain as heat. ☐
c A puppy fed 1 kg of dogfood a week will increase in mass by 500 g each week. ☐
d A pyramid of numbers is used to calculate the number of living things in a habitat. ☐
e A pyramid of biomass shows the mass of the organisms at each level of a food chain in an ecosystem. ☐

7 a Stream water will collect dissolved chemicals as it passes over rocks and soil. ☐
b Rainwater is the purest form of water available. ☐
c When water leaves a sewage works it is fit for drinking. ☐
d Filtering removes all chemical substances from water. ☐
e Acid rain is caused partly by burning coal, oil and gas. ☐

8 a Humans make reservoirs to stock with fish for anglers. ☐
b Using a lake or stream as a source of drinking water is dangerous. ☐
c Management of the water supply should include using water for sports and recreation. ☐
d There is always enough rain to supply us with all the water we require. ☐
e Water is too precious a resource to be used for generating electricity. ☐
f Water used by industry and returned to rivers should be carefully tested. ☐

9 a Wood is a natural resource that should be used. ☐
b The slag heaps seen beside mines spoil the environment. ☐

continued ▶

c It is more important to supply raw materials to industry than to conserve the countryside. ☐

d Damage caused by taking raw materials from the environment can be corrected. ☐

10 a Human activity always causes environmental problems that could be avoided. ☐

b The benefits to humans and the harm caused to the environment should be considered before starting a project. ☐

11 a As the human population increased the damage to the environment increased. ☐

b Alterations to the environment were necessary to support industry. ☐

c Humans have always made large, permanent changes to their surroundings. ☐

d The human impact on the environment has always caused problems. ☐

e If humans demanded less luxury the environment might improve. ☐

Extensions

12 a Microbes are examples of decomposers. ☐

b Photosynthesis and respiration are two important processes in the carbon cycle. ☐

c Adding too much fertiliser to the soil upsets the carbon cycle. ☐

d Bacteria in the soil play an important part in the nitrogen cycle. ☐

e Burning fuels has no effect on the nitrogen cycle. ☐

f Most plants get the nitrogen they need directly from the air. ☐

13 a Plants can grow normally in water if the water is pure. ☐

b Iron is the most important plant mineral. ☐

c A plant with yellow leaves might be short of magnesium. ☐

d Plants produce simple sugars by photosynthesis. ☐

e The glucose made in photosynthesis is used up to supply the plant with energy. ☐

f Plants get food from the soil. ☐

g Glucose is changed by the plant into new substances. ☐

Name _____

Complete each sentence. Put the correct word(s) in each blank space.

1 Ecology is the study of _____ and their _____.

Living things are put into large sets called _____ for identification

and naming. Each of these is then divided into smaller sets.

For example, the animal kingdom is divided into these main sets:

- _____
- _____
- _____

- _____
- _____
- _____

- _____ .

The plant kingdom is divided into these sets:

- _____
- _____
- _____

- _____
- _____
- _____ .

2 The living things found in a habitat are well _____ to that habitat.

An example is

_____.

Animals also survive in their habitat because of their _____. An

example of this is *Daphnia* moving towards _____.

3 Living things in an _____ are linked by food _____

and food _____. These show the flow of _____. They

always begin with _____ which trap _____ by the

process of _____.

Another way to show the energy flow is by drawing a _____ of

biomass or _____. Energy is lost at each link because of

- _____
- _____
- _____ .

4 It is important that essential minerals are _____ through the

ecosystem. Two examples are the _____ and _____

cycles.

continued ▶

Name _____

A group of living things called _____ are involved in the decay of

dead material. Three examples are

● _____ ● _____ ● _____.

Things decay fastest when the material is compacted together,

_____ and _____.

5 There is a need to manage the environment. This means measuring and controlling

_____.

Water management means _____

_____.

6 Artificial _____ can be used to improve the growth of plants. Three

things to consider when using these chemicals are

● _____ ● _____ ● _____.

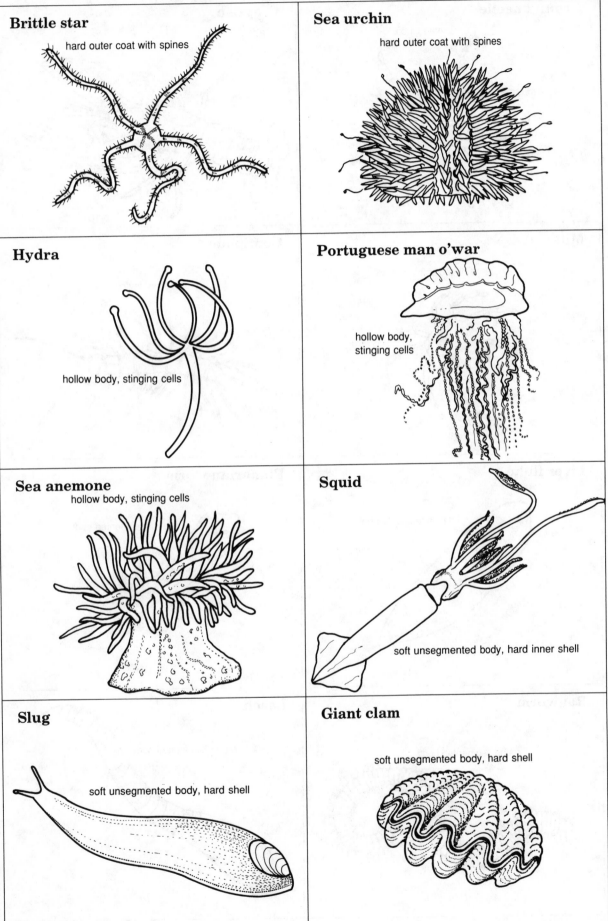

Brittle star
hard outer coat with spines

Sea urchin
hard outer coat with spines

Hydra
hollow body, stinging cells

Portuguese man o'war
hollow body, stinging cells

Sea anemone
hollow body, stinging cells

Squid
soft unsegmented body, hard inner shell

Slug
soft unsegmented body, hard shell

Giant clam
soft unsegmented body, hard shell

1 of 2

Ground beetle

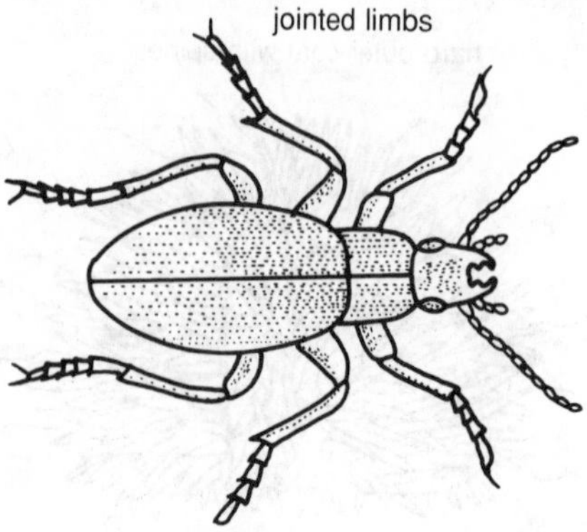

jointed limbs

Crayfish

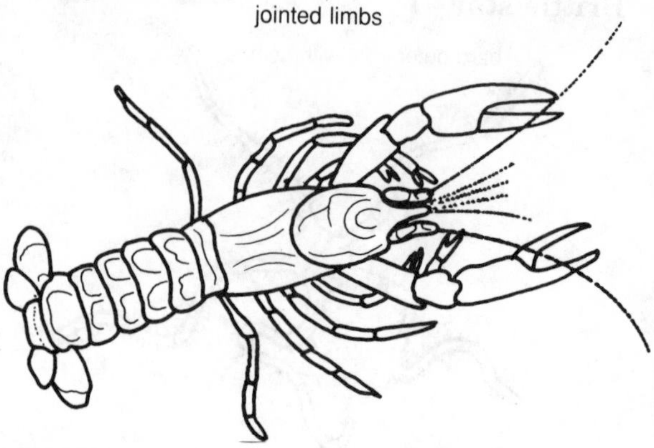

jointed limbs

Mite

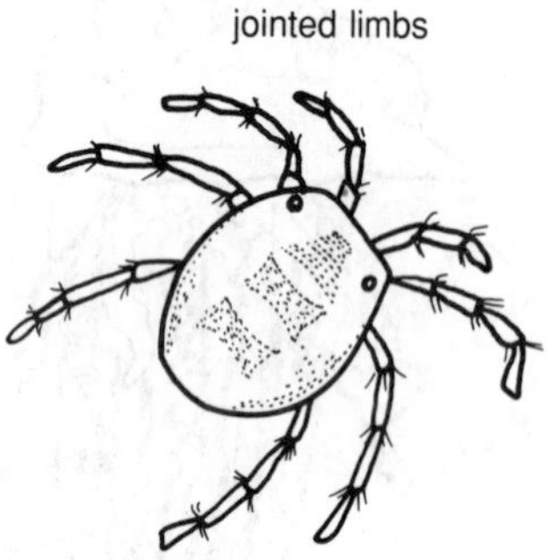

jointed limbs

Centipede

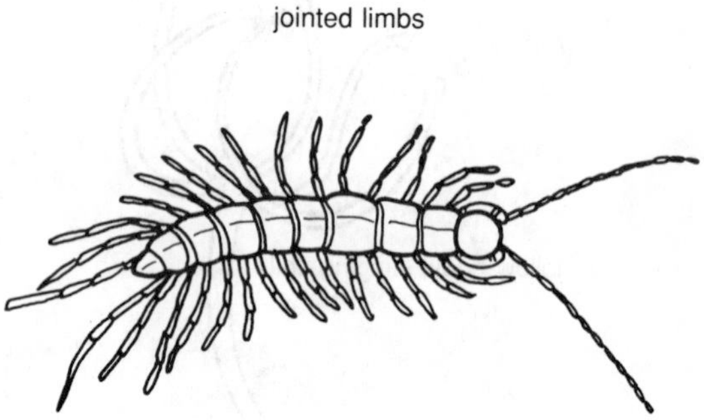

jointed limbs

Liver fluke

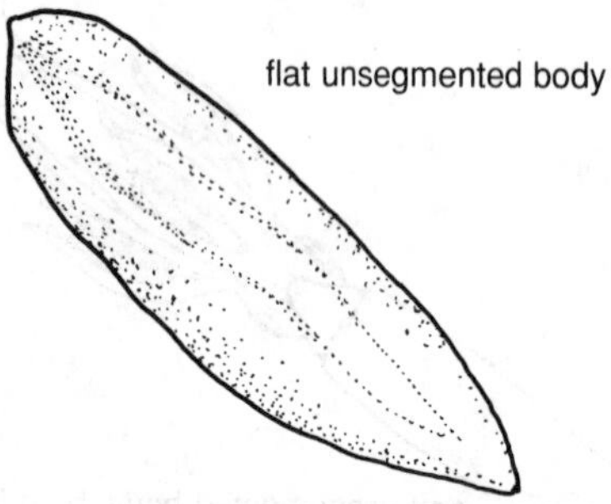

flat unsegmented body

Planarian worm

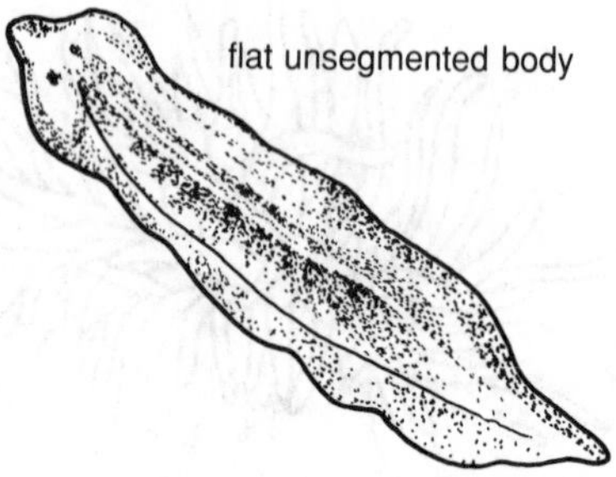

flat unsegmented body

Ragworm

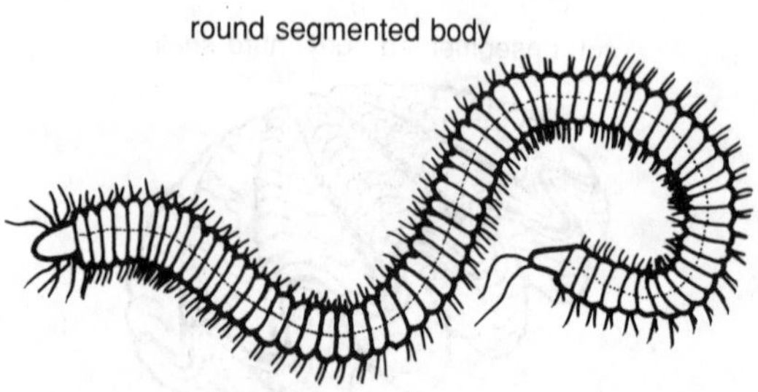

round segmented body

Leech

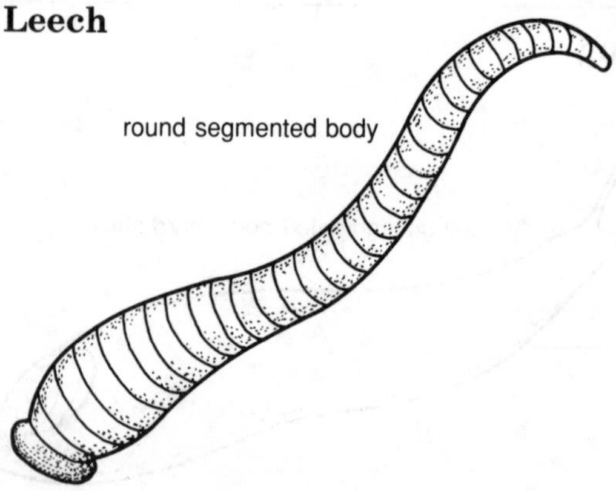

round segmented body

Animal kingdom table

Animal group	Important features	Examples
Echinoderms		
Coelenterates		
Flatworms		
Molluscs		
Segmented worms		
Arthropods		
Vertebrates		

Plant kingdom key

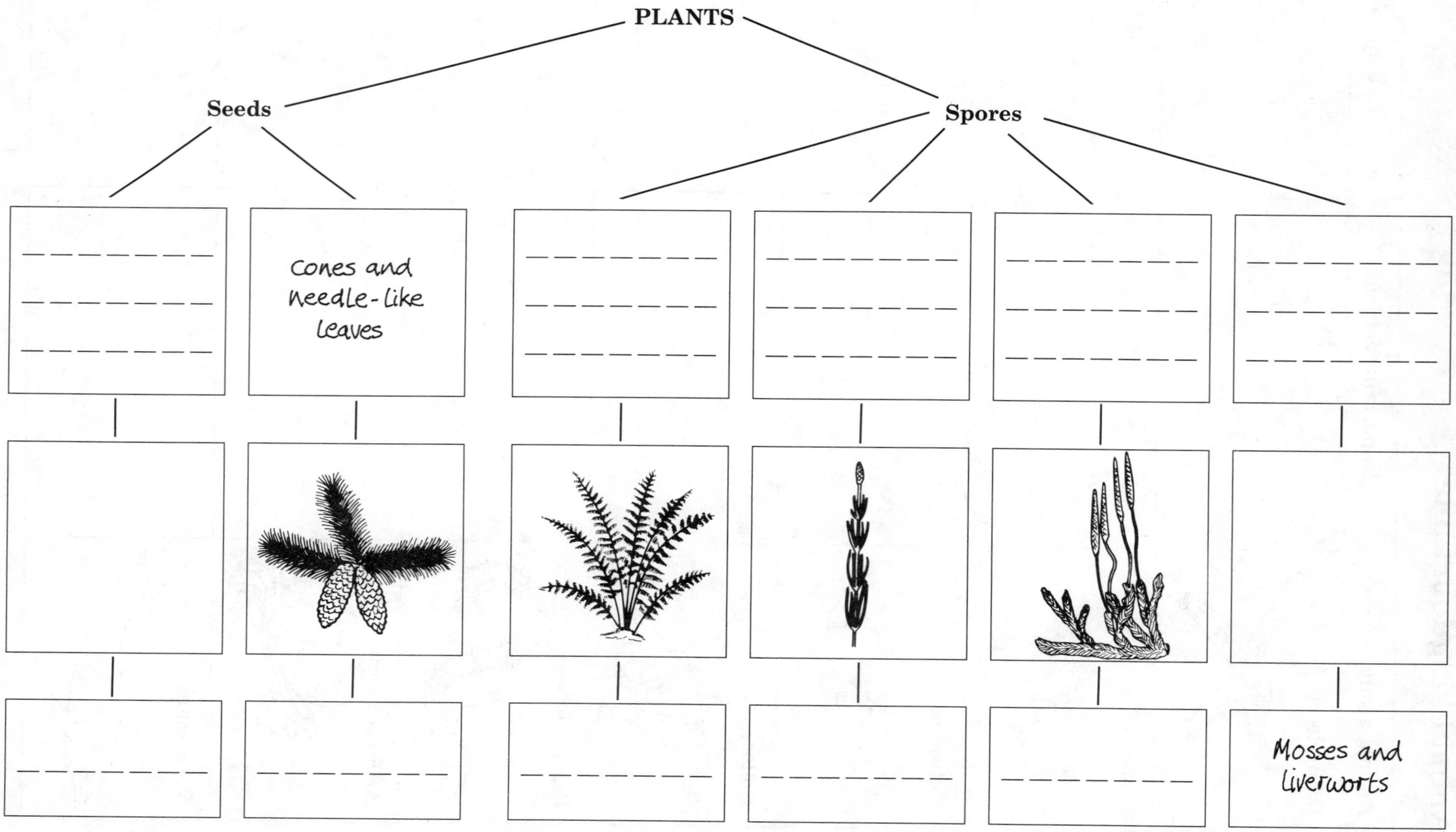

PLANTS

Seeds

Spores

Cones and needle-like leaves

Mosses and liverworts

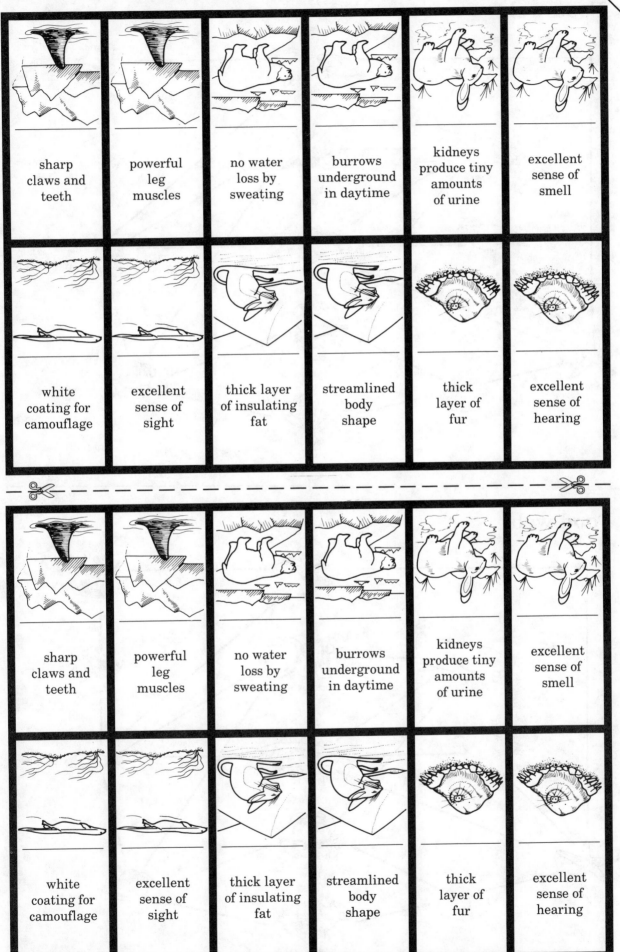

sharp claws and teeth	powerful leg muscles	no water loss by sweating	burrows underground in daytime	kidneys produce tiny amounts of urine	excellent sense of smell
white coating for camouflage	excellent sense of sight	thick layer of insulating fat	streamlined body shape	thick layer of fur	excellent sense of hearing
sharp claws and teeth	powerful leg muscles	no water loss by sweating	burrows underground in daytime	kidneys produce tiny amounts of urine	excellent sense of smell
white coating for camouflage	excellent sense of sight	thick layer of insulating fat	streamlined body shape	thick layer of fur	excellent sense of hearing

Food web

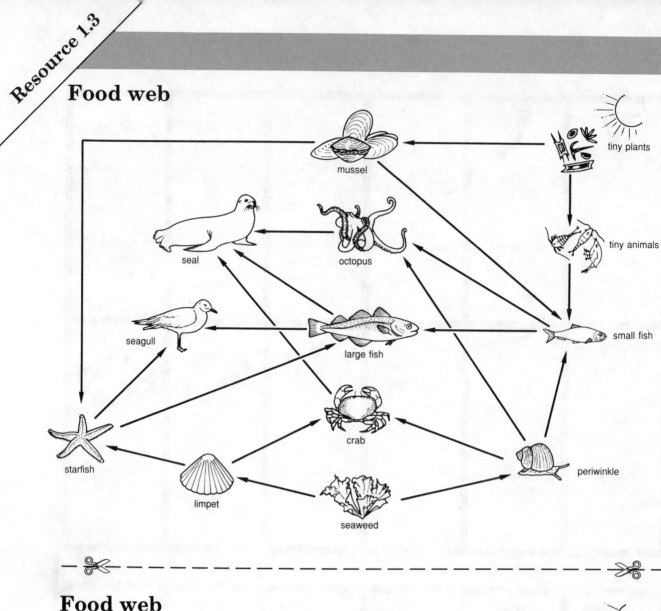

Food web

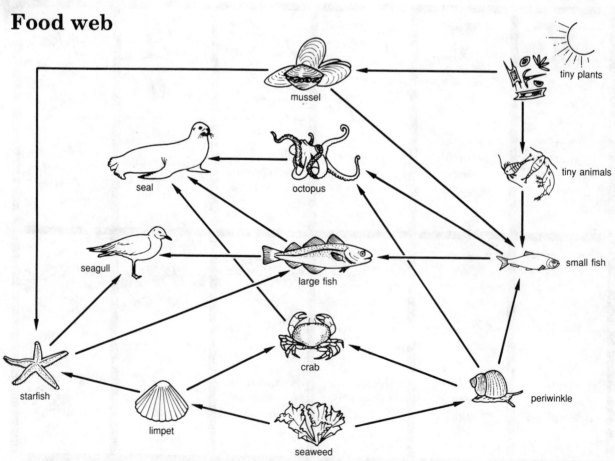

The carbon cycle

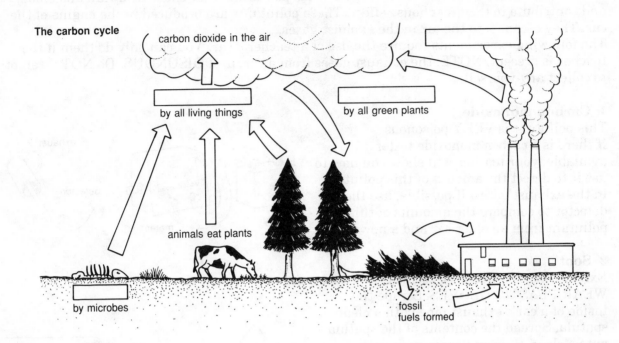

The carbon cycle

carbon dioxide in the air

by all living things

by all green plants

animals eat plants

by microbes

fossil
fuels formed

✂ – ✂

The nitrogen cycle

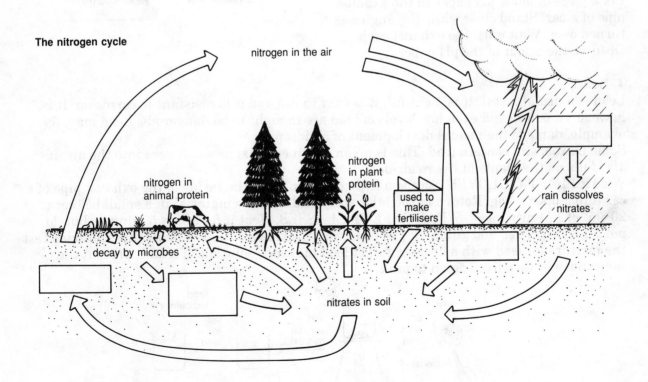

The nitrogen cycle

nitrogen in the air

nitrogen in
animal protein

nitrogen
in plant
protein

used to
make
fertilisers

rain dissolves
nitrates

decay by microbes

nitrates in soil

Car pollution card

Cars are the greatest producers of the major air pollutants that cause acid rain and smog, and contribute to the greenhouse effect. These pollutants are produced in the engine of the car. They escape into the air in the exhaust gases.

The following experiments require the use of a teacher's car. You can only do them if the teacher is present. NOTE: the exhaust gases from a car are POISONOUS. Do NOT attempt to collect any yourself.

1 Carbon monoxide

This pollutant is VERY poisonous. If there is a carbon monoxide tester available, your teacher will show you how to use it to detect the amount of this pollutant in the exhaust gases. If possible, use the detector to compare the amounts of this pollutant from an older car and a newer car.

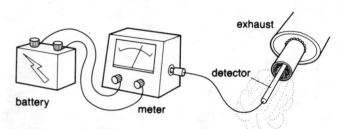

2 Soot

Exhaust gases contain soot which can cause smog. WEAR PLASTIC GLOVES. Scrape the inside of a car's exhaust pipe with a clean spatula. Spread the contents of the spatula onto a clean slide and examine it with a microscope. Is there any evidence of soot? You could also collect the soot by running the car exhaust gases over a slide smeared with Vaseline, as shown.

3 Acid gases

Exhaust gases contain gases like sulphur dioxide and nitrogen dioxide which dissolve in water to give acid rain.

Fix a piece of moist pH paper in the exhaust pipe of a car. Stand clear while the engine is turned over. Wait until the exhaust cools. Observe the colour of the pH paper.

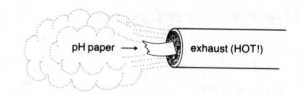

4 Lead

Lead is a useful metal. It is plentiful, it is easy to use and it is resistant to corrosion. It is, however, a poison and even low levels of lead are thought to be dangerous. Lead may, for example, damage the mental development of children.

Some petrols still contain lead. This is given out in exhaust gases. It goes into the air. It also falls on the plants at the roadside.

WEAR PLASTIC GLOVES. Scrape a little of the solid on the inside of the exhaust pipe of a car into a plastic bag. Return to the laboratory and add this material in a small beaker to 20 cm^3 of 1 M nitric acid. WEAR SAFETY GLASSES. Heat it for about 5 minutes but do not let it boil. Then add 20 cm^3 of 1 M sodium hydroxide solution to neutralise the acid. Test the mixture for lead with a dropper full of lead-indicator solution. If lead is present the indicator will turn from green to pink.

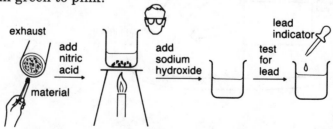

Water test card 1

Collect

Spotting tile
Universal indicator paper
pH colour chart

pH test
Pure water has a pH of 7.
When water has a pH greater than 7 it is alkaline.
When water has a pH of less than 7 it is acid.
Note: pH of 6 will kill some tadpoles.
pH of 5 will kill frog spawn and affect some fish.
pH of 4 will kill many fish.
pH of 3 will kill all fish.

1 Add a drop of the test water to the indicator paper.
2 Compare the colour of the paper with the chart and read the pH number.
3 Your teacher may let you check the value with a pH meter.

Water test card 2

Collect

Long turbidity tube

Turbidity test
Good water is clear. You can see through it to a depth of over 500 mm.
Poor water is much more difficult to see through because it contains substances and microbes which prevent light from getting through.

1 Draw a cross on a piece of paper.
2 Stand the tube so that the bottom is over the cross.
3 Look down the tube. Pour water into the tube until the cross disappears. Stop.
4 Measure the depth of the water in the tube.

Water test card 3

Collect

Filter funnel
Filter paper
Measuring cylinder
Beaker

Suspended solids
Water may have small pieces of mud, plants and even animals spread through it. These bits are small enough to stay suspended in the water. They never settle to the bottom.

1 Put 20 cm³ of your sample into a measuring cylinder.
2 Pour the sample through the filter paper.
3 Use the scale below to estimate the amount of suspended solid.

5
lots of suspended solids

4

3

2

1
no suspended solids

Water test card 4

Collect

Beaker
Tripod and gauze
Heatproof mat
Bunsen burner
Measuring cylinder
Safety glasses

Dissolved solids
As water passes over soil and rock, it dissolves small quantities of many substances. Other soluble substances like nitrates and salt can be added by people by mistake.

1 Put exactly 20 cm³ of the water sample into the clean beaker.
2 Evaporate the water with care using a Bunsen burner.
3 When dry, inspect the beaker for any solid.

Information sheet 2: Building roads

Roads are needed for fast transport. Modern motorways are designed to be wide and fairly straight so that vehicles can travel fast. Some of the effects are shown below.

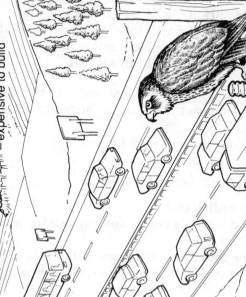

Disadvantages
- route often straight through wildlife areas
- cutting down trees destroys habitats
- large number of animals killed on roads
- pollution from large numbers of vehicles
- salt in winter damages some plants
- expensive to build

Advantages
- fast movement possible
- people get to countryside more easily
- freight transport provides prosperity
- towns by-passed
- lower accident rate on motorways
- less fuel used when cruising
- only small amount of land affected
- some wildlife not affected:
- kestrels flourish
- new trees can be planted on verges

Information sheet 1: Nuclear power

Nuclear power stations use the energy from radioactive substances to produce heat. The heat energy is then used to drive the turbines which make electricity. The left-overs of the nuclear fuel are very radioactive. They must be disposed of very carefully because radioactivity is dangerous to living things. Radioactive substances give out dangerous invisible rays or particles. These can cause cancer: in high amounts they can kill.

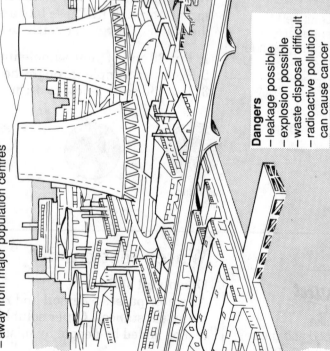

Advantages
- electricity produced cheaply
- safe careful management possible
- away from major population centres

Dangers
- leakage possible
- explosion possible
- waste disposal difficult
- radioactive pollution
  can cause cancer

Information sheet 4: Acid rain

Acid rain is caused when pollutants in the air react with water in snow, mist and rain. Acid rain causes damage to trees and to fish. The diagram below shows some of the problems.

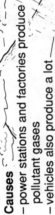

Causes
– power stations and factories produce pollutant gases
– vehicles also produce a lot
– amount of pollutant gases steadily increasing
– these react with water in the air to give rain with a low pH
– this affects the environment
– it travels long distances

Effects
– the lake has become acid
– fish and plants die
– trees lose leaves and needles
– the soil becomes poorer
– important wild habitats are depleted

Solutions
– power stations can reduce sulphur dioxide emissions
– car exhausts can be fitted with catalytic converters
– acid lakes can be neutralised with limestone

Information sheet 3: Using fertilisers

Fertilisers are chemicals that are used to increase the growth of crop plants. More food can thus be produced from the land.

Advantages
– produce a bigger crop – about a 40% increase
– spread easily on fields
– fairly cheap

Problems
– fertilisers in food crops taken into body
– fertilisers run off into the water supply and increase nitrate levels
– too much nitrate increases algae, oxygen used up, fish die

Finding out about being human

This unit builds on those aspects of unit 3 in Book 2 that introduced health and fitness. The revision work therefore refers to cell structure, organ systems, nutrition, keeping physically fit and avoidance of harmful substances. The next five topics introduce genetics and inheritance, and aspects of growth and development: there is a more detailed treatment of digestion, the eye and sight and the ear and hearing. Pupils take an active part in their learning through structured and open-ended practical work and are encouraged to express their own ideas and views on health issues. Individual and co-operative group work is developed throughout. The final three topics comprise an open-ended construction problem for a team to solve, a discussion that challenges their views on personal and social responsibility, and an exercise that demands background reading on a health problem. This unit deals largely with Attainment Targets 3 and 4 of the 1989 National Curriculum. In addition to meeting the general requirements of Attainment Target 1, this unit deals specifically with AT 1 levels 5b, 5d, and 7.

Core and Reinforcement

2.0 Revision—Health check

Revise background work.
Complete a revision question sheet.
Discuss and record a 'radio phone-in programme' on health issues.   *page 24*

Revise earlier work.
Apply knowledge in an imaginative way.

2.1 Who are you?   *AT 4–4a, 5a, 6a,b*

Collect and graph data on variation in hand span.
Complete a family tree to show the inheritance of some characteristics.
Identify examples of genetic and environmental variation from pictures.
          page 26

Measure and record systematically.
Apply a scientific law to solve qualitative problems.
Recognise examples of two forms of variation.

2.2 Grow up   *AT 3–6c,d*

Summarise information on physical development in a flow diagram.
Solve a series of mental puzzles.
Identify and describe essential needs for the complete development of a baby from pictures.   *page 30*

Extract relevant information from text and diagrams.
Communicate ideas in graphical form.
Use imagination to solve puzzles.

Extension

AT 4–7a

Describe the inheritance of sex.
Investigate the incidence of colour blindness amongst classmates.
          page 141

Extract information from a passage.
Communicate scientific ideas by diagrams.
Recognise a pattern in experimental data.

AT 3–6e

Summarise the effects of solvent abuse.
Produce a poster describing the effects of alcohol abuse.
          page 142

Communicate scientific facts and ideas logically and concisely.

Core and Reinforcement

2.3 Food for thought   *AT 3–4b, 5c, 7b*

> Design and carry out an investigation into the
> effect of bile on the speed of digestion of fat.
> Make a flow diagram to show the sequence of
> organs in the digestive system.
> Make a model of the small intestine.   *page 32*

Extract relevant information and translate this from
text to flow diagram.
Design and carry out experiments for a given
purpose.
Draw conclusions from experimental data.
Build a model to demonstrate a scientific idea.

2.4 See here   *AT 15–4a, 6b*

> Complete a diagram to show eye structures
> and their function.
> Investigate features of sight by experiment.
> Build and use a pinhole camera to investigate
> how the eye functions.   *page 34*

Extract relevant information.
Observe and record accurately.
Draw conclusions from experimental observations.
Use a model to explain scientific facts.

2.5 Hear here   *AT 14–6b*

> Complete a diagram showing ear structures
> and their function.
> Investigate features of hearing by experiment.
> Classify hearing defects.   *page 36*

Extract relevant information.
Observe and record accurately.
Draw conclusions from experimental observations.
Recognise examples of a given category.

2.6 Problem—Teamwork

> Design and build a structure to deliver a
> marble from one point to another in a given
> time.   *page 38*

Design and build an object for a given purpose.
Apply scientific methods and ideas to solve a
problem.
Work as part of a team.

2.7 Talkabout—Making decisions   *AT 3–6d*

> Discuss and consider responsible behaviour
> in four given contexts.   *page 39*

Evaluate social and economic implications of health
issues.
Make decisions based on evidence and arguments.

Extension

AT 3–7b

> Design and carry out an investigation into the
> effect of pH on amylase activity.
> Write a scientific report.
>
> *page 143*

Design and carry out experiments for a given
purpose.
Draw conclusions from experimental data.
Communicate scientific ideas logically and
concisely.

AT 3–7c

> Explain behaviour in terms of stimulus,
> receptor and response.
> Study the escape response of an earthworm.
> *page 144*

Suggest an explanation of a familiar observation.
Apply a pattern to describe familiar actions in a
scientific manner.

> Communicate simple words and ideas by
> Morse code, Sign language, Braille and
> symbols/diagrams.
> *page 145*

Communicate in a variety of forms.

Core and Reinforcement

2.8 Readabout—Medical matters   AT 3–5d

> Locate and compile information on a medical problem.
> Give an oral presentation of the response to the problem.   *page 40*

Extract and collate relevant information from a variety of sources.

Equipment
required for each pupil group

2.0—Revision—Health check
- Revision question sheet
- Tape recorder
- Blank audio tape

2.1—Who are you?
- Graph paper
- Hand-span sheet **(R2.1A)**
- 3 beakers
- Beads of two different colours (e.g. popper beads)
- Coloured pencils
- Family-tree sheet and diagram **(R2.1B)**

Extension
- Colour-blind test cards (Ishihara cards)

2.2—Grow up
- Graph paper
- Size data sheet **(R2.2)**
- Spent matches
- 6 coins or metal discs

Notes

Pupils will find it easier to generate health issues after completion of the revision question sheet. Access to copies of *Understanding Science 1* and *2* will allow pupils to check their work and look for information they are unsure of.

Pupils require a certain minimum vocabulary before genetics can make sense. Although many pupils will have some problem in understanding beyond a very superficial level they can normally complete the family tree exercise with increasing confidence.

Colour blindness is a sex-linked recessive trait. About 7% of males and less than 1% of females are affected. The most common form is red–green colour blindness.

Developmental stages take place sequentially and although specific behaviour may seem to regress, development is not thought to be reversible nor can stages be skipped.
An individual's developmental stage can be consolidated by practice and repeated experience. Progress can be encouraged by example and explanation.
Pupils may wish to work out solutions to the puzzles with real matchsticks and coins.
Solutions: **A**—**(i)** 17; **(ii)** 13, 34. **B**—snail, turtle, hare, mouse.

C (i)   C (ii)

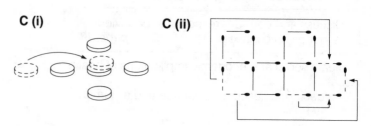

Equipment

Extension

- Health Education Council pamphlets or posters
- Coloured pencils
- Magazines
- Glue
- Scissors
- Stencils

2.3—Food for thought

- Fresh lipase solution (5 g/100 ml water)
- Fresh milk
- Detergent/washing-up liquid
- Universal indicator solution/pH paper
- Spotting tile
- 3 test tubes
- 2 beakers
- 25 ml measuring cylinder or graduated pipette
- Timer
- Teat pipette
- Scissors
- Glue/sticky tape
- 3 sheets scrap paper

Extension

- Freshly made amylase or diastase solution (5 g/100 ml water)
- Dropper bottle of dilute iodine solution
- Dropper bottle of dilute HCl solution
- Dropper bottle of dilute $NaHCO_3$ solution
- Starch solution (5 g/100 ml water)
- Test tubes
- Universal indicator solution/pH paper
- Spotting tile
- Teat pipette

2.4—See here

- Sheep, or pig, eye
- Dissecting board
- Dissection kit
- Experiment cards **(R2.4A 1–6)**

Experiment 2: Seeing colours

- Coloured pencils
- Metre rule

Experiment 4: Shine a light

- Torch

Experiment 6: See through

- Cardboard tube from roll of foil/cling film etc.

Notes

There is an opportunity to introduce AIDS education and to discuss responsible sexual behaviour at this point. All LEAs will have material on both topics.

Digestion and absorption is a difficult topic for pupils. They benefit from revision of particle theory before attempting the investigation. The concept of chemical digestion by enzymes is very abstract. Pupils find explanatory models helpful (e.g. breaking bead models, cutting lengths of wool etc.). Bile improves the activity of lipase by emulsifying the fat and so providing a larger surface area of substrate for the lipase to react with. Pupils should see the universal indicator solution changing colour faster when 'bile' is added to the reactants.

Pupils should be able to stick strips from at least two sheets of paper onto a third piece. This gives a concrete illustration of the increased surface area on the inner lining of the small intestine.

Non-human amylase should be used, or alternatively diastase.
The optimum pH is slightly alkaline.
When testing saliva, pupils should only use their *own* saliva.

Bullocks' eyes are much easier to dissect but may not be available or may be banned. Ask biologist colleagues to demonstrate the best dissecting technique and key structures. Alternatively use video material or models.
Put each experiment card and associated equipment in separate polythene bags for easy storage and class management.
1 Pupils get quantitative data on range of vision.
2 Yellow and red are easiest to see.
3 The blind spot experiment only works if pupils fix their eyes and don't try to look from dot to cross.
4 The pupils dilate in the dark.
5 Our binocular vision provides the brain with overlapping images. This allows us to judge distance accurately.
6 As you move your hand away from your eye you appear to see through a hole in it. This is because of the overlapping images created by binocular vision.

Equipment

- Tin can with top and bottom removed
- Black paper
- Greaseproof paper
- 2 elastic bands
- Candle and holder
- Matches
- Pin
- Glass rod
- Convex lens
- Eye diagrams **(R2.4B)**

Extension
- Earthworm
- Petri dish

2.5—Hear here
- Experiment cards **(R2.5A 1–3)**

Experiment 1: Sound sense
- Stethoscope
- 2 rulers/metal rods/wooden dowels
- Access to sink or glass trough

Experiment 2: Co-ordination
- Ping-pong ball
- Ear plugs/muffs

Experiment 3: Direction of hearing
- Blindfold
- Ear diagram **(R2.5C)**
- Hearing defects sheet **(R2.5B)**

Extension
- Pin
- Coloured pencils

2.6—Problem—Teamwork
- Marble/ball bearing
- Timer
- Sheet of cardboard
- Sheet of poster paper
- Newspaper
- Roll of sticky tape
- 3 plastic caps
- Box of pins
- 3 elastic bands
- 1 metre of string
- Plasticine

Notes

The black paper (iris) and greaseproof paper (retina) must be taut on the pin-hole camera. Pupils start with the smallest hole and see a clear inverted small image. Larger holes make the image brighter and bigger but fuzzier. Lenses can be used to focus the image.

The earthworm contracts its longitudinal muscles when its tail is touched. If this happens too often there is no response—the worm has learned to ignore the stimulus (habituation).

Bag experiment cards with associated equipment.

Sound travels best in solids, then liquids, then air.

Catching is more difficult when there is no sound to aid judgement of pace off surface.

Detecting the direction of sound is more difficult when it comes from somewhere along the centre line between the ears.

This exercise could lead to a discussion on the integration of disabled people into mainstream schools.

This is a 'fun' exercise that can be solved very successfully within about one hour if the group works effectively as a team. Team selection will determine the likely degree of success and consolidates earlier ideas on social and emotional development.
The most successful structures are the simplest – helter-skelter or slide structures. The pins and Plasticine can be used to adjust the speed of the marble.

Equipment

2.7—Talkabout—Making decisions

No equipment required

2.8—Readabout—Medical matters

- Access to biology textbooks, HEA posters and pamphlets on: viral infections and antibiotics, immunisation and whooping cough, insecticides and malaria, noise pollution, need for sleep, posture and healthy feet, typhoid and cholera, sewage works
- Tape recorder
- Blank audio tape

Assessment 2

The questions are designed to assess the skills and knowledge developed in the unit, as shown in the table. The Attainment Target assessed by each question is also shown. A selection of questions would be appropriate for a unit test.

Topic	Core	Attainment Target
2.1	1	AT 4–4a
	2	AT 4–5a
	3, 5	AT 4–6a
	4	AT 4–6b
2.2	6	AT 3–6d
	7	AT 3–6c
2.3	8, 9, 10	AT 3–7b
2.4	11, 12, 13	AT 15–6b
2.5	14, 15, 16, 17	AT 14–6b
2.8	18	AT 3–5d
	Extension	
2.1	19, 20	AT 4–7a
2.2	21, 22	AT 3–6e
2.3	23, 24	AT 3–7b
2.4	25, 26	AT 3–7c

Answers

1 a Bar graph with axes labelled, correct scales and plotting; **b** 200; **c** 55–59;
d environmental;
2 A/F, B/F, C/T, D/F, E/T, F/T
3 Genetic variation—A, B, F.
Environmental variation—C, D, E, G.

Notes

This topic deals with responsible behaviour, and the examples can be extended or replaced to focus on issues of particular relevance; e.g. drug abuse, alcoholism, sexual behaviour.
Some background reading on such issues:
Drugwise, Institute for the Study of Drug Dependence/Teachers Advisory Council on Alcohol and Drug Education/Lifeskills Associates (1986); *Values, Cultures and Kids*, M Bovey (Developmental Education Centre 1982); *Balancing Acts in Personal, Social and Health Education*, J Ryder and L Campbell (Routledge 1988); *School Sex Education—Why, What and How?* D Massey (FPA 1988).

Information on all issues should be readily available within the school. Some background material can be found in *Understanding Science 2*.
The Health Education Authority, Hamilton House, Mabledon Place, London WC1H 9TX can offer advice and provide a range of support material suitable for many aspects of this unit.

4 The idea of following the incidence of the diseases through a family tree; looking for a pattern across several generations.
5 a Brown.
b Both parents carry one allele for black (the idea of heterozygous parents).
6 a Physical, mental.
b Thinking about others; any two reasonable answers.
c Listens to other people's views, understands rules and regulations, enjoys company of people of own age.
7 A—3, B—2, C—2, D—1, E—1, F—1, G—2/3.
8 C—A—D—B—F—E.
9 1—stomach, 2—produces enzymes, 3—digests and/or absorbs food, 4—large intestine.
10 A—5, B—4, C—1, D—3, E—2.
11 a 1—focus light, 2—retina, 3—changes light to electrical impulses, 4—cornea, 5—maintains shape of eye, 6—iris.
b Optic nerve.
c Judgement of distance is better, better co-ordinated movement.
d Diameter of pupil larger in B than in A and iris diameter the same in both eyes.
12 A—these colours are the easiest to see.
B—eyes accustomed to dark take a little time to adjust to light/takes time for the iris to adjust size of pupil.
C—better judgement of distance.
D—no distractions from peripheral/side vision.
13 a Cornea—liquid—iris—lens—liquid—rentina—optic nerve.
b (i) Cornea, lens.

(ii) The pupil is not a structure, it is a hole.
(iii) Iris, lens.
14 a 1—Changes sound/vibrations into electrical impulses.
2—Keeps air pressure the same on each side of the ear drum.
3—Ear drum.
4—Vibrates when sound hits it/transmits sound.
5—Small bones/hammer, anvil, stirrup.
b By vibrations/as sound waves.
15 Control of variables—Distance of meter from source of sound, —loudness of sound, —amount of insulation added; repetition of experiment.
16 A—Collect sound from all areas, detect direction of sound. B—Pressure on ear drums. C—Sound reaches one ear before the other so the brain can interpret the direction easily.
17 A—1, B—3, C—2, D—1/2, E—1.
18 Longer sleep/earlier to bed, more suitable/less tight clothes, proper meals, no smoking, avoid stress/do homework, take exercise, any other sensible comment based on the passage (*any five correct*).
19 Description of sex chromosomes—XX female, XY male;
description of sex chromosomes carried by sex cells—sperm X or Y, eggs X only;
demonstration of how this generates a 50 : 50 ratio of males to females.

20 Female—sperm X, egg X, fertilised egg XX.
Male—sperm Y, egg X, fertilised egg XY.
21 a Alcohol slows down nervous system;
b Glue fumes slow down breathing and heart rate: *or* answers relating to damage to brain and liver (alcohol & glue) and kidneys (glue) which state the function of these organs.
22 Glue—B, E, F; alcohol—A, H, I; both—C, D, G.
23 Carbohydrate—amylase—maltose.
Fat—lipase—fatty acids and glycerol.
Protein—protease—amino acids.
24 Correct mixture—starch and amylase.
Range of temperature—at least four temperatures.
Means of following reaction—negative test for starch with iodine.
Means of identifying best temperature.
Control of variables—volumes of liquid, pH.
25 List 1—pop music, sunshine, perfume, heat.
List 2—hamstring muscle, biceps muscle.
List 3—eye, skin, ear, tongue.
26 a Effector—arm muscle; stimulus—heat; co-ordinator—brain; receptor—skin.
b Light, sound, pressure, cold, gravity, smells/tastes/chemicals (*any three*).
c Eye, ear, skin, semi-circular canals, tongue, nose (*any three*).

True/false 2

Each statement is marked as either true or false by the pupil. This gives a rapid assessment of a pupil's grasp of the Attainment Targets covered in the unit. This list gives the Attainment Targets covered by each set of statements.

1	AT 3–5d	7	AT 4–6b
2	AT 3–6c	8	AT 14–6b
3	AT 3–6d	9	AT 15–6b
4	AT 3–7b	10	AT 3–6e
5	AT 4–5a	11	AT 3–7c
6	AT 4–6a	12	AT 4–7a

Unit 2 Body and mind

Name _____

1 Write the meaning of each word or phrase in the space provided. The figures in brackets are references to *Understanding Science*, Books 1 and 2 (**book number, page number**). Use the references to *check* your answers.

- an animal cell (**1**, 95)
- a plant cell (**1**, 95)
- the function of the cell nucleus (**1**, 95)
- the function of a white blood cell (**1**, 96)
- sexual reproduction in humans (**1**, 139)
- the circulatory system (**2**, 44)
- the nervous system (**2**, 44)
- the digestive system (**2**, 50)
- balanced diet (**2**, 47)
- malnutrition (**2**, 47)
- being fit and healthy (**2**, 44).
- the importance of exercise (**2**, 54)
- the dangers of smoking (**2**, 56)
- the dangers of drinking alcohol (**2**, 57)
- the dangers of drug abuse (**2**, 145).

2 The spider diagram shows some connections between these terms. Complete the diagram with the correct words.

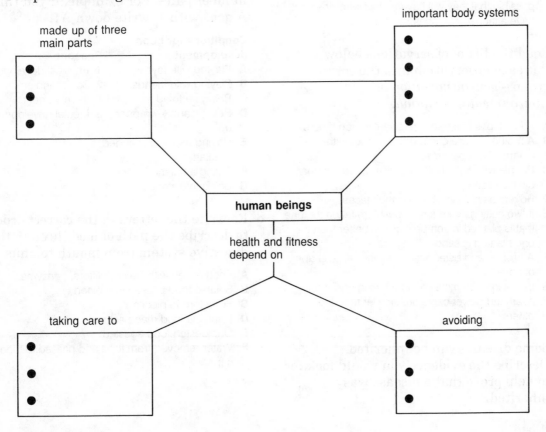

1 Plums were picked and sorted into groups by weight. The table below gives the results for the plums picked by one person from a single tree.

Weight range (g)	45–49	50–54	55–59	60–64	65–70
Number of plums	18	42	65	48	27

   a Draw a bar graph of the results.
   b Calculate the total number of plums picked.
   c What was the most common weight range of plum?
   d Is this an example of genetic or of environmental variation?

2 Having attached ear lobes is an inherited characteristic.
   Answer the following questions *true* or *false*.

   A A person born with attached ear lobes can lose this characteristic in later life.
   B Ear-lobe information can only be passed to the child by its mother.
   C Ear-lobe information is carried by a gene.
   D The appearance of your ear lobes can be affected by changes in the season.
   E If both parents have attached ear lobes it is likely that they will have a child who has attached ear lobes.
   F If both parents have attached ear lobes it is possible that they will have a child who does not have attached ear lobes.

3 Read the list of observations below. Put each observation into the correct group – *genetic variation* or *environmental variation*.

   A Some types of apples are sweeter than others.
   B A mother mouse can produce a litter with different coat patterns.
   C People who eat a balanced diet do not get the disease scurvy.
   D Boxers often have scars on their faces.
   E If two cuttings from a rose bush are taken the one that is planted in compost grows better than the one planted in sand.
   F A brother and sister often have the same shape of nose.
   G In a field of corn the plants growing under an overhead power cable are smaller than the others.

4 Some diseases can be inherited. Describe the evidence you would look for to help prove that a disease was inherited.

5 The results of a genetic investigation into coat colour of mice is shown below.

	Colour of male mouse	Colour of female mouse	Colour of baby mice
1	brown	black	all brown
2	brown	brown	mostly brown with a few black
3	black	black	all black

   a What colour seems to be dominant?
   b How can the results of the second mating be explained?

6 Growth and development is very complicated.
   a Social and emotional changes are only part of growing up. Name two other parts.
   b What does responsible behaviour mean?
   c What emotional development takes place in the teenage years?

7 Babies develop very quickly. Match the conditions for good development with the correct reason. Write down the correct letter and number pairs. For example, if you think A goes with 1, write down A1.

Conditions for good development
   A Playing with toys
   B Playing with friends
   C Being cuddled
   D Being warmly wrapped up
   E Having nappies changed regularly
   F Eating a balanced diet
   G Being told stories

Reasons
   1 Physical development
   2 Social and emotional development
   3 Mental development

8 Re-write the letters in the correct order to describe the path of food through the digestive system from mouth to anus.

   A Food mixed with several different enzymes
   B Soluble food passed into blood
   C Food torn to pieces
   D Insoluble food made soluble
   E Undigested food egested
   F Water removed from food and passed to blood supply

continued ▶

9 Look at the diagram of the human digestive system below.

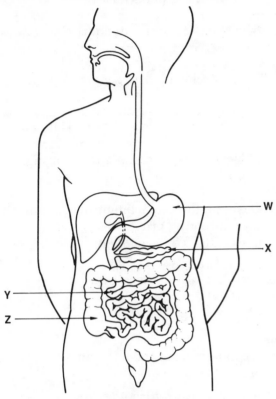

Copy and complete the table with the names of the missing parts and descriptions of what the parts do.

Letter	Name of part	What the part does
W	1	stores and mixes food
X	pancreas	2
Y	small intestine	3
Z	4	absorbs water

10 Damaged parts of the digestive system can be removed in hospital. The patient is given advice on possible problems and on how to keep healthy.
Match the advice below with the part of the digestive system removed. Write down the correct letter and number pairs.

If this was removed . . .	the advice would be
A Stomach	**1** Avoid fatty food.
B Teeth	**2** Less water will be absorbed.
C Gall bladder	**3** Less food will be digested.
D Part of small intestine	**4** Eat softer food.
E Part of large intestine	**5** Eat smaller meals.

11 The diagram below shows a cross section of the human eye.

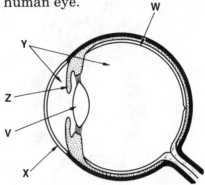

a Copy and complete the table with names of the parts and a description of what the parts do.

Letter	Name of part	What the part does
V	lens	1
W	2	3
X	4	tough window lets light in
Y	liquid	5
Z	6	controls amount of light entering the eye

b Name the part of the eye that takes electrical impulses to the brain.
c Why should it be easier to play tennis if you have two eyes rather than one?
d Copy both drawings below and complete *drawing B* to show the appearance of the eye in dim light.

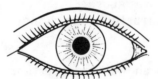   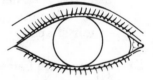

A the eye in normal light   **B** the eye in dim light

12 Explain each of the following observations.

A Fire engines are usually painted yellow or red.
B People coming out of a cinema on a sunny day cover their eyes.
C Mammals that are predators have eyes that face forward.

continued ▶

D Race horses often wear blinkers.

13 a The main structures of the eye are listed below in alphabetical order. Write a list that describes the path of light through the eye from the time it enters to the time nerve impulses are sent to the brain.

- cornea
- iris
- lens
- liquid
- optic nerve
- retina

b (i) Which two structures are involved in bending light to a focus?
(ii) Why is the pupil not present in the list of structures above?
(iii) Which two structures can change their shape?

14 The diagram below shows a cross section of the human ear.

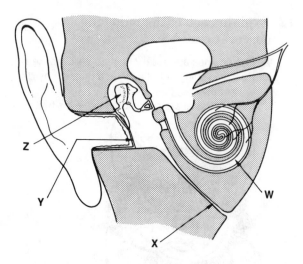

a Copy and complete the table with the names of the parts and a description of what the parts do.

Letter	Name of part	What the part does
W	cochlea	1
X	Eustachian tube	2
Y	3	4
Z	5	transmits sound across the middle ear

b How is sound transmitted through the air?

15 Design a fair experiment to compare the soundproofing properties of two materials. You are given

- a bag of cotton wool
- a bag of cardboard egg cartons
- a sound meter
- a room with cavity walls
- a bell.

16 Explain each of the following observations.

A Many animals can move their ears.
B When you dive deep underwater your ears hurt.
C The direction of sound is easier to detect when it comes from the left or right side than it is when it comes from the front or rear.

17 Hearing defects are quite common and are caused in many ways. Several parts of the ear can be affected.
Match the cause of a hearing defect with the part of the ear most likely to be affected. The parts of the ear can be used more than once. Write down the correct letter and number pairs.

If this happened . . .	this part of the ear would be affected
A pushing a sharp object into the ear	**1** ear drum
B listening to loud music over a long time period	**2** Eustachian tube
C having a very heavy cold and/or blocked nose	**3** cochlea
D blowing the nose too hard	
E having too much wax in the outer ear	

continued ▶

18 Read the page from a friend's diary.

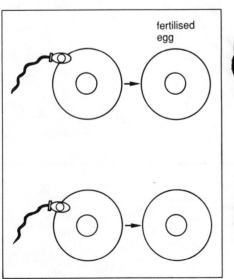

MONDAY
What a day! I got to bed really late as usual last night. I slept in and I only had time to squeeze into my jeans (they are a size too small, but you have to be fashionable don't you?), teeshirt and old trainers which are a bit on the tight side, grab a handful of biscuits and rush for the bus. Homework wasn't finished so. I was worried sick all through Science. I was given one more day to complete it — what a great teacher.
I skipped PE because I just hate exercise, and lunch because I was desperate for a cigarette. By the end of the afternoon I felt awful.

Suggest five changes to your friend's lifestyle that would improve their health.

Extension questions

19 Explain why, when babies are born, about half are female and half male.

20 The sex of a baby depends on which two sex chromosomes it inherits.
Copy and complete the diagrams in the box below; show how the sex of a baby is controlled by writing the correct sex chromosome(s) in each cell.

Sharon

Frank

fertilised egg

21 Describe how one body process is affected by
a drinking alcohol;
b sniffing glue.

22 The list below describes risks to health.
Copy and complete the table to show which risks are caused by sniffing glue *or* by drinking alcohol *or* by both.
Put the letters of each risk in the correct column in the table.

Risks to health
A addiction
B spots around mouth
C brain damage
D liver damage
E kidney damage
F lower breathing rate
G unpredictable behaviour
H gaining weight
I malnutrition

Sniffing glue	Drinking alcohol	Both

23 In digestion each food type is broken down by a different enzyme to make a product.
Copy the three lists below.

Food type	Enzyme	Product
carbohydrate	amylase	amino acid
fat	protease	maltose
protein	lipase	fatty acids and glycerol

Draw a line to link each food to the enzyme that breaks it down.
Draw a line to link each enzyme to the product it makes.

24 Design an experiment to investigate the effect of temperature on the action of the enzyme amylase.

continued ▶

25 Read the three lists below.

From list 1 write down every example of a stimulus.

From list 2 write down every example of an effector.

From list 3 write down every example of a receptor.

List 1

pop music, big toe, hair, sunshine, perfume, hamstring muscle, heat

List 2

drum beat, hamstring muscle, television screen, brain, biceps muscle, North Sea gas, moon beam

List 3

hamstring muscle, eye, skin, dirty socks, ear, Radio 1, tongue

26 a Here is what happens when you warm your hands by an open fire.

You feel the **heat** on the **skin** of your hands. Your **brain** thinks 'that feels good'. Your **arm muscles** move to make your hands rub together.

Match each of the words in **bold type** to the correct word in the list below.

effector
stimulus
co-ordinator
receptor

b Write down three other examples of stimuli.

c Write down three other examples of receptors.

Unit 2 Body and mind

Name_____

Put a tick after the statements that are true.
Put a cross after the statements that are false.

1 a All diseases are caused by microbes. ☐
  b The scientific term for microbe is bacterium. ☐
  c Your emotional state affects how healthy you feel. ☐
  d The shoes you wear and the way you stand can cause health problems. ☐

2 a Young children only cry to get attention. ☐
  b The younger the child the more sleep it requires. ☐
  c Because young children need lots of food they should be allowed to eat anything they like. ☐
  d Young children need love and affection for normal development. ☐

3 a As you grow from baby to teenager your co-ordination gets worse. ☐
  b The time of most rapid growth is the baby stage. ☐
  c Puberty is reached before full emotional development. ☐
  d Playing with others prevents good social development. ☐
  e Responsible behaviour cannot be learned; it comes naturally. ☐
  f A child of two does not have a well-developed sense of fair play. ☐

4 a The liver produces a chemical called bile. ☐
  b Each food type is digested by a different enzyme. ☐
  c In digestion food molecules are made larger. ☐
  d Enzymes pass food from the large intestine into the blood supply. ☐
  e Most chemical digestion takes place in the stomach. ☐
  f Proteins are changed to amino acids by digestion. ☐

5 a You cannot inherit characteristics from both your mother and father. ☐
  b Human information is carried on a pair of genes. ☐

c Some of your features will be passed on to your children in your genes. ☐
  d Your genes change as you grow older. ☐
  e Dominant characteristics are more common than recessive characteristics. ☐

6 a Variation is caused by the environment only. ☐
  b Genetic variation is inherited. ☐
  c The colour of your eyes depends on the weather. ☐
  d A tree grows less quickly in the cold than in the warm. This is an example of environmental variation. ☐
  e Some people wear a watch on their right arm, others on their left arm. This is environmental variation. ☐

7 a Some diseases can be inherited. ☐
  b If a person is treated for an inherited disease, the disease cannot be passed on to their children. ☐
  c Information for inherited diseases is passed from one generation to the next by microbes. ☐

8 a Sound is caused by vibrations. ☐
  b Sound travels best in air. ☐
  c The ear drum sends messages to the brain. ☐
  d One form of deafness can be treated by removing the tiny bones in the middle ear. ☐
  e A blockage in the Eustachian tube can affect hearing. ☐
  f The cochlea allows us to detect the direction of sound. ☐

9 a The lens changes shape to control the amount of light entering the eye. ☐
  b The part of the eye sensitive to light is the retina. ☐
  c The pupil gets larger in bright light. ☐
  d The auditory nerve controls eye movement. ☐
  e If you close one eye it is easier to judge distance. ☐

continued ▶

Understanding Science 3

49

f Light is focused onto the retina by the cornea and the iris. ☐

Extensions

10 a Alcohol damages the kidneys. ☐
b Trying a drug once only cannot cause any harm. ☐
c Solvent abuse can cause brain damage. ☐
d Chemicals bought from shops are unlikely to be harmful because they have been tested. ☐
e Alcohol has lots of calories. ☐
f If drugs are taken in a group it is safer and more sociable. ☐
g Glue sniffing can cause heart failure. ☐

11 a The eye, ear, nose and tongue are all examples of receptors. ☐
b At its most simple, behaviour is a response to a stimulus. ☐
c A stimulus provides the link between the receptor and the effector. ☐
d The co-ordinator in humans is the muscle system. ☐

12 a The sex of a baby depends on the month in which it is conceived. ☐
b The sex of a baby is inherited from its mother only. ☐
c Females have two similar sex chromosomes. ☐
d Males have two Y chromosomes. ☐
e There is an equal chance of having a boy or girl baby. ☐

Name _____

Complete each sentence. Put the correct word(s) in each blank space.

1 Human variation can have _____ or environmental causes.

Eye colour is an example of _____ variation. Two other examples

are ● _____ ● _____ .

Environmental factors can cause variation by affecting the way

_____ work. Two examples of environmental variation are

● _____ ● _____ .

2 Information in the form of _____ is passed from one

_____ to the next. Genes can have a _____ form or a

recessive form.

Some diseases such as _____ can be inherited.

3 Growing up involves several types of changes such as

● _____

● mental development

● _____ .

There are some conditions and experiences that very young children need for their

complete growth, such as

● _____

● _____

● _____ .

4 Digestion involves breaking large, _____ molecules into

_____ , soluble molecules. These can then pass from the

_____ into the _____ supply.

Digested food goes to every body _____ where it can be used to

provide _____ or to repair tissue or to build new tissue.

continued▶

Name _____

5 Most of the chemical breakdown of food takes place in the _____

and requires special chemicals called _____ .

One organ that produces these substances is the _____ .

6 The inside of the small intestine has a very large _____ to absorb

food. Extra water is removed from the food in the _____ .

Undigested food is eventually _____ at the

_____ .

7 Light enters the eye through a clear window called the _____ .

It then passes through the pupil. The size of the pupil is controlled by the

_____ which gives the eye its colour. Next comes the lens which

can _____ the light onto the _____ . Messages

are produced here and carried by _____ to the brain.

8 Two eyes allow us to judge _____ well and give us a wide

_____ of vision.

9 We hear because of _____ which makes the

_____ vibrate. These vibrations are passed to the ear

_____ , then to the _____ . Here the vibrations

are turned into _____ impulses and sent to the

_____ .

10 Hearing can be damaged when

- the _____ of vibrations through the ear is disturbed

- the cochlea or the _____ nerve is damaged

- there are problems with air _____ in the ear.

11 Mature behaviour means being responsible for

- _____

- _____

- _____ .

Hand-span sheet

Name _____ Class _____

My hand span is _____ mm.

Class Results

Span (mm)	120–134	135–149	150–164	165–179	180–194	195–209	210–224
Number of pupils							

— ✂ — ✂ —

Hand-span sheet

Name _____ Class _____

My hand span is _____ mm.

Class Results

Span (mm)	120–134	135–149	150–164	165–179	180–194	195–209	210–224
Number of pupils							

— ✂ — ✂ —

Hand-span sheet

Name _____ Class _____

My hand span is _____ mm.

Class Results

Span (mm)	120–134	135–149	150–164	165–179	180–194	195–209	210–224
Number of pupils							

— ✂ — ✂ —

Hand-span sheet

Name _____ Class _____

My hand span is _____ mm.

Class Results

Span (mm)	120–134	135–149	150–164	165–179	180–194	195–209	210–224
Number of pupils							

Family tree sheet

A family tree can be used to show how some characteristics are inherited in a family.

The genes are represented by beads, a dark bead for the DOMINANT allele of a gene and a light bead for the RECESSIVE allele.

Place 12 dark beads in a beaker and label it '*DOMINANT*'.

Place 12 light beads in a second beaker and label it '*RECESSIVE*'.

Place 6 dark and 6 light beads in a third beaker. Label it '*MIX*'.

Use these beads to show the inheritance of:

a Eye colour – BROWN is DOMINANT and BLUE is RECESSIVE;
b Hair line – WIDOW'S PEAK is DOMINANT, STRAIGHT HAIR-LINE is RECESSIVE;
c Hair colour – DARK HAIR is DOMINANT, BLOND HAIR is RECESSIVE.

Refer to the family tree diagram. The alleles of the genes carried by both grandparents for each characteristic are shown in the boxes beside the face shapes.

1 To find the alleles of the eye-colour genes inherited by MOTHER 1
— take one bead from the '*MIX*' beaker (this is the allele carried by the grandfather's sperm)
— take one bead from the '*MIX*' beaker (the allele carried by the grandmother's egg).
You will have one of the sets of beads shown below.

       ● ○   *or*   ● ●   *or*   ○ ○

Both these sets produce the DOMINANT characteristic – BROWN EYES.

This set gives the RECESSIVE characteristic – BLUE EYES.

2 Show the genes inherited by MOTHER 1 in the box beside her face. Return the beads to the '*MIX*' beaker.

3 Repeat this to find the genes inherited by MOTHER 2.

4 Keep repeating this method until you have found the eye colour for everyone in the family tree. Remember to take a bead from the '*DOMINANT*' beaker if the person has only DOMINANT alleles of the gene for eye colour (such as FATHER 2). Similarly take a bead from the '*RECESSIVE*' beaker if the person has only RECESSIVE alleles of the gene. Colour in everyone's eyes.

5 Repeat this to find the hairline and hair colour inherited by everyone. Draw these in.

Family tree diagram

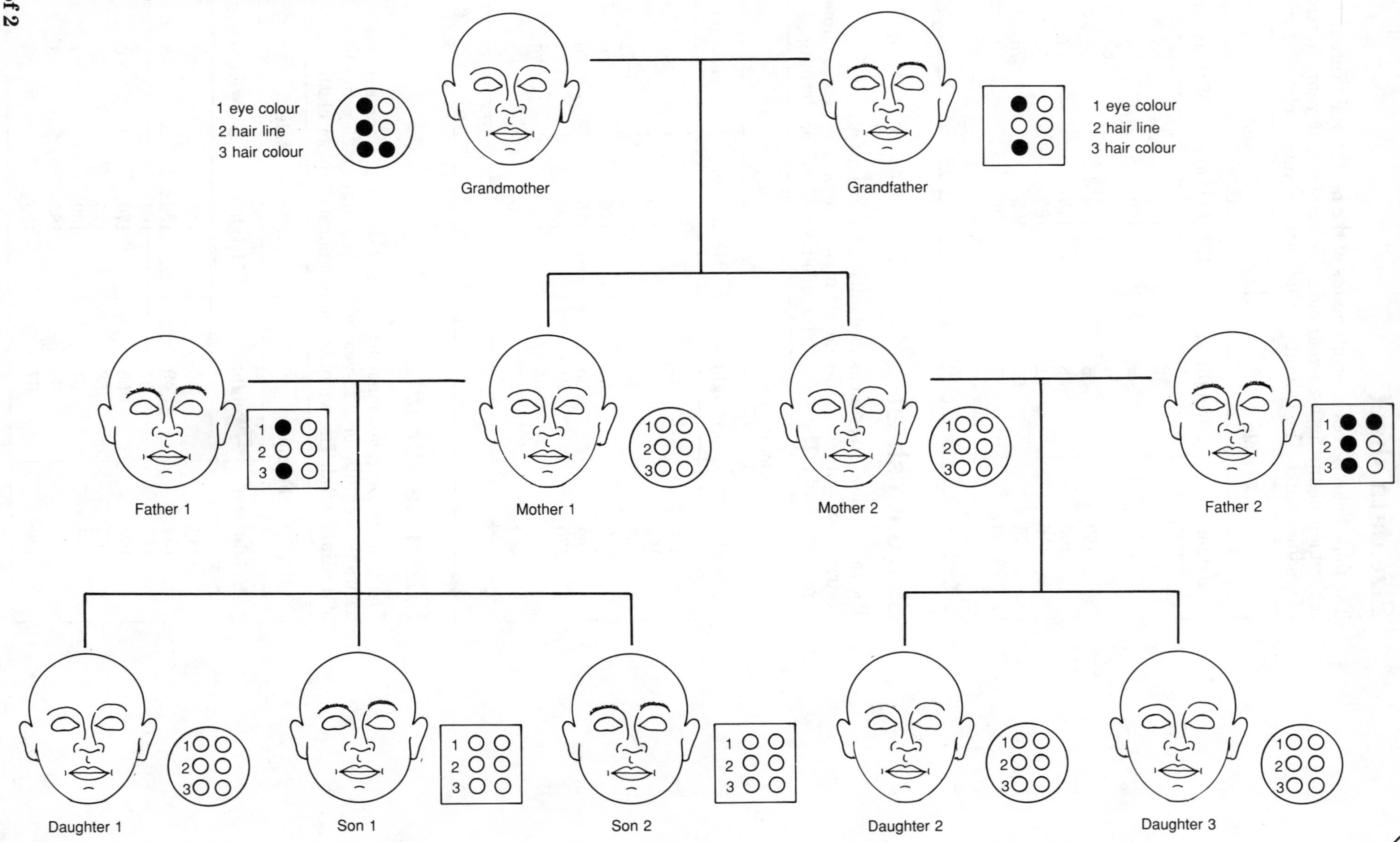

1 eye colour
2 hair line
3 hair colour

1 eye colour
2 hair line
3 hair colour

Grandmother

Grandfather

Father 1

Mother 1

Mother 2

Father 2

Son 1

Son 2

Daughter 1

Daughter 2

Daughter 3

Size data sheet

The table below gives measurements of the height and average desirable weights for a 25-year-old male and for a 25-year-old female of medium build. The weights include normal indoor clothing.

Female		Male	
Height (cm)	**Weight** (kg)	**Height** (cm)	**Weight** (kg)
145	46	155	56
150	49	160	59
155	51	165	62
160	55	170	66
165	58	175	70
170	61	180	74
175	65	185	78
180	67	190	82

Size data sheet

The table below gives measurements of the height and average desirable weights for a 25-year-old male and for a 25-year-old female of medium build. The weights include normal indoor clothing.

Female		Male	
Height (cm)	**Weight** (kg)	**Height** (cm)	**Weight** (kg)
145	46	155	56
150	49	160	59
155	51	165	62
160	55	170	66
165	58	175	70
170	61	180	74
175	65	185	78
180	67	190	82

Size data sheet

The table below gives measurements of the height and average desirable weights for a 25-year-old male and for a 25-year-old female of medium build. The weights include normal indoor clothing.

Female		Male	
Height (cm)	**Weight** (kg)	**Height** (cm)	**Weight** (kg)
145	46	155	56
150	49	160	59
155	51	165	62
160	55	170	66
165	58	175	70
170	61	180	74
175	65	185	78
180	67	190	82

Experiment 1: *Range of vision*

Find your range of vision.

1 Look straight ahead.
  Bring your arms forward slowly. Stop when you see your hands. Note the position of your arms. Measure the distance between them.

2 Look straight ahead.
  Slowly lower your top hand and raise your bottom hand. Stop when you can see both.
  Measure the distance between them.

1 Draw the view from above your head to show your range of vision to each side. Record the distance between your hands.
2 Copy the second diagram. Record the distance between your hands on your diagram.
3 Predict what the range of vision of a rabbit would be (its eyes are on the side of its head).
  How does this help the rabbit?

Experiment 2: *Seeing colours*

Find out if some colours are easier to see than others.

1 Sit on a stool facing forward. Look straight ahead only.
  Place a metre rule on the floor about 1 m to the left of your stool.
  Your partner stands behind you about half a metre to the side.

2 Your partner holds up a coloured pencil at arm's length, starting at the end of the rule. Your partner then moves forward very slowly.

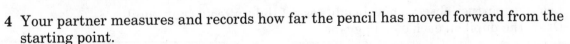

3 Say '*stop*' when you are sure you can see the colour of the pencil. Don't guess!

4 Your partner measures and records how far the pencil has moved forward from the starting point.

5 Repeat this with other colours, change positions with your partner.

1 Which colour did you see most easily?
  Make a list of colours from *easiest* to *most difficult to see*.
2 Suggest suitable colours for ambulances and fire engines.
3 Explain the colouring you see in bees and wasps.

1 of 4

Experiment 3: *Spot the dot*

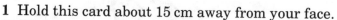

1 Hold this card about 15 cm away from your face.
2 Close your left eye. Focus your right eye on the cross.
3 Slowly move the card away from your face. Notice what happens to the dot.

> There are no light sensitive cells on the retina where the optic nerve leaves the eye. This area is called the *blind spot*. If an image is focused on this spot, it cannot be seen.

1 Draw the cross and dot in your book – about 10 cm apart.
2 Describe what happens in the experiment.
3 Copy the information in the box above.

 ✂ ---------------------------- ✂

Experiment 4: *Shine a light*

1 Copy the three outline drawings of the eye into your book.

Normal light   Brighter light   Dimmer light

2 Look at your partner's eyes. Observe the size of the pupils. Measure them if you can.

3 Investigate the effect of brighter and of dimmer light on the size of the pupils.

4 Let your partner observe how brightness of light affects your pupils.
Draw the pupil on each eye diagram.

1 Make up a rule that describes how brightness of light affects pupil size.
2 Describe how the change in pupil size is brought about.
3 Bushbabies are nocturnal animals (they are active at night). Draw the sort of eyes you would expect a bushbaby to have. Explain your prediction.

Experiment 5: *Seeing double*

1 – Now you see it, now you don't

a Close your *right* eye.
Hold your right arm out in front of you
and stick up your first finger.

b Look at a door or window frame across
the room. Cover an edge of the frame
with your first finger. Don't move.
Close your left eye and open your right
eye. Now look with both eyes.

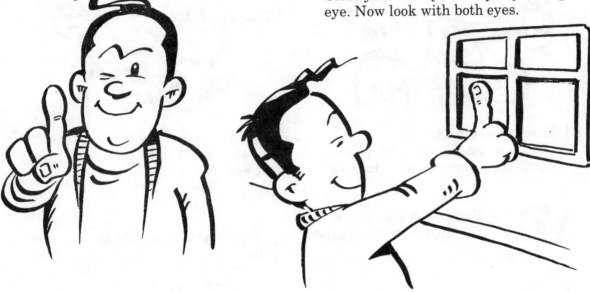

2 – Judging distance

a Sit at your desk with one arm at your
side. Point your first finger off to one
side.
Close *both* eyes.
Your partner holds a pencil upright on
the desk some distance from you.

b Open *one* eye only.
Swing your arm forward and try to
touch the pencil with the *tip* of your
finger. Try this several times.
Try it with both eyes open.
Change positions with your partner.

1 Describe what happened in activity 1.
2 How is the image that you see with both eyes made?
3 Describe what happens in activity 2.
4 Why are two eyes best for judging distance?

3 of 4

Experiment 6: *See through*

Try this experiment after you have completed *Experiment 5: 'Seeing double'*.

1 Keep both eyes open.
Look through the tube with one eye.
Cover the other eye with your hand.

2 Keeping both eyes open, move your hand slowly along the tube away from your eye.

1 Draw what you saw.
2 Explain the result of the experiment (Experiment 5 should help you).

- - - ✂ - ✂ - -

Experiment 6: *See through*

Try this experiment after you have completed *Experiment 5: 'Seeing double'*.

1 Keep both eyes open.
Look through the tube with one eye.
Cover the other eye with your hand.

2 Keeping both eyes open, move your hand slowly along the tube away from your eye.

1 Draw what you saw.
2 Explain the result of the experiment (Experiment 5 should help you).

Eye diagrams

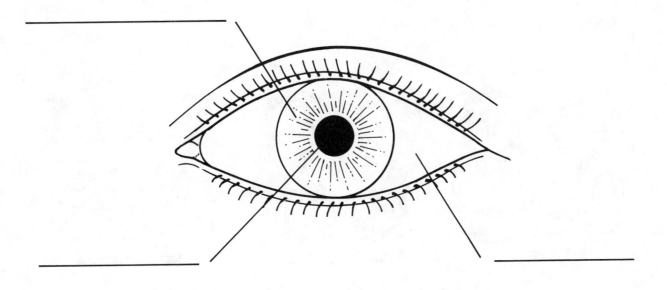

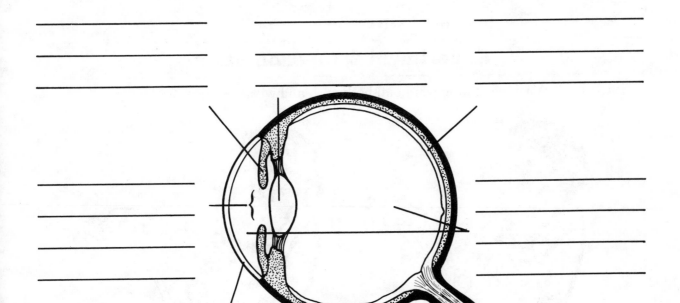

Experiment 1: *Sound sense*

Investigate how easily sound travels through a solid, a liquid and a gas.

Use a stethoscope to detect the sound.

1 Write a short report on the experiment.
2 Why is it difficult to obtain reliable results from this experiment?

Experiment 2: *Co-ordination*

Try to catch a bouncing ping-pong ball both with and without earmuffs on.

1 Describe the difference in your ability to catch the ball. Try to explain how sound is involved.
2 Why do tennis players ask the crowd to be quiet during play?

Experiment 3: *Direction of hearing*

Copy the drawing below.

1 Blindfold your partner.
Do not speak.
Snap your fingers or make a sharp noise at any of the points shown on your diagram.

2 Your partner describes exactly where the noise came from.
Put a tick on the diagram for a correct description; put a cross for wrong.

3 Quietly move to a new position and repeat the test. Do this until most or all of the positions have been tested.

4 Now your partner can test your hearing in the same way.

1 When is it easy to judge from where a sound comes?
2 When is it difficult to judge the direction of a sound?

- - - - - ✂ - ✂ - -

Experiment 3: *Direction of hearing*

Copy the drawing below.

1 Blindfold your partner.
Do not speak.
Snap your fingers or make a sharp noise at any of the points shown on your diagram.

2 Your partner describes exactly where the noise came from.
Put a tick on the diagram for a correct description; put a cross for wrong.

3 Quietly move to a new position and repeat the test. Do this until most or all of the positions have been tested.

4 Now your partner can test your hearing in the same way.

1 When is it easy to judge from where a sound comes?
2 When is it difficult to judge the direction of a sound?

2 of 2

Hearing defects

Discuss the causes of hearing loss described below. Decide what the result of each would be and put a tick in the correct column.

Stick this sheet into your book.

Cause	Result		
	Nerve damage	Pressure altered	Faulty transmission
A heavy cold blocks the Eustachian tube			
The ear bones join together and stop vibrating			
An ear injury makes a hole in the ear drum			
Wax builds up in the outer ear			
Very loud noises damage tiny hairs in the cochlea			
In glue ear, fluid builds up behind the ear drum			
The nose is blown too hard causing the ear drum to be pushed out of shape			
A head injury damages the hearing centre of the brain			

Many ear defects last for a short time only.
More serious defects can be helped by hearing aids or by operations.

Hearing defects

Discuss the causes of hearing loss described below. Decide what the result of each would be and put a tick in the correct column.

Stick this sheet into your book.

Cause	Result		
	Nerve damage	Pressure altered	Faulty transmission
A heavy cold blocks the Eustachian tube			
The ear bones join together and stop vibrating			
An ear injury makes a hole in the ear drum			
Wax builds up in the outer ear			
Very loud noises damage tiny hairs in the cochlea			
In glue ear, fluid builds up behind the ear drum			
The nose is blown too hard causing the ear drum to be pushed out of shape			
A head injury damages the hearing centre of the brain			

Many ear defects last for a short time only.
More serious defects can be helped by hearing aids or by operations.

Understanding Science 3

Ear diagram

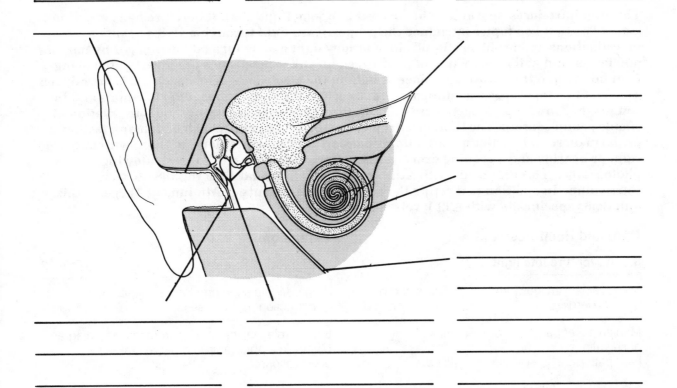

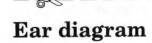

Ear diagram

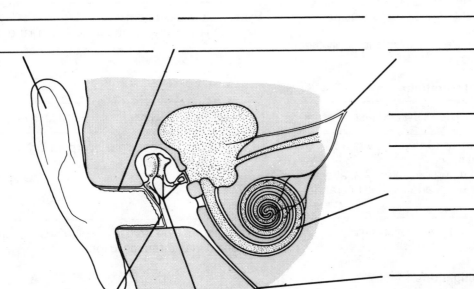

Finding out about light and sound

This unit introduces new areas not covered in Books 1 and 2, and therefore has no revision work. The first two topics introduce the properties of light through a series of simple investigations and problems. Pupils look at how light can be formed into images by mirrors and lenses and at the correction of poor eyesight. Other properties are investigated using light beams and the nature and place of light in the electromagnetic spectrum is introduced. The next two topics present students with a series of investigations into vibrations and the sounds they produce. Concepts are built up through direct experience and observation of simple sound sources. The final three topics comprise a design, construction and testing problem on sound insulation, a group discussion about the problems of those with impaired sight or hearing and a reading exercise about early scientific work foreshadowing photography. This unit deals with Attainment Targets 14 and 15 of the 1989 National Curriculum. In addition to meeting the general requirements of Attainment Target 1, this unit deals specifically with AT1 levels 5d, 6 and 7.

Core and Reinforcement

3.1 Adventure into light

> Investigate images formed by mirrors and by a converging lens. *page 8*

Manipulate apparatus in order to make observations.
Find patterns in observations obtained.

3.2 Streaks of light   *AT15–3a,3b, 4a, 5a, 6a*

> Use a light beam to investigate reflection, absorption and scattering.
> Observe how lenses can focus light and how prisms can reflect and disperse it.   *page 44*

Manipulate apparatus, observe and look for patterns.
Report results, deduce principles and apply them to further problems.

3.3 The sound of vibrations   *AT14–3a, 5a*

> Use the body to make slow and fast vibrations.
> Construct apparatus to study how rapid vibrations make sound.
> Investigate and report on factors that affect vibrations, frequency, and the audible range of frequency.   *page 46*

Use manipulation and observation skills.
Report on findings.

3.4 Sound investigations
  AT12–7c; AT14–3a,b, 4a

> Study the nature of sound waves.
> Investigate and report on the speed of sound and its transmission by various materials.   *page 58*

Exercise observation and design skills.
Make predictions from acquired knowledge.

Extension

AT15–16c

> Investigate short and long sight and their correction using lenses.   *page 146*

Extract relevant information from text and diagrams.
Manipulate apparatus in order to make observations.

AT15–7a,b

> Study the nature, production and use of light and other electromagnetic radiations.
> *page 147*

Extract information from text.
Use scientific knowledge to explain familiar events.

PoS

> Investigate the effect on sound of an air cavity and reverberation.
> Report on reverberation, incorporating experimental results.
> *page 148*

Extract information from text. Follow instructions presented in diagrammatic form.

AT14–5b, 7c

> Investigate how the height and length of waves relate to volume and pitch.
> *page 149*

Manipulate apparatus in order to make observations.
Use experimental data to derive patterns.

Core and Reinforcement

3.5 Problem—Noise annoys   AT14–5c

> Design, make and test sound insulation for reducing noise.
> Report and comment on results.   *page 50*

Consider a technological problem.
Choose and use materials.
Design and evaluate a solution.

3.6 Talkabout—Lacking sight or hearing

> Discuss aids for the deaf and blind.
> Discuss potential problems in the school facing deaf or blind children, and possible solutions.   *page 51*

Gather information.
Demonstrate communication skills.
Consider the effect of science on society.

3.7 Readabout—The beginnings of photography   AT17–4a, 7b

> Read about an unexpected discovery by Johann Schultze and how he followed it up.
> *page 52*

Extract information from a passage and represent it diagrammatically.
Identify good scientific practice.

Equipment

required for each pupil group.

3.1—Adventures into light

Note—Reversal of images by mirrors

When you look at a friend's face in a mirror, the images of his eyes do not cross over. His left eye appears on the left of the image and his right eye on the right. The reason the mirror image looks different is because, if your friend took the position of the image, he would have turned through 180 degrees. So his left eye would be on the right side of his head from your point of view. The mirror does not cross the eyes over like this and so the image looks strange. In *this* sense it is correct to say that the mirror image is the 'reverse' of the normal face you see, because the left side of the image is the right side of the face and vice versa. This reversal however is due to the rotation of the *object*, and *not* due to 'lateral inversion' by the mirror. True lateral inversion would mean that the image of the left eye would appear on the right and this obviously does not happen. Also, if 'lateral inversion' *did* occur in a mirror, vertical inversion would happen also, otherwise the mirror would have different properties in the horizontal and vertical planes.

Notes

- Reasonably large mirror, e.g. about A3 size
- Large sheet of glass
- 2 identical candles
- Matches
- Heatproof mat
- Ruler
- Glass of water
- Mirror writing sheet (R3.1)
- Empty camera
- Sheet of tissue or tracing paper
- Torch or table lamp

It is best to have the edges of the glass polished to avoid cuts.
Blackout is needed for the ghostly illusion.

The laboratory should be blacked out.

Equipment	Notes

Equipment

- Convex lens +7D or 14 cm focal length
- Small piece of white card

Extension

- Poor eyesight sheets **(RE3.1)**
- Ray box apparatus with multiple slits
- Rectangular lens of focal length +75 mm (standard ray box lens)
- Selection of weak converging and diverging lenses

Notes

The ray box lens, placed at X on the diagrams, represents both the eye's cornea and its lens.

3.2—Streaks of light

- Light-beam path sheet **(R3.2A)**
- Ray box apparatus with single slit and 3 slits
- White paper
- 2 small mirrors
- Aluminium foil
- Small piece of coloured glass or plastic
- Copy of secret message cartoon **(R3.2B)**
- Sheet of white paper
- Rectangular lens of about +7D
- 45/45/90-degree perspex prism

Black-out will be needed.

A 60-degree glass prism, if available, produces a better spectrum.

Extension

- Electromagnetic wave information sheet **(RE3.2)**

3.3—The sound of vibrations

The following arranged in a circus

- Bicycle wheel, or motor with cog
- Pieces of cardboard
- Sticky tape
- Rulers of several types
- Tuning forks and rubber bung(s)
- Plasticine
- Collection of narrow-necked bottles, e.g. milk bottle, medicine bottle, conical flask
- Water supply
- Petri dish (or similar)
- Ping-pong ball
- Thread

Pupils should investigate each instrument and report on the sound it makes and how to alter that sound.

Tuning forks should be struck on a soft surface such as a rubber bung. They can be altered in pitch by attaching Plasticine to the prongs.

Class demonstration

- Audio-signal generator
- Loudspeaker and leads
- Some musical instruments, e.g. guitar, whistle, recorder

The instruments can be used to give further frequencies for activity 2.

Extension

- Tuning fork
- Hollow wooden box
- Large sheet of card
- Staple gun

The equipment is best left available for extension pupils to do as a circus.

Equipment

- Guitar
- Scarf
- Gloves
- Mug
- Rubber band
- Sock

3.4—Sound investigations

- Vacuum pump driven by a motor, or other safe machine with moving parts
- Piece of broomstick
- Cup
- Plastic filter funnels
- 50 cm of rubber tubing to fit the funnels
- Measuring tape
- Stop clock or watch

Extension

- Small microphone
- Oscilloscope
- Leads

3.5—Problem—Noise annoys

- Cardboard box
- Noise source
- Assorted materials, e.g. egg boxes, newspaper, paper and wood straw (messy!), plastic chips, expanded polystyrene, wood shavings.

Notes

These experiments need a quiet place!

Pupils could be sent out to a reflecting wall in small groups, to work co-operatively. The group results could then be compared.

It is quite tricky to get the rhythm correct. The best way is to first make a good echo, then to speed up the clap rate until the echo cannot be heard because it is covered by the claps. The clapper can then nod to the timekeeper to start the clock and time 20 claps, counting the first as zero. The air temperature should be measured as it affects the speed of sound.

A computer simulation for the BBC computer is available to give the pupils a chance to practise in real-time before trying the measurement outside. The listing is on **R3.4.** This program and the one on **R7.1** can be obtained from Peter Warren, Acton High School, Gunnersbury Lane, London W3 8EY, by sending a blank disc and postage.

If a direct electronic timing method is available it might be preferred.

If enough oscilloscopes are available this can be done in groups. Small loudspeakers can be used as microphones.

A computer and interface (e.g. BBC and Unilab interface) can be used to obtain 'frozen' wave forms (see ⅃pils' book p. 149). This can be printed out by th￼ ‚omputer printer.

Copi￼ for the class can be made by putting a 'Banda' carbon under the print-out paper. This can then be used as a 'Banda master' to run off copies.

A 'bleeping' watch is a convenient noise maker of constant loudness that is likely to be available to the pupils.

Pupils could be asked to bring boxes and materials from home.

The testing could prove to be a challenge. It may be necessary to let groups go outside to find a large quiet space to do the testing.

Equipment

3.6—Talkabout—Lacking sight or hearing

● Science texts giving further information about properties of the types of electromagnetic radiation.

3.7—Readabout—The beginnings of photography

● Some books on the development of photography, showing early photographic methods.

Assessment 3

The questions are designed to assess the skills and knowledge developed in the unit, as shown in the table. The Attainment Target assessed by each question is also shown. A selection of questions would be appropriate for a unit test.

Topic	Core	Attainment Target
3.1	1	AT15–3b
	2	AT15–7c
3.2	3	AT15–3a
		AT15–3b
		AT15–5a
	4	AT15–4b
	5	AT15–4a
	6	AT15–6a
	7	AT15–6a
3.3	8	AT14–3a
	9	AT14–5a
	10	AT14–5a
3.4	11	AT14–4a
	12	AT14–6a
		AT14–3b
	13	AT14–5c
Extension		
3.1	14	AT15–6c
3.2	15	AT15–7b
	16	AT15–7a
3.4	17	AT14–5b

Answers

1 a C.
b To the right of the writing.
By looking through the page.

2 a 2—forms the image, 3—keeps light off the film until it is needed, 1—stores the image, 4—keeps light off the film.
b same, different, different, different, same.
3 a C, F.
b Light is reflected by a mirror at equal angles.
4 a B.
b Rays of light travel in straight lines.
5 His face scatters the sunlight in all directions so that his classmates can see it. His watch reflects the light in only one direction so that only his teacher can see it.
6 a Reflected 90° down;
b reflected 90° down then 90° left; **c** converge.
7 See illustration in the Pupils' book, page 45.
8 Make the rubber band tighter, make the blade shorter, make the lips vibrate faster.
9 C.
10 A = 20 kHz, B = 16 kHz, C = 20 Hz
11 a Sound takes time to travel to the wall and back.
b An equal distance behind the wall.
12 a Earth and rock; **b** metal; **c** fluid, flesh and air; **d** water.
13 a Someone crossing the road; a person in bed.
b The mother or father when the child is in need; neighbours.
c The casualty or the drivers of vehicles in the way; anyone else trying to work or sleep.
14 Behind, Long sight, Positive (convex).
In front of, Short sight, Negative (concave).
15 a Infrared; **b** radio; **c** light; **d** X-rays; **e** gamma.
16 a X-ray, ultraviolet, infrared, radio. **b** gamma.
17 a Microphone and oscilloscope; **b** A and B; **c** D; **d** C.

True/false 3

Each statement is marked as either true or false by the pupil. This gives a rapid assessment of a pupil's grasp of the Attainment Targets covered in the unit. This list gives the Attainment Targets covered by each set of statements.

1	AT 15–3a	9	AT 14–3b
2	AT 15–3b	10	AT 14–4a
3	AT 15–4a	11	AT 14–5a
4	AT 15–4b	12	AT 14–5c
5	AT 15–5a	13	AT 14–6a
6	AT 15–6a	14	AT 15–6c
7	AT 15–7c	15	AT 15–7a
8	AT 14–3a	16	AT 15–7b
		17	AT 14–5b

1 a Which of these shows true mirror writing?

ecaf ehT The face ecaf ehT эɔɒʇ ɘ́ɥꓕ

   A   B   C   D

b Where would you place a mirror so that you can read the writing? How can you see the writing correctly without using a mirror?

2 a Copy and complete this table about a simple camera.

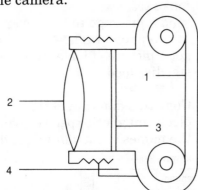

Part number	Description	Its job
	lens	
	shutter	
	film	
	enclosed box	

b Copy and complete the table below by putting 'same' or 'different' for an *object* and its *image* formed by a camera.

Colour	Size	Way up	Way round	Shape

3 a Which ray is reflected correctly in each of these pictures?

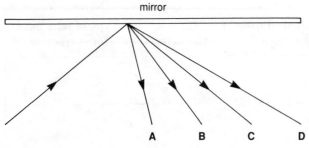

mirror

         A   B   C   D

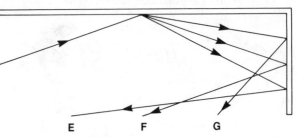

      E   F   G

b What idea did you use to work out your answer?

4 a An apple is placed between a torch and a white screen. One of the rays of light from the torch is shown just skimming the edge of the apple. Where would this ray hit the screen?

   C
   B
   A

b What idea did you use to find the answer?

5 A student dazzles his teacher by using his watch to reflect sunlight. The student's face also reflects the sunlight. Explain why all his classmates can see his face but only the teacher is dazzled by the light from the watch.

6 What happens to these rays of light?

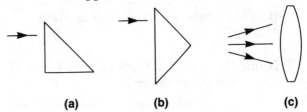

   (a)   **(b)**   **(c)**

Answer by describing or drawing a picture.

7 How can you arrange these items to make a bright spectrum of light? Draw a diagram to show their positions. Put an R on the screen to show where you would expect to see red light.

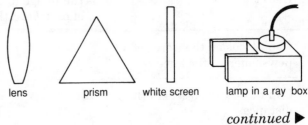

lens   prism   white screen   lamp in a ray box

continued ▶

8 How would you make these 'instruments' vibrate faster?

rubber band

hacksaw blade

'puttering' lips

9 What is meant by the frequency of a vibration?

  A The number of vibrations it makes.

  B How fast it vibrates.

  C The number of vibrations it makes in a second.

  D The number of vibrations it makes in a minute.

10 Match the letters in the table to the correct frequencies. Choose from 10 Hz, 20 Hz, 10 kHz, 16 kHz, 20 kHz, 40 kHz.

Highest frequency for normal ears	Highest frequency for recorded music	Lowest frequency that can be called sound
A	B	C

11 a Why is there a delay before you hear the echo of a clap?

b Where does the echo seem to come from?

12 Name the material through which sound travels in these examples.

  A An American Indian listening for horses by putting his ear to the ground.

  B A mechanic listening to an engine through a screwdriver.

  C A doctor listening to a patient's chest.

  D A sonar buoy listening for submarines.

13 Give an example of a person who would be helped by the following noises and one who would find them a nuisance.

  a car hooter

  b cry of a baby

  c ambulance siren.

Extension questions

14 Copy and complete the table at the foot of the page about eye defects.

15 Which electromagnetic radiation would you use to

  a make toast

  b send a message to the moon

  c take a photograph

  d get a picture of bones in the body

  e sterilise food.

16 a Copy this diagram of the electromagnetic spectrum and fill in the names of the missing radiations.

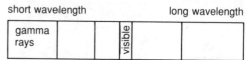
short wavelength   long wavelength

gamma rays			visible	

b Which radiation has the shortest waves?

17 a Name the two pieces of apparatus you need to make pictures of sound waves like these.

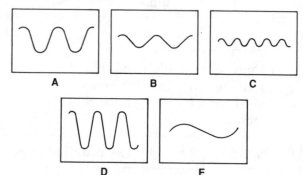

  A   B   C

  D   E

b Which two of the sounds have the same frequency?

c Which note is the loudest?

d Which note is the softest?

For question 14:

Defect	Is the image formed *in front* of or *behind* the retina?	Name of the defect	Type of lens used for correction
Can't focus on the words of a newspaper on the knee.			
Can't focus on objects in the distance.			

Understanding Science 3

Unit 3 Look and listen

Name_____

Put a tick after the statements that are true.
Put a cross after the statements that are false.

1 a Light rays always stop when they bump into things. ☐
   b A mirror is the only thing that can reflect light. ☐
   c The reflections of light from a mirror can make an image. ☐

2 a Mirrors always reflect light at equal angles. ☐
   b A mirror image shows a person as she is seen in a photograph. ☐
   c A mirror image is always formed an equal distance behind the mirror. ☐

3 a We can see a rose in a garden because it scatters light from the sun into our eyes. ☐
   b Our faces scatter light in all directions so that we can be seen from the front and the side at the same time. ☐

4 a Objects make shadows because light cannot bend round them. ☐
   b As you move an object away from a lamp its shadow gets larger. ☐

5 a A glass window does not reflect light, it only allows it to pass through. ☐
   b A ray of light and its reflection, make equal angles at a mirror. ☐

6 a A prism can spread white light out into a spectrum of colours. ☐
   b A lens can only focus light, it cannot form an image. ☐

7 a A camera uses a lens to form a real image on the film. ☐
   b The image is small and black-and-white. ☐

8 a Anything that vibrates makes a sound that we can hear. ☐
   b Sound can only travel through air. ☐

9 a We hear sound because the vibrations of noisy objects travel through the air and make our eardrums vibrate. ☐
   b Layers of air pass the vibrations along from one to the next until they reach our eardrums. ☐

10 a Sound travels at the same speed as light. ☐
   b Sound takes about 3 seconds to travel 1000 metres in air. ☐

11 a The frequency of a guitar string is the number of times it vibrates a second. ☐
   b A high frequency note sounds lower in pitch than a low frequency sound. ☐

12 a Loud noises cannot harm the body. ☐
   b Noise can spoil concentration and make people angry. ☐
   c Blankets can reduce the noise of an alarm clock. ☐

13 a Sound waves carry energy from the vibrating object to our eardrums. ☐
   b Sound waves can travel through a vacuum. ☐

Extensions

14 a People with short sight cannot focus clearly on distant objects. ☐
   b People with long sight cannot focus clearly on distant objects. ☐
   c Convex or positive lenses can correct long sight. ☐
   d Concave or negative lenses can correct short sight. ☐

continued ▶

15 a Light is a member of the electromagnetic family of waves. ☐

b Its wavelength lies between microwaves and radio waves. ☐

16 a X-rays, gamma rays, ultraviolet, light, infrared, sound and radio waves are all electromagnetic waves. ☐

b We cannot detect electromagnetic waves with any of our senses. ☐

c Infrared radiation can be used to cook food. ☐

17 a Large vibrations of a guitar string make a louder sound than smaller vibrations. ☐

b An oscilloscope will show that a soft sound is made by a larger wave than a loud sound. ☐

Name _____

Complete each sentence. Put the correct word(s) in each blank space.

1 Objects that give out _____ are luminous. Examples of luminous

objects are ● _____   ● _____

● _____ .

2 A mirror can form an _____ of our faces. This image is

_____ the same as a photograph or as others see us when they

_____ at us from the front. Glass can _____ like

a mirror and form reflected _____ . Glass can also let light through

when it acts like a _____ . Mirror images are an equal distance

_____ the mirror. A beam of light and its reflection make

_____ angles to a mirror.

3 Images formed by lenses can be _____ down and

_____ to _____ . A camera lens forms an image

like this on light-sensitive _____ .

4 A prism is a _____ piece of transparent material. It can

_____ light like a mirror or split it into _____ . The

colours of a white-light spectrum are ● _____

● _____   ● _____   ● _____

● _____   ● _____ .

5 Vibrating objects can send out _____ waves. Frequency is the

number of vibrations per _____ . We hear as sound frequencies

between _____ Hz and _____ kHz.

6 Sound can travel through _____ , _____ ,

_____ , but not through a _____ . Sound travels

at a speed of about _____ m/s or _____ m.p.h.

Mirror writing

There are two ways of reading this writing.
Can you find them?

> The face we see ★★ a mirror is not the ★★★★ that others see when they look ★★★★ at us. If we look ★★★★ a mirror and wink our right eye, the image winks ★★★★ with its ★★★★ eye. (Imagine you are the person in the mirror looking back.) Look at someone you know well in a mirror. They do ★★★ look 'normal', and yet this ★★ how they think they look. To see ourselves as we ★★★★ to others, we must ★★★★★★★★★★ on film or television. We ★★★ so used to our mirror image that a true-to-life photograph ★★★★★ strange. A mirror ★★★★★ also seems to lie behind the ★★★★★★ and not on the glass. Experiments show that it ★★★★ an equal distance behind the mirror. So if you want ★★ know what you look like from 50 cm away, you should ★★★★ into a mirror that is ★★ cm away.

Copy the sentences and fill in the blanks with ordinary words.

Mirror writing

There are two ways of reading this writing.
Can you find them?

> The face we see ★★ a mirror is not the ★★★★ that others see when they look ★★★★ at us. If we look ★★★★ a mirror and wink our right eye, the image winks ★★★★ with its ★★★★ eye. (Imagine you are the person in the mirror looking back.) Look at someone you know well in a mirror. They do ★★★ look 'normal', and yet this ★★ how they think they look. To see ourselves as we ★★★★ to others, we must ★★★★★★★★★★ on film or television. We ★★★ so used to our mirror image that a true-to-life photograph ★★★★★ strange. A mirror ★★★★★ also seems to lie behind the ★★★★★★ and not on the glass. Experiments show that it ★★★★ an equal distance behind the mirror. So if you want ★★ know what you look like from 50 cm away, you should ★★★★ into a mirror that is ★★ cm away.

Copy the sentences and fill in the blanks with ordinary words.

Poor eyesight sheet 1: *Short sight*

Use a ray box to get 3 or more parallel beams.

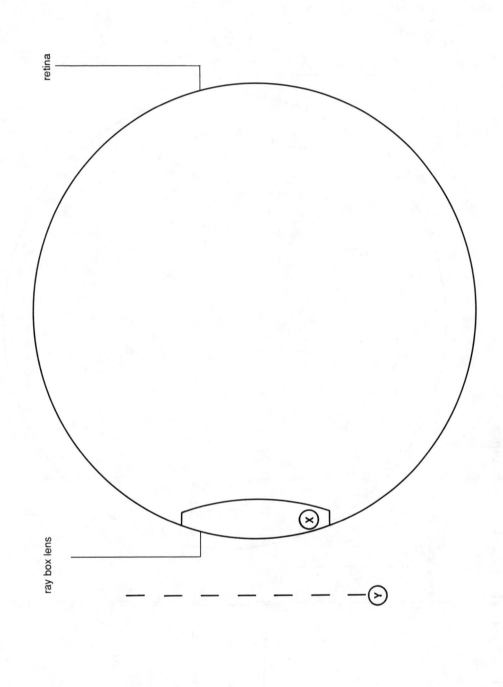

retina

ray box lens

X

Y

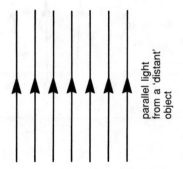

parallel light
from a 'distant'
object

1 of 2

Poor eyesight sheet 2: *Long sight*

Arrange beams from a ray box to spread out like this so that they focus somewhere near to Z.

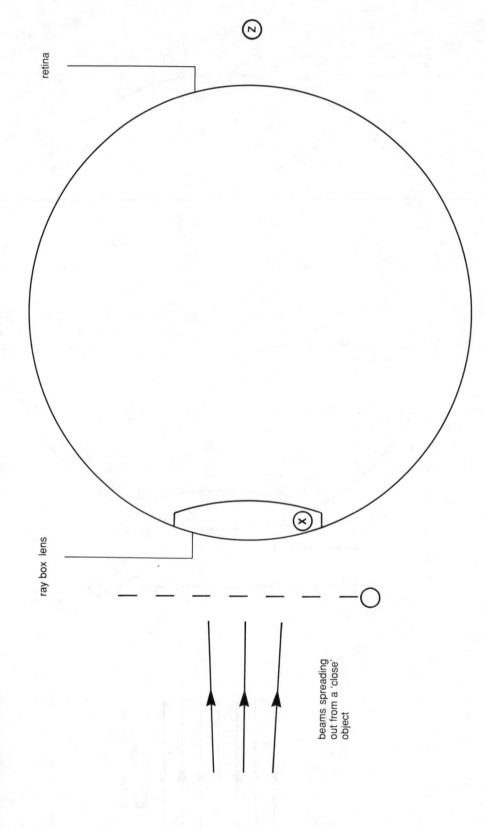

retina

ray box   lens

beams spreading
out from a 'close'
object

Light-beam path sheet

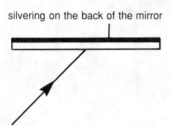

silvering on the back of the mirror

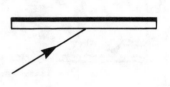

mirrors at right angles

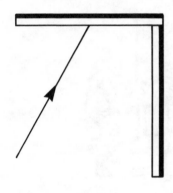
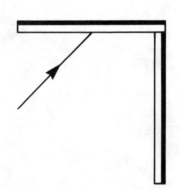
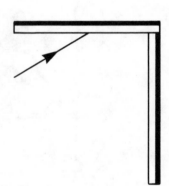

white card

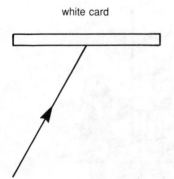

coloured glass

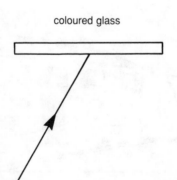

aluminium mirror

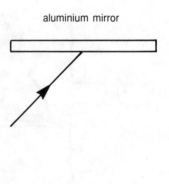

Marlon's secret message

✂- -✂

Marlon's secret message

✂- -✂

Marlon's secret message

Electromagnetic wave information sheet

Electromagnetic radiation brings us great benefits but it can also be dangerous. Cut out these fact cards about each of the main types of radiation and arrange them in 'wavelength order'.

Gamma rays
Energetic bursts of radiation from radioactive sources. They can be used to measure the thickness of metal sheets when these are being manufactured. They can destroy bacteria in food. They can pass right through the human body, and can destroy cancerous cells. They can also cause damage to cells, which later in life may become cancerous.

Radio waves
Artificial radio waves are used to broadcast TV and radio programmes and many other sorts of radio messages. They are used by the police and army, by taxi and courier firms, and for portable phones. They are used by hobbyists for amateur radio contacts and for radio-controlled models. They can invade our privacy, and carry propaganda.

X-rays
Energetic radiation made by X-ray machines. They can be used to find the structure of crystals and molecules, and to detect flaws inside metal objects. They can give pictures of bones and other internal parts of the body to help diagnose illness. They can kill cancer cells. They can also damage cells and later cause cancer.

Microwaves
Artificial microwaves can be used to cook food. They are used to transmit speech and pictures to satellites and between cities. In radar systems they are used for detection and navigation, for very accurate speed measurements, and for tracking storms. They can be dangerous to the body, and are suspected of causing headaches.

Ultraviolet
Produced inside fluorescent light tubes to make their surface glow. It is used to kill germs in hospitals. It is used to attract insects to be caught for study or killed to maintain hygene. It is the part of the Sun's radiation that causes chemical changes in the skin. It gives us a sun-tan. It can cause skin cancer.

Infrared
Can grill food, warm our bodies, and be used for remote control. It can be used by heat sensors to detect bodies and rocket engines, and in 'night sights' to see in the dark. It is the part of the Sun's radiation that warms the Earth and drives the weather; it generates hurricanes and storms.

Light
Our eyes respond to light and give us sight. Huge amounts of light are absorbed by green plants, providing the energy needed by all living things on Earth. Film and video cameras use light energy. Laser light can carry messages and do surgical operations. Light can blind you if it is too bright.

Speed of sound by echoes

This program allows you to practise the experiment on page 49. It
gives values for the speed of sound.

```
 10 REM Speed of Sound Measurement
 20 MODE1
 30 PRINTTAB(10,10)"SPEED OF SOUND"
 40 PRINTTAB(5,20)"Do you want instruct
    ions? Y/N"
 50 A$=GET$:IF A$="Y" OR A$="y" PROCins
    truct
 60 CLS
 70 ENVELOPE 1,129,0,0,0,2,2,2,120,-40,
    -40,-20,126,100
 80 REM Clap envelope.
 90 ENVELOPE 2,129,0,0,0,2,2,2,60,-20,-
    10,-10,100,90
100 REM Echo envelope.
110 PROCinit
120 *FX11,0
130 walk=35:y%=27:echo=0:No=0:start=0
140 DIM echo(20):clock=0:claps=0:DIM sp
    eed(20):delay=0
150 timeoff=0:timeon=0:clap=0:v=0
160 IF v=0 PROCrun
170 PROCcont
180 END
190 :
200 DEFPROCcont
210 CLS
220 PRINTTAB(0,15)"Press S for more rea
    dings, E to end."
230 REPEAT
240   IF INKEY(-82) PROCrun
250   IF INKEY(-35) PROCend:END
260 UNTIL FALSE
270 ENDPROC
280 :
290 DEFPROCrun
300 VDU23;8202;0;0;0:REM Turn off curso
    r
310 VDU19,2,3,0,0,0
320 COLOUR3
330 VDU23,249,48,48,240,240,255,0,0,0:R
    EM Graphic
340 VDU19,3,2,0,0,0:REM Change white to
    green
350 COLOUR2:REM Yellow
360 PROCshe(walk,y% )
370 PRINTTAB(walk,y%)she$
380 COLOUR3:REM Green
390 PROCgrass
400 COLOUR1:REM Red
410 PROCbrick
420 COLOUR2:REM Yellow
430 PROCsun
440 PROCflower
450 TIME=0:ping=0
460 PROCmove(-1)
470 REPEAT
480 REPEAT
490 *FX21,0
500 *FX11,0
510 IF INKEY(-26) PROCmove(-1)
520 IF INKEY(-122) PROCmove(+1)
530 IF INKEY(-1) PROCtimeit
540 IF INKEY(-99) PROCstop
550 IF INKEY(-83) AND delay <=0 PROCcla
    p
560 IF INKEY(-52) PROCtable:PROCcont
570 delay=delay-1
580 UNTIL TIME=echo(0) OR TIME=echo(0)+
    1 OR TIME=echo(0)+2
590 PROCecho
600 UNTIL FALSE
610 ENDPROC
620 :
630 DEFPROCtimeit
640 clock=1
650 timeon=TIME
660 claps=0
670 PRINTTAB(20,5)"TIMING NOW"
680 ENDPROC
690 :
700 DEFPROCshe(walk,y%)
710 VDU23,240,62,127,4,4,4,4,4,60
720 VDU23,241,5,13,60,60,12,12,12,28
730 VDU23,242,14,30,30,62,30,14
740 VDU 23,255,62,127,28,20,18,241,2,12

750 she$=CHR$ 242+CHR$8+CHR$10+CHR$241+
    CHR$8+CHR$10+CHR$ 240
760 leg$=CHR$242+CHR$8+CHR$10+CHR$241+C
    HR$8+CHR$10+CHR$255
770 PRINTTAB(walk,y%)she$
780 ENDPROC
790 :
800 DEFPROCgrass
810 VDU23,243,1,65,97,239,255,255,255,2
    55
820 FOR X=4TO 38
830   PRINTTAB(X,30) CHR$243:NEXT
840 ENDPROC
850 :
860 DEFPROCbrick
870 VDU23,244,0,255,255,255,255,255,255
    ,255
880 VDU23,245,0,254,254,254,254,254,254
    ,254
890 VDU23,246,0,254,254,254,254,254,254
    ,254
900 brick$=CHR$244+CHR$245
910 FOR X=1TO5 STEP 2
920   FOR Y=18TO30
```

continued ▶

```
930    IF (Y MOD 2=0) THEN c=1 ELSE c=0
940    PRINTTAB(X+c,Y) brick$
950   NEXT
960  NEXT
970  FOR Y=19 TO 29 STEP2
980    PRINTTAB(7,Y)CHR$246
990  NEXT
1000 ENDPROC
1010 :
1020 DEFPROCflower
1030 VDU23,247,48,48,48,48,48,48,48,48
1040 VDU23,248,170,126,254,63,256,126,25
     4,50
1050 flower$=CHR$248+CHR$8+CHR$10+CHR$24
     7
1060 FOR fl%=2TO6 STEP 2
1070   PRINTTAB(fl%,16)flower$
1080   PRINTTAB(fl%+7,28)flower$
1090 NEXT
1100 ENDPROC
1110 :
1120 DEF PROCclap
1130 echo(No)=TIME+return
1140 IF No=5 THEN No=0
1150 PRINTTAB(walk,y%+1)CHR$249
1160 SOUND 1,1,99,1
1170 delay=8:claps=claps+1
1180 FOR Q=walk-2 TO 8 STEP-2
1190   PRINTTAB(Q,27)pulse$
1200   PRINTTAB(Q+4,27);SPC(1)
1210 NEXT
1220 PRINTTAB(walk,y%+1)SPC(1)
1230 ENDPROC
1240 :
1250 DEFPROCsun
1260 VDU23,250,149,85,53,239,31,255,31,2
     55
1270 VDU23,251,31,255,31,239,31,53,85,14
     9
1280 VDU23,252,81,82,84,240,255,248,255,
     248
1290 VDU23,253,255,248,255,240,255,84,82
     ,81
1300 VDU23,254,5,5,5,5,5,5,5,5
1310 pulse$=CHR$254+CHR$254+CHR$254
1320 sun$=CHR$250+CHR$252+CHR$8+CHR$8+CH
     R$10+CHR$251+CHR$253
1330 PRINTTAB(30,16)sun$
1340 ENDPROC
1350 :
1360 DEFPROCecho
1370 FOR Q=8 TO walk-4
1380   PRINTTAB(Q,27)pulse$
1390   PRINTTAB(Q,27)SPC(1)
1400 NEXT
1410 PRINTTAB(walk-4,27)"       "
1420 SOUND 0,2,0,3
1430 ENDPROC
1440 :
1450 DEF PROCmove(go)
1460 IF walk>36 THEN walk=36
1470 IF walk<9THEN walk=9
1480 PRINTTAB(walk,y%)she$
1490 FOR k%=0TO2
1500   PRINTTAB(walk-go,y%+k%)SPC(1)
1510 NEXT
1520 walk=walk+go
1530 COLOUR1
1540 PRINTTAB(11,23)(walk-8)*10SPC(1)"me
     tres"
1550 COLOUR2
1560 return=INT(200*(walk-9)/33)
1570 ENDPROC
1580 :
1590 DEF PROCclock
1600 VDU19,2,13,0,0,0:PRINTTAB(20,5)"TIM
     ING    NOW "
1610 PRINTTAB(20,14)claps SPC(1)"claps"
1620 ENDPROC
1630 :
1640 DEFPROCstop
1650 clock=0
1660 timeoff=(TIME-timeon)/100
1670 clap=claps
1680 PRINTTAB(20,5)SPC(13)
1690 PRINTTAB(20,8)timeoff;SPC(1);"secs"

1700 PRINTTAB(20,10)clap;SPC(1);"claps"
1710 speed(v)=INT((walk-8)*clap*21.5/tim
     eoff)
1720 REM Speed of sound = 331 m/s. 21.5
     gives a fair answer with this progr
     am.
1730 PRINTTAB(20,12)speed(v);SPC(1);"m/s
     "
1740 IF v<20 THEN v=v+1 ELSE v=0
1750 wait%=INKEY(500)
1760 REPEAT UNTIL NOT INKEY(-99)
1770 ENDPROC
1780 :
1790 DEFPROCinit
1800 PRINTTAB(12,6)"SPEED OF SOUND"
1810 PRINTTAB(7,10)"KEY"
1820 PRINTTAB(7,12)"C         = clap"
1830 PRINTTAB(7,14)"SHIFT     starts the
      clock"
1840 PRINTTAB(7,16)"SPACE     stops the c
     lock"
1850 PRINTTAB(7,18)"> Arrow   moves the g
     irl away"
1860 PRINTTAB(7,20)"< Arrow   moves the g
     irl closer"
1870 PRINTTAB(7,22)"R         gives resul
     ts table"
1880 PRINTTAB(7,26)"Press any key to con
     tinue"
1890 REPEAT UNTIL GET<>0
1900 ENDPROC
```

continued ▶

```
1910 :
1920 DEFPROCtable
1930 *FX21,0
1940 CLS
1950 total=0
1960 PRINTTAB(8,7)"Speed of Sound"
1970 FOR U=0TO v-1
1980  PRINTTAB(10)speed(U)SPC(1)"m/s"
1990  total=total+speed(U)
2000 NEXT
2010 IF v=0 THEN 2040
2020 PRINT''
2030 PRINTTAB(1)"Average speed =";INT(to
     tal/v);" m/s"
2040 PRINT'''"Press COPY key to continue
     ."
2050 REPEAT UNTIL INKEY(-106)
2060 ENDPROC
2070 :
2080 DEFPROCend
2090 CLS
2100 PRINTTAB(14,12)"BYE BYE"
2110 PRINTTAB(6,15)"From the clapping Gi
     rl."
2120 TIME=0
2130 REPEAT UNTIL TIME=10000
2140 *FX12,0
2150 VDU4
2160 CLS
2170 ENDPROC
2180 :
2190 DEFPROCinstruct:CLS
2200 PRINTTAB(11,5)"INSTRUCTIONS"
2210 PRINT'"This program uses echoes to
     measure"
2220 PRINT"the speed of sound.  A little
      girl"
2230 PRINT"stands clapping and listens t
     o the"
2240 PRINT"echo from a wall.  (The echo
     time"
2250 PRINT"is real but the distance is t
     o scale)."
2260 PRINT'"Make her clap so that the cl
     aps"
2270 PRINT"coincide with the echoes.  Wh
     en you"
2280 PRINT"have the rhythm right start t
     iming."
2290 PRINT"Stop after about 20 claps."
2300 PRINT"The computer will count for y
     ou and"
2310 PRINT"calculate the effective speed
     ."
2320 PRINT'"Do the experiment several ti
     mes at"
2330 PRINT"different distances from the
     wall."
2340 PRINT"The computer will keep the re
     sults and"
2350 PRINT"work out the average result."

2360 PRINT'" Press any key to continue.
2370 A$=GET$
2380 CLS
2390 ENDPROC
2400 :
2410 REM Original by Peter Warren
          Revised by Wilf James 2/1/91
```

Unit 4 Back to Earth

Describing our planet

This unit builds upon those topics of units 1 and 5 in Book 2 that introduced aspects of the physical environment. The revision work therefore refers to landforms and their formation, rock types, the weather and the Moon's phases. The next three topics present some knowledge of basic astronomy and geology. Pupils extract and reorganise information presented in text, tables, diagrams and charts. They are asked to construct and use models to explain and aid their understanding of familiar and unfamiliar natural phenomena. Knowledge acquired is used to solve structured and open-ended problems. The final three topics comprise an open-ended problem, a discussion and a short reading exercise. Ideally videos could be used to support the class-based exercises. This unit deals with Attainment Targets 9 and 16 of the 1989 National Curriculum. In addition to meeting the general requirements of Attainment Target 1, this unit deals specifically with AT1 levels 5a, 5d, and 6.

Core and Reinforcement

4.0 Revision—Restless Earth

> Revise background work.
> Complete a revision question sheet.
> Give a written or oral report describing an erupting volcano.   *page 54*

Revise earlier work.
Apply knowledge in an imaginative way.

4.1 The mysterious universe
AT16–3a, 4b,c, 5a,b, 6a,b

> Extract information from a passage, diagrams and a bar chart.
> Make astronomical models and use these to demonstrate astronomical phenomena.
>   *page 56*

Extract information from a variety of sources and present it in a new form.
Use models to explain familiar and unfamiliar phenomena.

4.2 Rock groups
AT9–6a

> Examine a diagrammatic representation of the rock cycle.
> Complete a summary rock-cycle diagram.
> Use experimental models to demonstrate the formation of sedimentary and igneous rock.
> Use secondary sources to prepare a report on fossil fuels.   *page 60*

Extract relevant information.
Use a model to explain a natural phenomenon.
Investigate the relationship between two variables.
Observe accurately.

Extension

AT16–7a

> Read a passage describing evidence for a spherical Earth.
> Construct and use a simple measuring device to estimate the diameter of the Sun.
>   *page 150*

Extract information from a passage.
Build and use a measuring device. Use collected data to complete a numerical calculation.

AT9–6c, 7a

> Design an experiment to investigate the formation of sea and land breezes.
>   *page 151*

Devise and carry out an experiment to solve a given problem.
Use experimental data to make a prediction.

Core and Reinforcement

4.3 Rock roadshow   *AT9–6b*

> Conduct a variety of tests to compare the properties of mineral and rock samples.
> Use data collected to identify the best sample for a given purpose.   *page 62*

Observe, measure and record accurately and systematically.
Make decisions based on examination of evidence.
Communicate decisions in an imaginative way.

4.4 Problem—Is there anybody out there?

> Produce an interstellar message that comprises visual and audio elements and key artifacts.   *page 64*

Apply knowledge in an imaginative way.
Use symbols, sounds and artifacts to represent ideas and to convey meaning.

4.5 Talkabout—Rock history   *AT9–5a*

> Discuss photographic evidence of geological formations and suggest how they may have formed.
> Predict how they might change in the future.

Extract information from photographs.
Suggest scientific explanations of unfamiliar observations.
Make predictions based on scientific knowledge.

4.6 Readabout—A star's life
                              AT6–6e; AT16–6b, 7b

> Read a passage about the life cycle of a star.
> Answer questions on the passage.

Extract information from a passage.
Summarise information as a flow diagram.

Extension
                                                        AT9–7b

> Extract information from a passage about major Earth features.
>   *page 152*

Extract relevant information.
Communicate in written form.

Equipment

4.0—Revision—Energy and forces

- Revision question sheet
- Word processor *or*
- Tape recorder and blank audio tape *or*
- Telephone

4.1—The mysterious universe

- Solar system sheet **(R4.1A)**
- Earth orbit sheet **(R4.1B)**
- Scissors
- 2 paper fasteners
- Coloured pencils
- 1 bulb

Notes

Access to copies of *Understanding Science 1* and *2* will allow pupils to check their work and look for information they are unsure of.
The second activity can be handled in a number of ways depending on the availability of equipment:
- as a written exercise   ● as keyboard practice
- as role play.
The use of video material would provide an important stimulus.

Pupils are familiar with the basic astronomical ideas but will require help in operating the models to demonstrate the correct explanations.
Video material would again provide good reinforcement.
The Resource sheets function better if printed on card.

Equipment

- 1 cell (1.5V battery)
- 2 leads
- 2 balls of different size

Extension

- Retort stand (with flat base)
- Boss and clamp
- 2 sheets of card (A5 size)
- Sticky tape
- Metre rule
- Pin

4.2—Rock groups

- Large glass jar, e.g. coffee jar, gas jar, 250 ml measuring cylinder
- Soil sample (50 g)
- Rule
- Plastic bucket
- Microscope slides
- Water bath at 50°C
- Beaker of ice
- Teat pipette
- Salol (phenyl salicylate – m.p. 43°C)
- Microscope or hand lens
- Rock cycle diagram **(R4.2)**

Extension

- 2 plastic trays
- Fine dry sand
- Thermometer
- Bench lamp
- Timer

4.3—Rock roadshow

- 3 rock samples
- Mineral samples
- Rock information card **(R4.3)**
- Hand lens
- Iron nail
- Glass microscope slide
- Steel knife blade
- Metal file
- Dropper bottle of dilute hydrochloric acid
- Teat pipette
- Safety glasses

Notes

Do not forget that Pluto's eccentric orbit sometimes brings it closer to the Sun than Neptune, as for example between 1979 and 1999.

Pupils must be warned not to look directly at the Sun.
Some pupils will require help with the calculation. Answer 1 392 000 km. Pupils should obtain a result of this order of magnitude.

The first activity models the formation of sedimentary rock. The soil sample should contain a range of particle sizes from clay to coarse sand. The various particles will settle out quickly except for the clay, which will take several days to clear. This represents deposition and pupils will see a distinct banding. Changes in the water and sediment level over several lessons are due to compaction.
The 'sedimentary rock' should not be disposed of down the sink, but in the bucket.
In activity 2, pupils should establish the relationship between speed of cooling and size of crystals. Rapid cooling leads to small crystals. Heat from a microscope lamp may prevent crystallisation so use natural light or a hand lens.

Plastic meat trays or larger equipment trays can be used. Pupils have to identify and control variables and decide how best to use the timer. (It is best to measure temperature rise over 5 or 10 minutes.) Sand heats up and cools down more quickly than water. The difference in air pressures over land and sea creates a breeze which blows from sea to land in the day and from land to sea at night.

Select suitable rocks from the information card. Ideally one of the rocks should have 2 minerals. The composition of each of the minerals is as follows:
feldspar – Ca, Na, Al silicates
augite – Ca, Fe, Mg, Al silicates
quartz – SiO_2
mica – Si, K, Al oxides
hornblende – Ca, Mg, Fe, Na silicates
calcite – $CaCO_3$.
Pupils have to devise and carry out a matrix of tests and demonstrate systematic recording of results.
Pupils can carry out all tests and comparisons on the rocks (as suggested in the pupils' book) *or* on the discrete minerals.
Wrap sticky tape around the glass slide to prevent cuts if the slide breaks.

Equipment

Extension

- Access to resources on location of volcanoes and earthquake zones, and on the Mt St Helens eruption.

4.4—Problem—Is there anybody out there?

- Poster paper
- Coloured pencils
- Stencils
- Rulers
- Glue
- Tape recorder
- Blank audio tape

4.5—Talkabout—Rock history

No equipment required

4.6—Readabout—A star's life

No equipment required

Notes

The geography department is likely to have such resources, or a suitable video could be used.

Groups should be encouraged to use symbols and to think about the impact of their visual and aural messages.

Assessment 4

The questions are designed to assess the skills and knowledge developed in the unit, as shown in the table. The Attainment Target assessed by each question is also shown.

A selection of questions would be appropriate for a unit test.

Topic	Core	Attainment Target
4.1	1	AT16–4b,c, 6a,b
	2, 3	AT16–4b
	4	AT16–5a
	5, 6	AT16–5b
	7	AT16–6b
4.2	8, 9, 10	AT9–6a
4.3	11, 12, 13	AT9–6b
4.6	14	AT6–6e
		AT16–7b
	Extension	
4.1	15	AT16–7a
4.2	16, 17	AT9–6a, 7a
4.3	18, 19	AT9–7b

Answers

1 A—4, the Sun is a star, others planets.
B—3, planets out of sequence.
C—3, a measure of time, not of distance.
D—4, all others are astronomical terms that describe movement.
E—1, all others are astronomical phenomena.
2 a (i) 60 million km **(ii)** 150 million km.
b Mercury, Venus, Earth, Mars, Jupiter, Saturn, Uranus, Neptune, Pluto.
3 a A—Mars, B—Saturn, C—Pluto, D—Jupiter.
b A, D, C, F, E, B.
4 a A—2   B—4.

b (i) B   **(ii)** A   **(iii)** C.
5 a C—gibbous or half   E—gibbous or half.
b 28/29 January.
c As the Moon orbits Earth it keeps same side facing Earth at all times.
6 Explanation of phases of the Moon—Moon reflects sunshine, so when in line with the Sun can't be seen (new Moon), as it orbits Earth progressively more is lit by Sun (quarter Moon), until the full Moon is visible. The Moon then becomes less and less fully lit changing nightly to the next new Moon.
7 a A, B, E
b The nearest star is so far away that it would take light from the explosion 4.2 years to reach us.
8 a igneous—B, F
metamorphic—D, E
sedimentary—A, C.
b igneous rock—hard with crystals
sedimentary rock—soft in layers.
9 a A—sedimentary B—igneous
C—sedimentary D—metamorphic.
b A—by rapid cooling; B—by slow cooling.
10 a sedimentary.
b 1 and 2 heat and pressure, 3 weathering/erosion, deposition.
c volcanic eruption and cooling of lava.
d layers, usually not very hard.
11 A—waterproof/splits easily for correct shape/hard.
B—burns to produce good heat/releases heat energy/burns easily.
C—very soft/easily made into powder.
D—very hard/hard wearing.
12 Try to dissolve mineral—identify halite.
Scratch minerals—quartz is hardest *or* add acid to minerals—calcite fizzes.
13 A—**a** iron **b** strong and hard
B—**a** copper **b** conducts heat and electricity
C—**a** aluminium **b** lightweight and does not rust.

14 A, C.

15 Evidence from satellites, shape of eclipse shadows, circumnavigation of Earth, shadows from identical vertical sticks of two different places on same day not of equal length.

16 A—cold and wet   B—warm and dry
C—wet and warm   D—cold and dry.

17 a Show arrows swirling into centre of low in a counter-clockwise direction.

b B, A, C.

c **(i)** sea   **(ii)** sea to city   **(iii)** rapid heating and cooling over land compared to sea rise in temperature during day, fall in evening

18 Possible earthquakes and volcanoes.

19 a (i) B, A, C or C, B, A   **(ii)** volcanic eruption, earthquake/movement of Earth's plates   **(iii)** weathering and erosion

b (i) movement of the Earth's plates/continental drift   **(ii)** along the 'joins' of the two plates.

True/false 4

Each statement is marked as either true or false by the pupil. This gives a rapid assessment of a pupil's grasp of the Attainment Targets covered in the unit. The following list gives the Attainment Targets covered by each set of statements.

1 AT 9–6a	8 AT 16–6b
2 AT 9–6b	9 AT 16–7b
3 AT 16–4b	10 AT 6–6e
4 AT 16–4c	11 AT 9–6c
5 AT 16–5a	12 AT 9–7a
6 AT 16–5b	13 AT 9–7b
7 AT 16–6a	14 AT 16–7a

Unit 4 Back to Earth

Name _____

1 Write the meaning of each word or phrase in the space provided. The figures in brackets are references to *Understanding Science*, Books 1 and 2 (**book number, page number**). Use the references to *check* your answers.

- the Earth's crust (**2**, 23)
- landforms (**2**, 23)
- volcanoes (**2**, 23)
- earthquakes (**2**, 23)
- weathering (**2**, 23)
- erosion (**2**, 23)
- weather (**2**, 12)
- igneous rock (**1**, 119)
- sedimentary rock (**1**, 119)
- metamorphic rock (**1**, 119)
- fossil formation (**2**, 128)
- the solar system (**2**, 162)
- the phases of the Moon (**2**, 92).

2 The spider diagram shows some connections between these terms. Complete the diagram with the correct words.

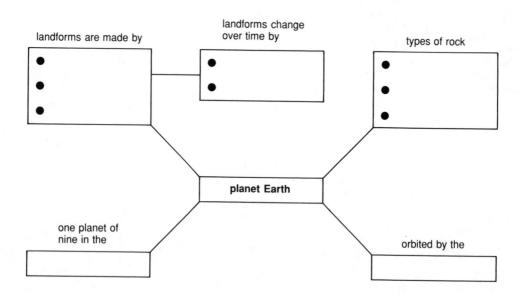

landforms are made by

landforms change over time by

types of rock

planet Earth

one planet of nine in the

orbited by the

1 Spot the odd one out in each of the following sets. Explain your choice.

A 1—Earth 2—Jupiter 3—Mars 4—Sun 5—Uranus

B 1—Saturn and Uranus
2—Earth and Mars
3—Saturn and Neptune
4—Mercury and Venus
5—Neptune and Pluto

C 1—cm 2—light years 3—second 4—metre
5—kilometre

D 1—rotation 2—revolution 3—orbit 4—gravity

E 1—clouds 2—eclipse 3—northern lights 4—tides.

2 Examine the bar chart below.

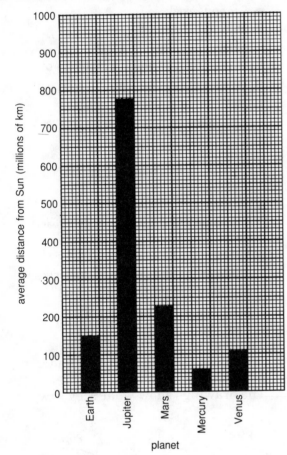

a What is the average distance from the Sun of
(i) Mercury
(ii) Earth?

b Write down the names of all nine planets in order of their average distance from the Sun.

3 a Identify each of the following planets from its description.

A The red planet

B The planet with giant rings

C The coldest planet

D The largest planet

b Write down the following in order of increasing size.

A The diameter of the Sun

B The diameter of the universe

C The distance from the Sun to the nearest star

D The distance from the Sun to Pluto

E The distance between galaxies

F The diameter of the Milky Way

4 a Examine the diagrams below.

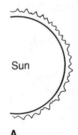 

A

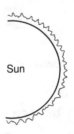 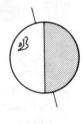

B

Match each diagram with the correct description.
Write down the correct letter–number pairs. For example, if you think diagram A matches statement 1 write down A1.

1—Summer in Australia
2—Night in the USA
3—Short days in Britain
4—Warm weather in Britain
5—Short nights in Australia

continued ▶

b The diagrams below show the position of the Sun in the sky at mid-day at three times in the year.

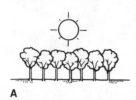
A

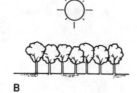
B

C

(i) Which drawing was made on 30th May?

(ii) Which drawing was made on the coldest day of the year?

(iii) Which drawing shows the Sun's position all the year round at the equator?

5 Look at the drawings of the Moon below.

 A **B** **C** ? **D** **E** ? **F**

new Moon

a Draw the Moon as it would appear at points C and E.

b If shape A is seen on the 1st of January when would shape A be seen next?

c Why is only one side of the Moon ever visible from the Earth?

6 Explain why the appearance of the Moon changes each month.

7 a Which of the following statements are true?

A The Sun is part of the solar system

B Our galaxy is part of the universe

C The galaxy is outside the solar system

D There are many galaxies in every solar system

E A spaceship would travel across the Milky Way more quickly than it would travel across universe

b If the star nearest to the sun suddenly exploded we would not see the explosion for 4.2 years. Explain this true statement.

8 a The following are important processes in the formation of three types of rock.

Processes	Rock types
A deposition	
B volcanic eruption	igneous
C weathering	metamorphic
D crushing at high pressure	sedimentary
E heating at high temperature	
F rapid cooling of lava	

Write down the letters of two processes involved in the formation of each rock type.

b Describe two features of
● igneous rock
● sedimentary rock.

9 a Read the following descriptions of rocks.

Rock A
A rock that can be scratched easily and has a striped appearance.

Rock B
A rock made up of a number of interlocking crystals. It is hard.

Rock C
This has a smooth texture and contains many fossils.

Rock D
This seems to be made of several different rocks that have been crushed together.

Identify each rock as igneous, metamorphic or sedimentary.

b Two pupils examined different crystals of the same mineral under a microscope.
The drawings show what they saw.

Pupil **A**

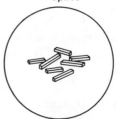

Pupil **B**

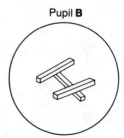

If you had been given a hot solution of the mineral how would you have produced each size of crystal?

continued ▶

10 The diagram below shows how the three rock types can be recycled.

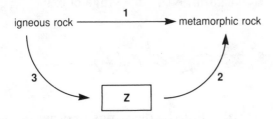

a What rock type should be shown in box Z?
b Name the processes at points 1, 2 and 3.
c Describe how igneous rocks form.
d Explain how you would recognise a rock of type Z.

11 Some rocks are important raw materials.
State one property you would expect each rock described below to have.

A Slate is used for roofing tiles

B Coal is used as a fuel

C Talc is used for talcum powder

D Granite is used for walls of buildings

12 The table below describes the properties of three common minerals that have a very similar appearance.

Mineral	Soluble	Reaction with acid	Hardness
halite	yes	none	2/3
calcite	no	fizzes	2/3
quartz	no	none	7

Imagine you have been given a sample of each mineral. Explain how you would be able to identify which was which.

13 Some minerals are mined because they contain metals that are important raw materials.

A Haematite contains a metal used for making girders for buildings, car bodies, cookers and many other heavy-duty household goods.

B Malachite is a green mineral that contains a metal used for cooking pots and for electrical wiring.

C Bauxite contains a metal that is shiny and is often used for window frames.

a What metal is present in each of these minerals?

b Suggest two important properties of each metal for the uses given.

14 Which of the following diagrams correctly show how the force of gravity acts?

A		The force of attraction between two planets
B		Gravity pulling a space station back to Earth
C		A ball falling to the ground
D		The Moon rotating round the Earth
E		A black hole pulling a comet towards it

Extension questions

15 Describe three pieces of evidence that show that the Earth is not flat.

16 Forecast the weather you would expect to get at point X in each of the situations below. The arrows show the direction of the airstream.

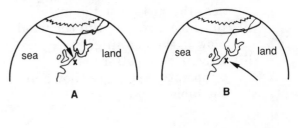

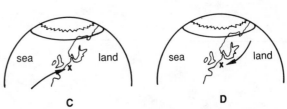

17 a Copy the drawing of an area of low pressure below. Add arrows to the drawing to show the direction of wind.

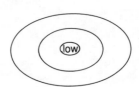

continued ▶

b Place these 'lows' in order of windspeed produced, from highest windspeed to lowest windspeed.

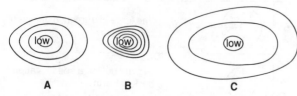

A   B   C

c The table gives the temperature change in the three areas shown on the map.

Place	Temperature change 9a.m.–12a.m.	5p.m.–8p.m.
city	+15°C	−12°C
desert	+14°C	−11°C
sea	+10°C	−8°C

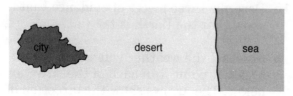

city   desert   sea

(i) Where is the air pressure highest near the surface at 12a.m.?

(ii) In which direction will the wind blow in the morning?

(iii) Describe the pattern of temperature changes shown in the table.

18 What are the risks of living near a zone of active crust?

19 a Examine the drawings below.

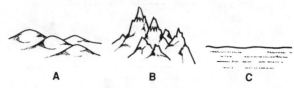

A   B   C

(i) Put the drawings in order of age of landscape, from oldest to youngest.

(ii) Name two processes that might have formed the landforms seen in diagram B.

(iii) What two processes cause the changes in the landscape?

b The drawings below show changes in a huge landmass on an alien planet. They took place over millions of years.

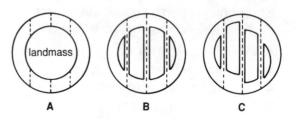

landmass

A   B   C

(i) What causes the change seen from A to C?

(ii) Where would you be most likely to find volcanoes in diagram B?

Name _____

Put a tick after the statements that are true.
Put a cross after the statements that are false.

1 a Sedimentary rocks are formed when a volcano erupts. ☐
  b Igneous rocks always contain crystals. ☐
  c Large crystals form when molten rock cools slowly. ☐
  d A piece of rock with layers or bands running through it is likely to be metamorphic. ☐
  e Igneous rock can be changed into sedimentary rock by heat and pressure. ☐
  f A rock is made up of a number of different minerals. ☐
  g Igneous rock can be recycled into sedimentary rock by weathering, erosion and deposition. ☐
  h Sedimentary and igneous rock are changed into metamorphic rock by processes on the Earth's surface. ☐

2 a A raw material is something that must be heated before it can be used. ☐
  b Coal is used as a fuel because it burns. ☐
  c A mineral that was very hard and shiny could be used as a raw material for jewellery. ☐
  d Talc is a raw material for the cosmetics industry because it is very soft. ☐
  e Granite is easy to find and easy to identify. These are two important properties of granite. ☐

3 a The solar system is made up of the Sun, the Earth and the Moon. ☐
  b There are nine planets in the solar system. ☐
  c The distance between planets is measured in tens of thousands of kilometres. ☐
  d A spaceship launched from Earth takes several months to pass out of the solar system. ☐

4 a The Sun is part of a burning planet. ☐
  b Stars can only be seen at night when they start to shine. ☐
  c The Sun is a star. ☐
  d Some objects in the night sky look like stars because they reflect starlight. ☐

5 a Day and night are caused by the Moon passing between the Sun and planet Earth. ☐
  b The Earth rotates once every 24 hours. ☐
  c The tilt of the Earth's axis causes the seasons in the northern and southern hemispheres. ☐
  d The Earth revolves around the Sun four times each year – once per season. ☐
  e The position of the Sun in the sky at mid-day is the same in July as it is in January. ☐
  f Day length is the same throughout the year at the equator. ☐
  g England is closer than Scotland to the 'Land of the Midnight Sun'. ☐

6 a The shape of the Moon seems to change in a predictable pattern every two months. ☐
  b A new Moon cannot be seen from Earth with the naked eye. ☐
  c The shading on the Moon is caused by the Earth's shadow. ☐
  d The shape of the Moon we see depends on how brightly it is shining. ☐

7 a One revolution is the time taken for the Earth to pass once around the Sun. ☐
  b The orbits of the planets cross each year. ☐
  c The planets are always the same distance apart. ☐
  d The same side of the Moon always faces the Earth. ☐
  e A solar eclipse occurs when the Moon passes directly between the Sun and Earth. ☐
  f The four planets closest to the Sun are, in order: Mercury, Mars, Venus, Earth. ☐

continued ▶

8 a The constellations we see in the night sky will always look the same. ☐

b New stars are forming all the time. ☐

c The Milky Way is another name for the universe. ☐

d There are more stars than there are galaxies. ☐

e There are likely to be many thousands of different solar systems in one galaxy. ☐

f An order of increasing size is: solar system, galaxy, universe. ☐

9 a A falling ball is pulled by gravity to the centre of the Earth. ☐

b Gravity is always a force of attraction. ☐

10 a When an empty tin with its lid on is heated gently the lid blows off because the volume of air inside the tin has increased. ☐

b Pushing in the handle of a bicycle pump increases the pressure on the air and increases its volume. ☐

c Hot air expands. ☐

Extensions

11 a An airstream is the movement of air from one particular direction. ☐

b A northerly airstream is likely to bring colder weather. ☐

c Airstreams cause changes in the tides. ☐

12 a Air moves into the centre of an area of low pressure in a clockwise direction. ☐

b The type of weather depends on the direction of the airstream. ☐

c A sea breeze develops in warm weather at night time. ☐

d Wind moves towards an area of higher air pressure. ☐

e When air gets hot it rises creating an area of low pressure. ☐

13 a At one time there was only one very large continent on Earth. ☐

b The position of the continents is changing slowly. ☐

c The Earth's crust is made up of one large plate which slowly moves around. ☐

d Areas of active crust are closest to the centre of each plate. ☐

e Volcanoes and earthquakes are most likely where two plates meet. ☐

14 a There is no scientific proof that the Earth is flat. ☐

b If the Earth was flat boats would fall off the edge. ☐

c Photographs from space prove that the Earth is not flat. ☐

Unit 4 Back to Earth

Name _____

Complete each sentence. Put the correct word(s) in each blank space.

1 We live on _____ which is one of 9 planets in the

_____ system. The planets move round the _____ .

The planet nearest the Sun is _____ and the planet farthest from

the Sun is _____ .

The 7 planets in between are, in order:

- _____
- _____
- _____
- _____
- _____
- _____
- _____ .

2 Our Sun is one of many millions of _____ that are part of a

_____ called the Milky Way. The Milky Way is only one of many

thousands of _____ that make up the _____ .

3 All the planets _____ the Sun. The time taken to go once round the

Sun is a _____ and it takes _____ for the Earth to

do this.

The rotation of the Earth causes _____ and _____ .

The Earth spins on its _____ at an angle. This is why we have four

_____ of the year when there are differences in

_____ and _____ .

The tilt of the Earth also explains why the angle of the _____ in the

sky varies with the time of year.

- _____ in the sky in summer
- _____ in the sky in winter.

continued ▶

Name _____

4 The Moon _____ around the _____ . The phases of

the Moon are caused by the way in which the _____ , Moon and

_____ line up. The phases are shown below.

new Moon   full Moon   new Moon

5 The force of gravity always acts towards the _____ of every

astronomical body.

6 There are three types of rock:

- _____ formed by _____

- _____ formed by _____

- metamorphic formed by _____ .

These rocks can be _____ from one form into another by

_____ processes such as weathering, _____ and

_____ . Underground processes such as _____ and

_____ are also involved.

Two examples of rocks changing are: ● limestone to _____

● _____ to _____ .

7 Rocks are made up of a number of different _____ which are

chemical compounds.

When used as raw materials they must have the right _____ for the

job. For example, marble is used in building because it is _____ and

colourful.

Solar system disc

1 Cut out both circles and the window in the smaller circle.

2 Join them at their centres with a paper fastener, so that the smaller disc rotates on the larger one.

3 Complete the information about each planet in the window area. Colour each planet appropriately.

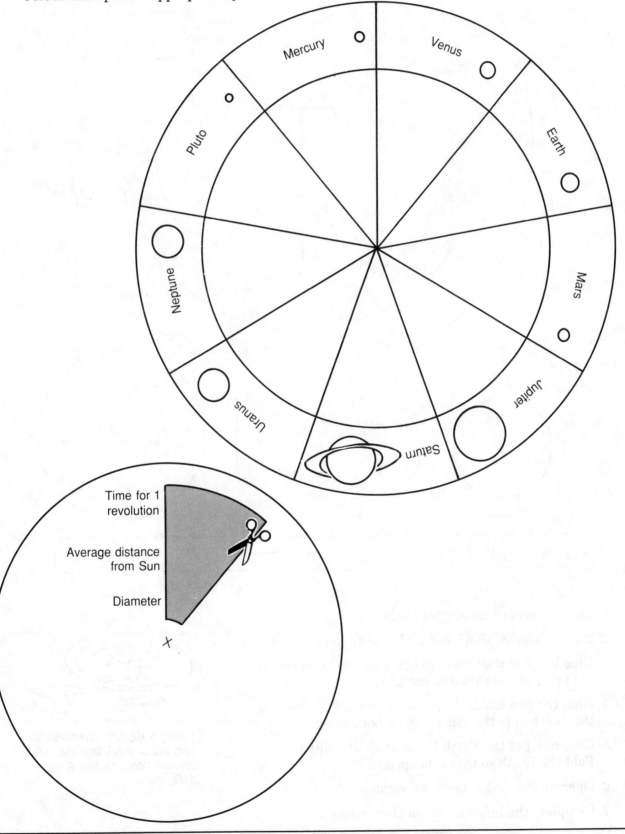

Earth orbit model

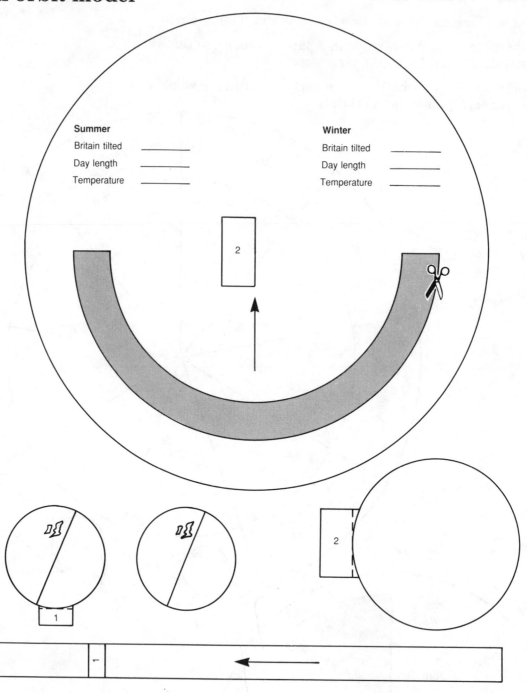

Summer

Britain tilted _____

Day length _____

Temperature _____

Winter

Britain tilted _____

Day length _____

Temperature _____

1 Cut out each of the shapes above.

2 Cut the shaded shape out of the large circle.

3 Glue box 2 of the Sun onto box 2 on the large circle. Fold the Sun so that it is upright.

4 Glue the two Earth shapes back to back. Make sure the axis points the same way on both sides.

5 Glue box 1 of the Earth to the stick at point 1. Fold the Earth so that it is upright.

6 Operate the model as shown right.

7 Complete the information on the model.

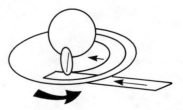

Make sure the arrows on the stick and on the circle always point in the same direction.

Understanding Science 3

Rock cycle diagram

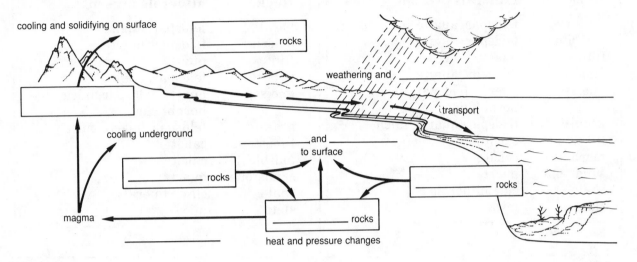

Rock type

2 examples

_____ _____ _____
_____ _____ _____
_____ _____ _____

Rock cycle diagram

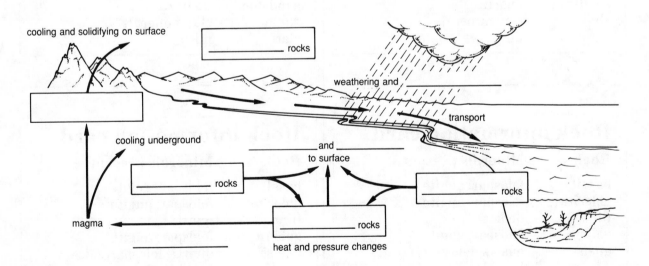

Rock type

2 examples

_____ _____ _____
_____ _____ _____
_____ _____ _____

Rock information card

Rock	Minerals present
basalt	feldspar, augite
dolerite	feldspar, augite
flint	quartz
gabbro	feldspar, augite
gneiss	quartz, feldspar, mica, hornblende
granite	feldspar, quartz, mica
limestone	calcite
marble	calcite
sandstone	quartz
shale	clay minerals
slate	mica

Rock information card

Rock	Minerals present
basalt	feldspar, augite
dolerite	feldspar, augite
flint	quartz
gabbro	feldspar, augite
gneiss	quartz, feldspar, mica, hornblende
granite	feldspar, quartz, mica
limestone	calcite
marble	calcite
sandstone	quartz
shale	clay minerals
slate	mica

Rock information card

Rock	Minerals present
basalt	feldspar, augite
dolerite	feldspar, augite
flint	quartz
gabbro	feldspar, augite
gneiss	quartz, feldspar, mica, hornblende
granite	feldspar, quartz, mica
limestone	calcite
marble	calcite
sandstone	quartz
shale	clay minerals
slate	mica

Rock information card

Rock	Minerals present
basalt	feldspar, augite
dolerite	feldspar, augite
flint	quartz
gabbro	feldspar, augite
gneiss	quartz, feldspar, mica, hornblende
granite	feldspar, quartz, mica
limestone	calcite
marble	calcite
sandstone	quartz
shale	clay minerals
slate	mica

Rock information card

Rock	Minerals present
basalt	feldspar, augite
dolerite	feldspar, augite
flint	quartz
gabbro	feldspar, augite
gneiss	quartz, feldspar, mica, hornblende
granite	feldspar, quartz, mica
limestone	calcite
marble	calcite
sandstone	quartz
shale	clay minerals
slate	mica

Rock information card

Rock	Minerals present
basalt	feldspar, augite
dolerite	feldspar, augite
flint	quartz
gabbro	feldspar, augite
gneiss	quartz, feldspar, mica, hornblende
granite	feldspar, quartz, mica
limestone	calcite
marble	calcite
sandstone	quartz
shale	clay minerals
slate	mica

Investigating energy, forces and movement

This unit builds upon those aspects of unit 4 in Books 1 and 2 that introduced the concepts of energy, forces and friction. The revision work therefore refers to these concepts. The next six topics introduce energy changes, energy conservation and the transfer of heat: the force of friction and its effect on motion is considered, and further work on force covers its deforming effects on materials, the concept of pressure, and how force can be changed by the use of machines. The final three topics comprise a discussion on the greenhouse effect and global warming, a reading exercise about early scientists' search for a vacuum, and a technological design problem utilising air pressure. This unit deals with Attainment Targets 10 and 13 of the 1989 National Curriculum. In addition to meeting the general requirements of Attainment Target 1, this unit deals specifically with AT1 levels 6 and 7.

Core and Reinforcement	**Extension**

5.0 Revision—Energy and forces

Revise background work.
Complete a revision question sheet.
Report on an energy-driven toy. *page 68*

Revise earlier work.
Apply knowledge in an imaginative way.

5.1 Using energy *AT13–4c, 6a,d*

Follow the processes of energy changes and representation using energy arrows.
Design and perform energy-changing activities corresponding to given data.
Learn that energy chains start with the Sun. *page 70*

Devise an activity for a stated purpose.
Communicate information in written and diagrammatic form.
Follow written instructions.

AT13–6b, 7b

Understand the principle of the conservation of energy.
Observe examples of energy transfer and compare the useful outcomes.
Learn that energy is measured in joules. *page 153*

Present information as a chart.

5.2 Heat on the move *AT13–7a*

Measure the rate of conduction.
Observe convection currents.
Describe everyday examples of heat transfer in terms of conduction and convection. *page 72*

Follow written instructions.
Communicate the method, result and conclusions of an experiment in written form.
Extract information from a diagram.

AT13–5a, 7a,c

Learn how houses lose heat by conduction.
Measure rate of conduction through a variety of materials.
Understand the concept of a fair test. *page 154*

Design an activity for a stated purpose.
Present information as a chart.

5.3 Heat radiation *AT13–4d, 7a*

Learn that heat can be transferred by radiation.
Measure the effect of surface colour in the rate of absorption of radiant heat.
Investigate the rate of transfer of radiant heat from an electric heater. *page 74*

Follow written instructions.
Draw graphs to show results.
Evaluate and improve apparatus.

AT11–6d

Learn how to read two types of electricity meter.
Extract information from an electricity bill.
Calculate cost of domestic electrical energy consumption. *page 155*

Extract information from diagrams.
Carry out arithmetic calculations.

Core and Reinforcement

5.4 Speed
AT10–4b, 5c, 7a

> Investigate ways of reducing friction between a moving object and a surface.
> Investigate the effect of speed and friction on braking distance.
> *page 76*

Carry out investigation with due regard to safety.
Prepare an appropriately structured and illustrated report.

5.5 Shaping up to force
AT10–3a, 4d, 5b, 6b, 7b

> Consider the effect of force on everyday materials.
> Build a structure with spaghetti to withstand the maximum force for least cost.
> Investigate the relationship between area, force and pressure.
> Measure weight in newtons.
> *page 78*

Design, build and evaluate a structure.
Formulate a testable hypothesis.
Measure and record accurately.
Carry out arithmetic calculations.

5.6 Be more forceful
AT10–6c, 7a; AT13–6c

> Learn how levers and pulleys increase turning force.
> Build different pulleys and compare the force needed to lift a load.
> Investigate force and distance moved by the pedal and wheel on a bicycle.
> *page 80*

Follow diagrammatic instructions.
Observe, measure and record accurately and systematically.
Use experimental data to recognise patterns and to deduce relationships.

5.7 Talkabout—The greenhouse effect
AT5–7a; AT13–7a

> Learn about some causes and effects of global warming.
> Prepare a short talk based on information selected from the text and other sources.
> *page 82*

Extract information from a variety of sources.

5.8 Readabout—No pressure at all!
AT6–5a; AT17–5b

> Learn that gases have weight.
> Read about the ideas of the ancient Greeks, Galileo and other Italian scientists concerning the nature of air.
> *page 85*

Extract relevant information.

Extension

AT10–4a, 6a, 7a

> Measure the time taken for vehicles to cover a given distance.
> Calculate speed.
> *page 156*

Process data using a computer spreadsheet or by calculations.

AT10–3a, 5a, 7a

> Learn that when an object is not moving balanced forces are acting upon it.
> Design and build a Plasticine boat which can carry the maximum weight.
> *page 157*

Design, build and evaluate a structure.

AT10–7a; AT13–6a,c, 7b

> Learn that efficiency is a measure of how much energy is transferred in an intended way.
> *page 158*

Manipulate apparatus to achieve stated result.
Carry out arithmetic calculations.

Core and Reinforcement

5.9 Problem—High pressure energy

> Learn how energy can be stored in
> compressed gases.
> Design, build and evaluate a machine which
> uses compressed gas. *page 84*

Devise, build and evaluate an apparatus which applies
scientific knowledge to meet a given specification.

Extension

Equipment
required for each pupil group

5.0—Revision—Energy and forces
- Revision question sheet
- Simple powered toy, e.g. clockwork car

5.1—Using energy

- Energy story cards **(R5.1)**

5.2—Heat on the move
- Potato
- 250 ml beaker
- Tripod
- Gauze
- Bunsen burner
- Heatproof mat
- Tongs
- Stop clock
- Kitchen knife
- Small round-bottomed flask
- Aluminium powder
- Spatula
- Washing-up liquid
- Pieces of ice
- Candle
- Low-voltage heater
- Power supply
- Stands and clamps

Extension
- Electric iron
- Drawing pin
- Grease
- Timer
- Sheets of test materials, e.g. heatproof mat, thick
  sheet of aluminium, magazine, sheet of wood.
- U-values sheet **(RE5.2)**

Notes

Access to copies of *Understanding Science 1* and *2*
will allow pupils to check their work and look for
information they are unsure of.
The mechanism of the toy should be visible: if
necessary the casing could be partially removed.

Equipment required for the energy-arrow activities
will depend on the pupils' designs. It may be
advisable to have the pupils carry out the activities
some time subsequent to their submitting their
designs, to allow time for appropriate equipment to
be collected.

The different groups could be told to cook the
potato for different times and the class results
collated at the end.
It is important to check the amount of cold water in
the beaker before it is boiled so that it does not
overflow when the potato is put in.

Great care must be taken to avoid inhaling the dust
when putting the aluminium powder into the flask.
Only a small amount is needed with two or three
drops of detergent to make a snow-storm effect.

The heater should be protected by a grid.

The materials should be of about the same
thickness.

This resource is provided especially for pupils in
Northern Ireland to address the requirements of
AT4–7d of the Science Curriculum.

Equipment

5.3—Heat radiation

- Copper sheets
- Radiant heater
- Thermometer
- Stop clock
- 1 metre of Nichrome wire
- Glass rod, diameter about 5 mm
- 2 block connectors
- 2 thick copper leads
- Screwdriver
- 100 ml beaker
- Thermometer
- Stop clock
- 12 V power supply

5.4—Speed

- Sheet of paper
- Small polystyrene beads in a tray
- Linear air track with accessories.
- Bicycle
- Crash helmet
- Tape measure
- Piece of chalk
- Stop watch
- Computer with spreadsheet program, e.g. *Beebcalc* or *Viewsheet*

5.5—Shaping up to force

- Spaghetti sticks
- Drawing pins
- Newton spring balance
- Hot-glue gun and heatproof board or sticky tape
- Masses
- Ruler
- Graph paper
- Centimetre-squared paper
- Newton (not kilogram) bathroom-type scales
- Computer with spreadsheet program

Extension

- Balloon
- String
- Scissors
- Access to aspirator bottle, water supply and gas supply
- Balloon-inflating instruction sheet **(RE5.5)**
- Plasticine or clay
- Newton masses
- Newton balance
- Bowl of water

Notes

The copper sheets should be blackened on one side and painted white on the other, with a pocket soldered on each side for the thermometer. The radiant heater should be protected with a grid.

Careful supervision is needed here.

Equipment	Notes

Equipment

5.6—Be more forceful

- 3 clamp stands
- 2 sets of bosses and clamps
- Strong string
- Suitable 'load', e.g. bag with handles
- 2 strong wood or metal rods
- 2 sets of masses on hangers
- Bicycle

Extension

- 2 sets of newton masses and hangers
- Suitable construction-kit parts, e.g. Fischer or Meccano.
- Thread or thin string
- Metre rule

5.7—Talkabout—The greenhouse effect

- Copy of global warming diagram **(R5.7)**

5.8—Readabout—No pressure at all!

No equipment required.

5.9—Problem—High pressure energy

- Copy of instruction sheet **(R5.9)**

Turbo lifter

- Sheet of thin card
- Scissors
- Plastic drinking straw
- Blu-Tack
- Knitting needle or stiff wire
- 2 large clothes pegs
- Washer
- Balloon
- Thread
- Mass hanger and masses

Balloon rocket

- Balloon
- Assorted washers
- Thread
- Plastic drinking straw
- Sticky tape

Notes

One stand should be of the three-legged type.

A suitable spring balance could be substituted for one set of masses.

Assessment 5

The questions are designed to assess the skills and knowledge developed in the unit as shown in the table. The Attainment Target assessed by each question is also shown. A selection of questions would be appropriate for a unit test.

Topic	Core	Attainment Target
5.1	1	AT13–4c
	2	AT13–6a, 6d
5.2	3, 4, 5	AT13–7a
5.3	6	AT13–7a
5.4	7	AT10–7a
	8	AT10–4b
5.5	9	AT10–3a
	10, 11	AT10–6b
5.6	12	AT10–6c
	13	AT13–6c
	14	AT6–5a
	Extension	
5.1	15	AT13–6b
5.2	16	AT13–7c
5.3	17	AT11–6d
5.4	18	AT10–6a
5.5	19	AT10–5a
5.6	20	AT13–7b

Answers

1 Chemical, gravitational, gravitational, kinetic, heat.
2 C, D, B, A.
3 Bad, bad, good, bad, good conductors. Good, good, bad, good, bad insulators.
4 See page 73 of pupils' book.
5 See page 73 of pupils' book.
6 B, C, E.
7 a Her speed will increase until the rocket is shut off.
b She will travel at a constant speed.
c By digging something into the ice *or* by spinning round and firing the rocket in reverse *or* any means of exerting a force in the opposite direction to the motion.
8 The braking distance will be larger than expected if the speed is high, the mass on the bike is high and the friction of the brake blocks is low, e.g. in the wet.
9 Possible answers could include:
a Push your thumb into the butter.
b Pull the lump of jelly.
c Bend the spaghetti strip.
d Break off a piece of cheese.
10 Small, small, large, small areas. Large, large, small, large pressures.
11 Sarah.
12 D.
13 a X and Z   **b** Z
14 a 1.4 g   **b** Water would be sucked into flask.
15 a 20 J
b Conservation of energy.
c Because the energy converted into heat is so spread around that it cannot be used.
16 Loft insulation because it makes major savings and only takes two years to pay back.
17 a 790   **b** 6.78 pence   **c** £63.83   **d** No
18 a 20 m/s, 2 m/s, 5 cm/s.
b from the push of the wings on the air, from the push of the feet on the ground, from the push of the tail on the water.
19 A + B + C = D
20 Push bike.

True/false 5

Each statement is marked as either true or false by the pupil. This gives a rapid assessment of a pupil's grasp of the Attainment Targets covered in the unit. The following list gives the Attainment Targets covered by each set of statements.

1	AT 13–4c	10	AT 10–7a
2	AT 13–6a	11	AT 10–7b
3	AT 13–6c	12	AT 6–5a
4	AT 13–6d	13	AT 13–6b
5	AT 13–7a	14	AT 13–7b
6	AT 10–3a	15	AT 13–7c
7	AT 10–4b	16	AT 10–5a
8	AT 10–6b	17	AT 10–6a
9	AT 10–6c	18	AT 11–6d

Unit 5 Energy on the move

Name_____

1 Write the meaning of each word or phrase in the space provided. The figures in brackets are references to *Understanding Science*, Books 1 and 2 (**book number**, page number). Use the references to *check* your answers.

- 'kinetic' or movement energy (**1**, 54)
- potential energy (**1**, 55,122)
- energy changes (**1**, 56,123)
- electrical energy (**1**, 54,129)
- stored energy (**1**, 55,122)
- contact forces (**2**, 65)
- non-contact forces (**2**, 66)
- friction (**2**, 68)
- balanced forces (**2**, 70)

2 The spider diagram shows some connections between these terms. Complete the diagram with the correct words.

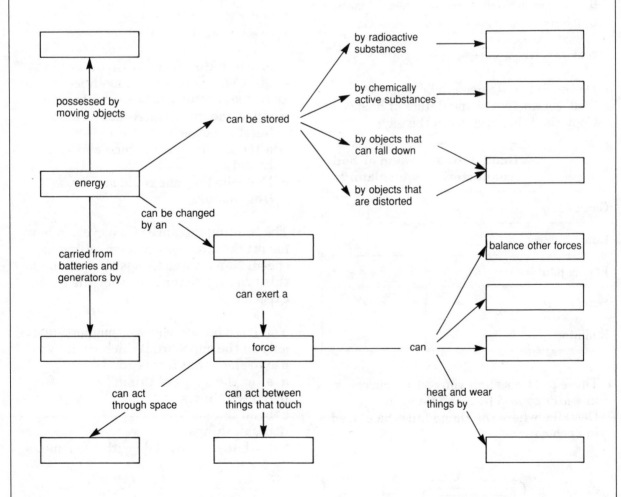

1 Write down the forms of energy that fit into the gaps in this story.

Doris climbed up the rope ladder to the top of the tower. She used some of the

_____ energy stored in her muscles and gained

_____ energy. She then grabbed a rope and swung down to the ground, digging her heels into the earth and sliding to a halt.

Her _____ energy was then

changed into _____ energy

and _____

2 Write the steps of this energy story in the correct order.

A Electricity is used to heat an electric iron

B A windmill turns a generator and makes electricity

C The Sun heats up the atmosphere and makes wind

D The winds blow and turn a windmill

3 Do the following need to be 'good' or 'bad' conductors or insulators of heat? Copy the table and fill in the gaps.

	Good or bad conductor?	Good or bad insulator?
Carpet		
Cup		
Frying pan		
Scarf		
Radiator		

4 These pictures show convection currents in water caused by a candle flame. Describe where the flame must be placed in each case.

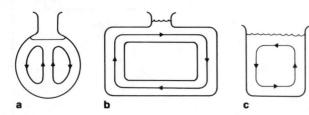

a   b   c

5 Describe or draw the convection currents you would expect around each of the items in the drawing below.

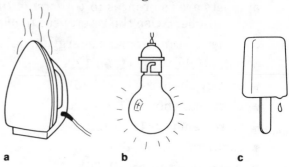

a   b   c

6 Which of the following use radiation to get rid of most of their heat?

A a boiling kettle

B the Sun

C an electric fire

D a cup of tea

E the filament of a light bulb

F an electric iron.

7 A brave skater, fitted with a rocket engine, stands on very smooth ice. Describe carefully how she will move

a when she gives the rocket a short burst of power

b after she has then turned off the rocket.

c Describe how she could stop herself from moving.

8 The braking-distance of a bicycle is how far it takes to stop when travelling at speed. Name three things that can make this braking distance further than you expect.

9 You have butter, cheese, spaghetti and jelly in the cupboard. Which would you use to show that force can

a alter the shape of things,

b stretch things,

c bend things,

d break things?

Say what you would do with each one.

continued ▶

10 Copy the table and fill in the gaps. For each of the examples say whether the area of contact and the pressure is *large* or *small*.

	Point of pencil	High-heeled shoe	Hovercraft	Spade
Area of contact				
Pressure				

11 Which of these people exerts the greatest pressure on the ground?

	Weight	**Shoe area**
Susan	400 N	200 cm^2
Sarah	600 N	150 cm^2
Sunil	600 N	200 cm^2

12 Which of these weights would be the easiest to wind up? Explain your answer.

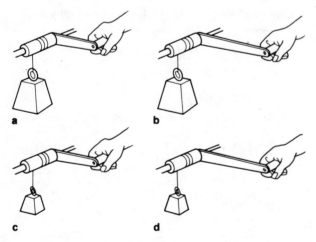

a   b

c   d

13 In each of the lifting machines shown below, a rope turns the large wheel which moves a parcel attached to the smaller wheel.

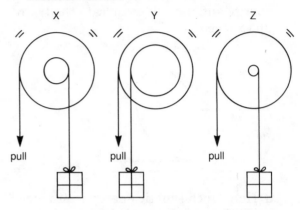

a As the rope is pulled down, which machines lift the parcel up?
b Which machine would need the least force to lift the parcel?

14 a The pictures show a strong flask on a balance. One shows the flask full of air and the other with the air pumped out. How much does the air weigh?

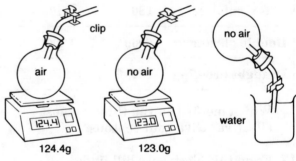

124.4g   123.0g

b How could you use the arrangement in the picture to show that there is such a thing as a vacuum?

continued ▶

Extension questions

15 The energy arrow is for a clockwork train. The spring is given 200 J of energy and used to accelerate the train up to speed.

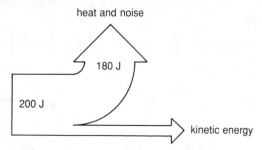

heat and noise

180 J

200 J

kinetic energy

a How much kinetic energy is produced?
b What principle is used in the calculation?
c Explain why the energy is less useful at the end of the operation.

16 A woman decided to cut her fuel bills by insulating her house. The costs and savings are shown in the table.

	Cost	Saving per year
Loft insulation	£80	£40
Double glazing	£6000	£200
Draught proofing	£30	£10

Which method do you think is most effective? Give your reasons.

17 From this electricity bill find:
  a the number of units used,
  b the cost per unit,
  c the total amount to pay,
  d whether the reading was taken by a visiting meter reader.

METER READING		UNITS USED	UNIT PRICE (pence)	V.A.T. code	AMOUNT £
PRESENT	PREVIOUS				
E 21773	E 20983	790	6.780	1	53.56
STANDING CHARGE				1	10.27
TOTAL CHARGES (EXCLUDING VAT)					63.83
VAT 1 £63.83 @ 0% DOMESTIC					0.00

E=Estimated Reading. Please read the advice given on the back of this bill.
C=Your own reading.

BALANCE TO PAY		63.83
VAT CHARGE THIS BILL		0.00

YOUR ACCOUNT NUMBER	BILL DATE/TAX POINT	READING DATE	NON-DOMESTIC USE
B/ 093.1125/015.120	21 JAN 91	21 JAN 91	0%

18 a Work out the speed of these animals. (Speed = distance/time)
  A A pigeon flies 200 metres in 10 seconds
  B A cat walks 50 metres in 25 seconds
  C A tadpole swims 10 cm in 2 seconds.

  b Describe how each animal produces the force it uses to get along.

19 A hot-air balloon is hanging suspended in the air and supports a basket containing two people. The following forces act on the balloon.
  A The weight of the people and basket.
  B The weight of the balloon and ropes.
  C The weight of the hot air in the balloon.
  D The buoyancy of the outside air.

Use the letters to write an equation that shows how the forces on the balloon balance.

20 Which of these machines is the most efficient?

	Energy put in	Energy got out
Push bike	500 J	400 J
Tube train	100 MJ	50 MJ
Car engine	200 kJ	50 kJ

Name_____

Put a tick after the statements that are true.
Put a cross after the statements that are false.

1 a Energy can be kept in store and held ready for use. ☐
  b Stored energy can be transferred to moving objects. ☐

2 a Petrol, gas and coal are energy sources that store energy in chemical form. ☐
  b The energy they store can be turned directly into any form we want. ☐

3 a We use machines to increase the force of our muscles. ☐
  b We use machines to increase the distance we move. ☐

4 a The Sun is the source of about half the energy we use. ☐
  b The Sun's main source of energy is nuclear. ☐

5 a Conduction of heat occurs without any visible movement of the material. ☐
  b Convection is the transfer of heat by the upward movement of cold liquids. ☐
  c Heat radiation is an electromagnetic wave. ☐

6 a Materials can change shape without forces acting on them. ☐
  b A rolling snooker ball will gradually stop without a force acting on it. ☐

7 a A heavy bicycle needs a greater force to stop it than a light bicycle travelling at the same speed. ☐
  b Braking distance does not depend on speed. ☐

8 a A force will make a bigger dent in a lump of butter if it is concentrated over a smaller area. ☐
  b The pressure is greater if the area of contact is greater. ☐

9 a It is harder to close a door by pushing it near to the hinges because your turning effect is less. ☐
  b You can get more turning force from a long spanner because the force you exert can be further from the pivot. ☐

10 a A snooker ball rolls to a stop because of friction with the table. ☐
  b You can decrease the pressure you make on the ground by standing on your toes. ☐
  c A small cat and a large dog have to use the same force to get the same acceleration. ☐
  d The speed of a body cannot change unless a force acts on it. ☐
  e Acceleration occurs when the speed of a body changes. ☐

11 a The frame of a bicycle should be made from a material that is strong, light, flexible and cheap. ☐
  b Strong materials are always heavy. ☐
  c The strength of a bicycle frame depends only on the materials used. ☐

12 a Air is weightless. ☐
  b An oxygen cylinder weighs more empty than full. ☐

Extensions

13 a When energy is changed from one form to another, a little bit is always lost. ☐
  b When energy is used, some is always spread around as heat and becomes useless. ☐

14 a An efficient machine uses less energy to do a job than an inefficient one. ☐
  b The efficiency of a machine is calculated from: energy put in – energy got out. ☐

15 a It does not matter how much fuel we use to get energy because there is plenty left. ☐

continued ▶

b To work out the best way of insulating your home you only need to know the cost of the materials. ☐

16 a If the forces balance on a moving car it will eventually stop. ☐

b The forces that act on a cup sitting on a table are exactly balanced. ☐

17 a Speed can be calculated by dividing *time taken* by *distance travelled.* ☐

b You can calculate the distance travelled by multiplying speed by the time of the journey. ☐

18 a Electricity meters measure the energy used in kilowatt-seconds. ☐

b To work out the cost of electrical energy you have used at home, you multiply the meter reading by the cost of one kilowatt-hour. ☐

Unit 5 Energy on the move

Name _____

Complete each sentence. Put the correct word(s) in each blank space.

1 Energy can be stored ready for use; for example

- a can of petrol stores _____ energy

- a bike at the top of a hill stores _____ energy

- a stretched catapult elastic stores _____ energy.

2 Energy can _____ easily from one type to another. Some

_____ energy is always produced when this happens.

Energy 'chains' usually start with _____ and finish as waste

_____ .

When energy changes, _____ is ever lost or destroyed.

3 There are three more ways to transfer heat energy

- _____ – the transfer of heat through materials without any

obvious movement

- _____ – the transfer of heat by the movement of hot liquids or

gases

- _____ – the transfer of heat by electromagnetic waves.

4 Loss of heat from a house can be reduced through

- the walls by _____

- the roof by _____

- the windows by _____ .

5 Speed = distance divided by _____ .

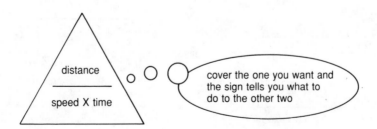

distance
————
speed X time

cover the one you want and the sign tells you what to do to the other two

continued ▶

Name _____

6 A force exerts a large pressure if it acts over _____ area.

Pressure = _____ divided by area.

A knife is used to produce a _____ pressure, a cushion is used to

produce a _____ pressure.

7 Machines like a lever or a wheel and axle are used to _____ force. A

machine like the bicycle is used to _____ speed or distance.

8 The efficiency of a machine is the energy got out divided by the energy

_____   _____ .

9 An unbalanced force always produces an _____ .

If the forces on a body balance it will either stay _____ or move at

a _____ speed.

Energy story cards

The climber uses his muscles to gain gravitational energy

Sunlight gave energy to trees that died long ago and turned into coal

The Sun heats up the air

Coal is burnt to make steam

The surfboard and sea warm up

Food provides energy for muscles

Warm air rises and winds blow

Plants are eaten as food

The surfboard takes energy from the wind

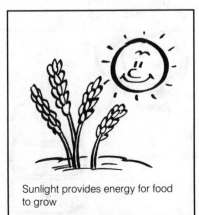

Sunlight provides energy for food to grow

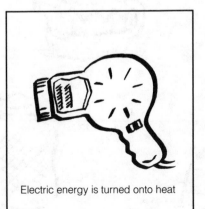

Electric energy is turned onto heat

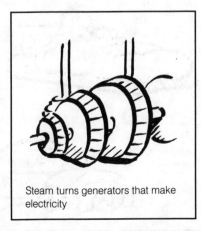

Steam turns generators that make electricity

U-values

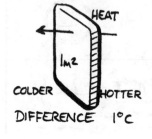

U-values are one way of measuring the insulating property of a material. It is a useful value to know for things like building materials, loft insulation, clothing and duvets.

The *U*-value of a material is defined as the heat energy that passes each second through one square metre, when one face is 1°C hotter than the other.

Typical values might be 0.6 for a lagging jacket for a hot water tank, and 70 for the rubber of a hot water bottle. The lower the *U*-value, the better the insulation.

If *U*-values, areas and temperatures are known it is possible to work out the loss of heat through an insulator.

For example, the loss of heat through the walls and roof of this strange little house can be calculated using the equation:

Heat loss per second =
U-value × area × temperature difference.

loss through walls = $1.7 \times 12 \times 10 = 204$ W
loss through door = $5.6 \times 4 \times 10 = 224$ W
loss through roof = $2.2 \times 8 \times 10 = 176$ W
total loss = 604 W

The electric fire and the man's body must produce heat at this rate to keep the house at 20°C.

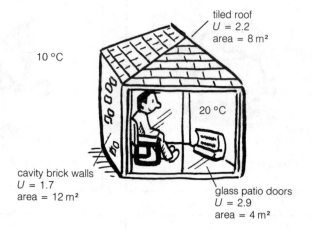

tiled roof
U = 2.2
area = 8 m²

10 °C

20 °C

cavity brick walls
U = 1.7
area = 12 m²

glass patio doors
U = 2.9
area = 4 m²

1 How much heating power would be needed to keep the house warm at 20°C if the cavity walls were filled with an insulating brick (reducing the walls to *U* = 0.6) and the patio doors were double glazed (*U* = 2.0)?

2 The pictures show other insulating materials in action. Use the values given to calculate the loss of heat per second for each example.

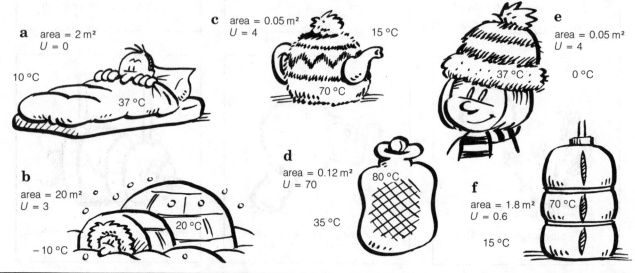

a area = 2 m²
U = 0

10 °C

37 °C

b
area = 20 m²
U = 3

−10 °C

20 °C

c area = 0.05 m²
U = 4

15 °C

70 °C

d
area = 0.12 m²
U = 70

80 °C

35 °C

e
area = 0.05 m²
U = 4

37 °C

0 °C

f
area = 1.8 m²
U = 0.6

70 °C

15 °C

How to fill a balloon with natural gas

1 Fill an aspirator bottle with water.

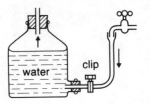

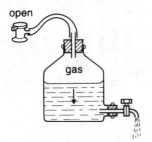

2 Connect to a gas tap.
   Let the water run out and fill the bottle
   with gas.

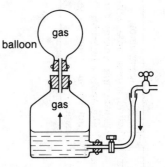

3 Fit the balloon onto the bottle.
   Fill the bottle with water and force the
   gas into the balloon.

WARNING Take great care that there are no flames about. When
you have finished with the balloon burst it, letting the
gas escape into the air.

How to fill a balloon with natural gas

1 Fill an aspirator bottle with water.

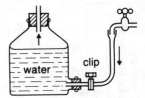

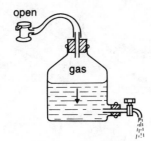

2 Connect to a gas tap.
   Let the water run out and fill the bottle
   with gas.

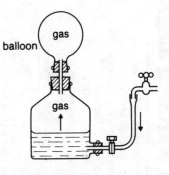

3 Fit the balloon onto the bottle.
   Fill the bottle with water and force the
   gas into the balloon.

WARNING Take great care that there are no flames about. When
you have finished with the balloon burst it, letting the
gas escape into the air.

Global warming diagram

The amount of CO_2 in the atmosphere is increasing. CO_2 traps the Sun's heat like a greenhouse. Earth's average temperature will probably rise by at least 2°C in the next 40 years.

Nuclear power stations make electricity without producing CO_2, but are expensive and dangerous.

Hydroelectric dams, wind, waves, tides and geothermal energy can also make electricity, but not yet on a very large scale.

Higher temperatures will dry out summer vegetation quicker, resulting in more fires.

Most modern transport – cars, planes, etc – burns fuels made from oil, producing more CO_2.

Coastal cities and even whole countries may be flooded by rising sea levels.

Algae in the sea absorb much CO_2, but pollution is killing them.

Poorer countries want to raise their living standards – as richer countries have done – by burning more fuels and making more electricity.

Ocean currents may change, causing local climate changes and movements of fish stocks.

As Earth gets warmer, more snow and rain will fall on the poles and on high ground.

Industrial countries burn coal to make electricity. This produces large amounts of CO_2.

Weather will generally become more extreme, with more blizzards and droughts.

Some cooler places will warm up enough to grow new and better crops.

Other places will become too hot and dry for the crops now grown there.

Trees absorb CO_2 as they grow, but forests are being cleared to give land for farming.

Wood is burned as fuel in poorer countries, releasing more CO_2.

As the sea warms up, storms and hurricanes will become more frequent.

Sea levels will probably rise by at least 30 cm in the next 40 years, mainly because water expands as it gets warmer.

How to build a compressed air machine

Turbo Lifter

1 Make a turbine wheel from thin card. Cut along the lines shown and curve the card to make blades.

2 Push a plastic straw through the middle of the wheel and fix it with Blu-Tack.

3 Put a needle or stiff wire through the straw to make an axle.

4 Support the axle by a peg at each end.

5 Fix the pegs to the table with pieces of Blu-Tack.

6 Fit a washer, with a medium-sized hole, into the neck of the balloon. This makes it easier to direct the jet of air onto the turbine blades.

7 Find how much weight your machine can lift.

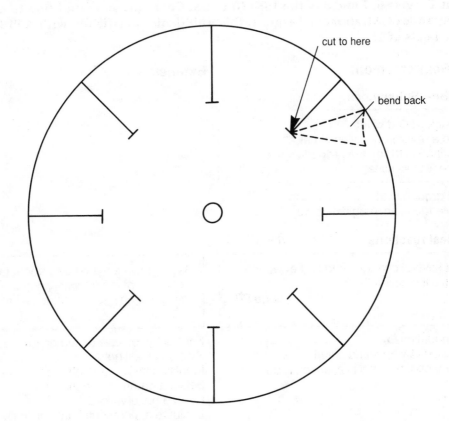

cut to here

bend back

Balloon Rocket

1 Fix a washer in the neck of the balloon (try different sizes to get the best effect).

2 Fix a short piece of plastic straw to the balloon with sticky tape.

3 Feed a long piece of thread through the straw and tie the thread across the room.

4 See if you can get your rocket to carry a payload or message.

Unit 6 Ideas of substance

Thinking about matter

This unit builds upon many aspects of unit 5 in Book 2 where the skills of hypothesising and prediction were introduced in the context of particle theory. The revision work therefore concerns the central ideas of elements, compounds, chemical reactions and the hypothesis that matter is made of tiny particles. The next three topics explore the nature of a chemical reaction, illustrating the qualitative effect of several variables on the speed of reaction. An investigative approach is encouraged and pupils are required to plan their practical work in advance, to identify and control relevant variables and to choose appropriate means of measurement. This approach is extended in the next two topics which ask pupils to research important chemical patterns, the reactivity series and the periodic table, and use them to make predictions. Although the unit exemplifies a way of approaching investigative work, key aspects of content are still presented within the practical context: basic knowledge about word equations, types of reactions (combustion, neutralisation, corrosion, oxidation, reduction, electrolysis), ways of increasing reaction rates, catalysts, enzymes, the reactivity series of metals, electrolysis and the movement of ions. The final three topics comprise the design and mapping of a local 'chemical trail', a group discussion activity on 'radiation' and a reading exercise about scientific models of the atom. This unit deals with Attainment Targets 6, 7 and 8 of the 1989 National Curriculum. In addition to meeting the general demands of Attainment Target 1, this unit deals specifically with AT1 levels 5a, 5b, 6a–d and aspects of 7.

Core and Reinforcement

6.0 Revision—Substances

> Revise background work.
> Complete a revision question sheet.
> Use imagination to link the properties of a substance with its uses. *page 88*

Revise background work.
Apply knowledge in an imaginative way.

6.1 Chemical reactions   *AT7–4a, 6c; AT8–6c*

> Carry out several changes and find evidence of a chemical reaction.
> *page 90*

Write word equations.
Identify reactions by applying criteria.
Communicate observations in a written report.

6.2 Speeding up reactions   *AT7–7a*

> Investigate the effects of temperature, particle size and concentration on the time taken to cook macaroni. Similarly investigate the effects on the rate of reaction of marble with hydrochloric acid. *page 92*

Plan an investigation.
Identify constant and changing variables.
Select a parameter to measure.
Record observations in a suitable form.

Extension

AT6–6d

> Write down a hypothesis about the order of reactivity of metals with vinegar. Plan and carry out an experiment to test the hypothesis.
> *page 159*

Form a hypothesis based on previous observations.
Plan an investigation.
Identify constant and changing variables.
Select a parameter to measure.
Record observations.
Evaluate experimental data critically.

AT7–7a

> Explain 11 everyday instances of speeding up reactions.
> *page 160*

Identify the changing variable in everyday reactions.

Core and Reinforcement	Extension

Core and Reinforcement

6.3 Catalysts
AT7–7a,b

Conduct an experiment to illustrate catalysis.
Investigate whether copper catalyses the reaction of zinc with acid.
Investigate ways of reducing the oxidation of apple.
page 94

Follow instructions.
Devise and carry out experiments for a given purpose.
Extract information.
Communicate observations in a written report.

6.4 Patterns in reactivity
AT6–6d, 7c

Investigate the reactivity series by reacting some metals with acid.
Research group similarities in one group of the periodic table.
page 96

Devise experiments to test given hypotheses.
Recognise and explain sources of unreliability.
Extract information.
Collate information from different sources and summarise it in written form.

6.5 Moving ions
AT7–6b; AT8–7b; AT11–7b; AT17–5b

Write on paper by using electricity to reduce iodide ions. Find out at which electrode a metal is discharged and make a hypothesis about the metal ion.
Use copper chromate to show that coloured ions are attracted to electrodes.
page 98

Follow instructions.
Form a hypothesis based on experimental observations.
Predict experimental results from a hypothesis.

6.6 Problem—Trail blazer
AT7–4a, 6c, 7d

Design and map a chemistry trail that will teach people about the chemical reactions in the local environment.
page 100

Devise a trail to present some local social, economic and environmental aspects of science.

6.7 Talkabout—Radiation
AT8–7d

Plan and record a 3 minute factual talk about radiation (group activity).
page 101

Extract relevant information from printed sources given key words.
Collate information.
Present information verbally.

Extension

AT7–7b

Design and carry out an experiment to find out if smelting of copper ore in a charcoal fire is feasible.
page 161

Devise and carry out an experiment for a given purpose.
Communicate in a written report.

AT6–6d

Use the reactivity series to predict some *dates of discovery* and *cell voltages*. Check the predictions.
page 162

Predict facts and experimental results from a given hypothesis.
Devise an experiment to test a prediction.

AT6–6c; AT8–7b

Use a conduction tester and chemical formulae to deduce whether given compounds are ionic or covalent.
page 163

Follow instructions.
Draw conclusions from experimental results.
Extract information.
Collate information from different printed sources and summarise it in written form.

6.8 Readabout—Atomic models   *AT17–7a,b*

> Read a short passage about the development
> of the modern model of the atom.   *page 102*

Extract information from printed sources.
Collate information and summarise it in written form.
Recognise that the study and practice of science
are subject to uncertainty.

Equipment
required for each pupil group

6.0—Revision—Substances
● Revision question sheet

6.1—Chemical reactions
● 3 prefilled oxygen tubes
  or
● Oxygen dispenser

● Iron powder
● Zinc powder
● Copper powder
● Burning spoon
● Bunsen burner and heatproof mat
● Safety glasses

Teacher's demonstration box
containing:
Activity 1
● Spray gun for misting plants
● Paraffin or turpentine
● Wire gauze, clamped vertically
● Bunsen burner and 2 heatproof mats
Activity 2
● Clear plastic tubing
● Cotton wool
● Filter funnel
● Shoe box with cut eyehole(s)
● Solution of luminol
  (3-aminophthalhydrazide)
● Solution of hydrogen peroxide

Notes

Access to copies of *Understanding Science 1* and *2*
will allow pupils to check their work and look for
information they are unsure of.

Allow pupils to fill boiling tubes with oxygen from a
Winchester bottle by displacement with water (as
shown below). NB. The boiling tube should remain
dry.

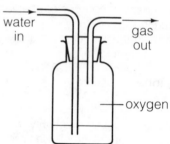

Powders are used in each case to make the
comparison fair. The powders need to be heated in
the Bunsen flame until glowing before being put
quickly into oxygen.
Encourage the pupils to look for an energy change
(taking the glowing metal as the starting point). The
order of activity is zinc, iron, copper.
Safety points: pupils work in pairs. One heats the
metal powder; when the metal is glowing the other
removes the stopper on the oxygen tube and **takes
hand away**. The spoon with the glowing metal is
then moved from flame to oxygen tube.

Spray a mist of flammable liquid **through** the wire
gauze. The gauze prevents flashback. Pupils should
stand behind a safety screen.
Position the gun 12 cm in front of the gauze and the
Bunsen burner 12 cm behind it.

As the solutions mix in the tube they react to
produce a pale light. Cotton wool soaked in the
solutions looks like a glowing solid.

Or classroom blackout facilities if available.

0.02 g plus 10 g sodium hydroxide in 200 cm³ of
water.

0.05 g of potassium hexacyanoferrate(III) in 200 cm³
of water plus 2 cm³ of 3% hydrogen peroxide.

Equipment

Pupils' activities boxes
containing:
- Appropriate activity card (R6.1)

Activity 3
- Solid ammonium chloride, sodium nitrate, sodium chloride, ammonium carbonate
- Spatula or wooden splint
- Test tube

Activity 4
- 100 cm^3 measuring cylinders labelled A and B
- Solution A

- Solution B
- Flask

Activity 5
- 3 small test tubes
- Alka Seltzer tablet
- Sodium carbonate solution (1M)
- Hydrochloric acid (1M)
- Lead nitrate solution (0.1M)
- Potassium iodide solution (0.1M)

Activity 6
- Low voltage electric motor
- Fresh lemon (or orange)
- Voltmeter (d.c. 1–2 V)
- Large zinc and copper plates
- Connecting leads with crocodile clips

Activity 7
- 100 cm^3 plastic beaker
- Copper sulphate solution (0.1M)
- Pieces of zinc foil (Approx 3 cm by 1 cm)
- Thermometer
- Stirring rod

Activity 8
- Boiling tube
- Sodium silicate solution (water glass)
- Crystals of cobalt(II) chloride, nickel(II) chloride, copper(II) chloride, manganese(II) sulphate

Fact-finder
- Access to a camera if possible

Extension
- Ethanoic acid (2M) labelled *vinegar*
- Metal foil: copper, zinc, iron
- Metal powder: copper, zinc, iron
- 3 test tubes and rack
- Dropper bottle of detergent (TeePol)

Notes

One activity per box.
Two sets of activities per class.

Some solids give out energy when dissolved and the tube becomes hotter. Others take in energy and the tube becomes colder.

Equal amounts of 0.5M sulphuric acid and 0.1M sodium iodide.

Equal amounts of 1vol hydrogen peroxide, fresh starch solution and 0.01M sodium thiosulphate solution.
This is an example of a clock reaction.

All concentrations are approximate.

Stick a shaped piece of foil onto the motor rotor to represent the helicopter blades.

The plates must be within 2 mm of each other to generate the necessary voltage.

Solution should have specific gravity = 1.6

Equipment

- Ruler
- Heatproof mat
- Scissors
- Tongs
- Thermometer
- Stirring rod
- Access to clock
- Safety glasses

6.2—Speeding up reactions

- Macaroni (quick-cook)
- Bunsen burner and heatproof mat
- Graph paper
- Blank white A4 paper
- Access to clock
- Beaker
- Thermometer
- Tile (to test stickiness of macaroni)

- Hydrochloric acid (2M)
- Hydrochloric acid (0.1M, labelled *dilute*)
- Cotton wool
- Marble chips (big and small)
- Conical flask
- 100 cm^3 measuring cylinder
- Balance
- Safety glasses

Extension

- Solid sodium hydrogen carbonate (flakes or chunks)
- Solid tartaric (or citric) acid crystals
- Bunsen burner and heatproof mat
- Beaker
- Access to balance
- Access to mortar and pestle
- Access to thermometer

6.3—Catalysts

- 5 vol hydrogen peroxide solution
- Two 100 cm^3 beakers
- Spatula
- Manganese(IV) oxide powder
- Bunsen burner and heatproof mat
- Safety glasses
- Zinc granules
- 1p (copper) coin
- Hydrochloric acid (2M)
- 2 boiling tubes
- Dropper bottle of detergent (TeePol)

Notes

Pupils will suggest other tests to measure the cooking time of the macaroni. There may be some hints on the packet itself. Discuss with each group how fair their test is.

Pupils must NOT boil or strongly heat the acid.

Can be graded by fitting through a plastic 'sieve'.

Interface an electronic balance with a computer if feasible.

Actually an alloy of copper.

Equipment

- Access to electronic balance
- Fresh apple
- Sugar solution
- Salt solution
- Starch solution
- Vinegar solution
- Food labels with E numbers in the contents list
- List of E numbers **(R6.3)**

Extension

- Malachite chunks if possible, copper(II) carbonate powder if not
- Bits of wood charcoal
- Tin lid
- Iron(II) oxide (labelled *iron ore*)
- Bunsen burner and heatproof mat
- Fire brick (if possible)
- Safety glasses

6.4—Patterns in reactivity

- Bottles of small pieces (cut foil/granules/filings) of Mg, Zn, Fe, Sn, Cu
- Hydrochloric acid (2M)
- Spatula
- Test tubes and rack
- Glassware
- Safety glasses
- Access to information about groups 1, 7 and 8 of the periodic table

Extension

- Reactivity series data sheet **(RE6.4)**
- Salt water
- Metal foil strips, about 5 cm by 2 cm, of Zn, Cu, Fe, Mg, Sn, Pb
- Filter paper
- 2 crocodile clips
- Voltmeter (1–2 V d.c.)
- Connecting leads

6.5—Moving ions

- Filter paper
- Potassium iodide solution (about 1M)
- 2 connecting leads (red and black) with 4 mm plug

Notes

Allow the pupils to build a 'fire' on the tin lid.

Ordinary stones can be placed around the 'fire' but some may crack and split at high temperatures.

Al could be included if desired, but it will not react as well as expected because of its oxide layer.

The key to this type of exercise is to provide a variety of resources and encourage pupils to find the information themselves. For example, a short video sequence is appropriate here. Also provide a *range* of textbooks if possible (check the index of each one for suitable keywords). Commercial/industrial wall posters and in-house productions made from pictures and magazine articles are a further useful source of information. Several computer programs allow a periodic table database to be searched.

The missing dates are

Na	1807
Zn	Sixteenth century
Sn	Prehistoric
Ag	Prehistoric

The missing voltages are

Cu + Zn	1.08 V
Cu + Fe	0.75 V
Cu + Mg	2.71 V
Cu + Pb	0.47 V
Pb + Zn	0.63 V
Fe + Zn	0.35 V

An alternative is to soak the paper in a mixture of sodium chloride solution and phenolphthalein.

Equipment

- 2 crocodile clips
- d.c. power supply (variable 12 V max)
- Tin(II) bromide solution (about 0.5M)
- Zinc iodide solution (about 0.5M)
- Copper(II) chloride solution (about 0.5M)
- 100 cm³ glass beaker
- 2 carbon rods
- U-tube containing copper(II) chromate solution in agar gel

Fact-finder
- Access to a photocopier if possible

Notes

A mixture of tin sulphate and sodium bromide solutions can be used.

Metal ions are positive and so the metal will always form at the negative electrode.

Make a cardboard lid for the carbon rods.

Prepare in advance. Make a saturated solution of copper(II) chromate in 2M ethanoic acid (about 2 g per 100 cm³). Add and dissolve 3 g of agar whilst heating. Pour into U-tubes and allow to set. Just before use, add a little 2M ethanoic acid to the tops of each limb. Electrolysis at about 12 V d.c. will cause a blue band to move to the negative electrode (the copper ions) and a yellow band to move to the positive electrode (the chromate ions). The tubes can be reused after reversing the polarity.

The fact-finder work also suggests using a video camera to make a short sequence. This can of course only be attempted by pupils who have some previous experience or tuition in the use of such equipment.
Note Aluminium is made by electrolysis of molten bauxite. Bauxite is a composite substance which can contain up to 60% aluminium oxide by weight. It is usually mined at open-cast sites. Aluminium is used for window frames, cooking utensils, aluminium paint, packaging, kitchen foil. It is also used to make light-weight alloys.

Extension

- Model of sodium chloride lattice

Either a commercial model or a home-made one as follows:

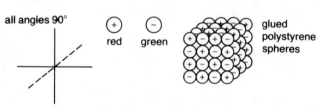

- Model of water molecule
- Solutions in boiling tube, each with inverted stopper containing two carbon electrodes, of
  sodium chloride
  copper(II) nitrate
  cobalt(II) chloride
  calcium oxide
  glucose (labelled *carbohydrate*)
  water (labelled *hydrogen oxide*)
  ethanol
- Bulb or ammeter (0–100 mA)
- Power pack (4 V d.c.)
- Connecting wires and clips

Molymod if possible.
As follows:

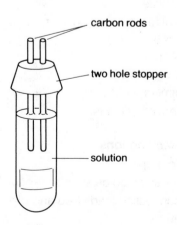

Equipment

- Formulae cards **(RE6.5)**
- Range of textbooks with information about properties of ionic/covalent compounds

Notes

Give pupils access to periodic tables.

Check index of books for relevant key words.

6.6—Problem—Trail blazer

- Map of school and the surrounding area
- Access to a word processor if possible
- Drawing instruments and black pen
- Access to a photocopier if possible

Base on the local town/area map (e.g. from tourist office or local authority information office). It may be necessary to take the pupils out on a guided walk around areas of chemical interest to illustrate what is expected (or take the class round a nearby nature trail). The most important points are that
(a) the pupils know what distance 20 minutes walking represents
(b) the importance of a concise guide is stressed
(c) the activities are varied.

6.7—Talkabout—Radiation

- A variety of resources that provide information on the three identified aspects of radiation
- Cassette tape recorder (with internal microphone)

Begin by showing a suitable video sequence if possible. Check any books for the specified key words. Use comics and science fiction as well as serious texts. Posters and work which other pupils have produced are also valid resources. Newspaper clippings are similarly very useful.

6.8—Readabout—Atomic models

- Access to books with information about Rutherford, Bohr and Chadwick

Most chemistry textbooks present some historical background to the development of the atomic theory.

Assessment 6

The questions are designed to assess the skills and knowledge developed in the unit, as shown in the table. The Attainment Target assessed by each question is also shown. A selection of questions would be appropriate for a unit test.

Topic	Core	Attainment Target
6.1	1	AT7–4a, 6c
6.2	2, 3, 4	AT7–7a
6.3	5	AT7–7a
	6	AT7–7b
6.4	7	AT6–6d
	8, 9, 10, 11	AT6–7c
6.5	12	AT6–6c; AT8–7b
	13, 14	AT7–7b; AT8–7b; AT11–7b
6.7	15	AT8–7d
	Extension	
6.1	16	AT6–6d
6.2	17	AT7–7a
6.3	18	AT7–7b; AT8–6c
6.4	19, 20	AT6–6d

Answers

1 a A—combustion, B—corrosion, C—electrolysis, D—combustion, E—neutralisation.
b Evidence of a chemical reaction is energy change plus a change in appearance.
2 a A + E; B + F; C + G; D + H.
b A + B; E + F.
3 a B + H
b Amount of water, size of crystals, amount of stirring.
4 Quickest is E then B, C, A, D, F.
5 a (i) 32, 199
(ii) A catalyst changes the rate of a chemical reaction and yet it remains unchanged at the end.
b (i) 171
(ii) An enzyme controls the rate of a chemical reaction in a living thing.
6 a Any suitable labelled arrangement. The method of comparison should be clear.
b The substance in contact with the avocado.
c Variables like: size of avocado piece, time of contact, area of contact, temperature, etc.
d Some way of measuring/estimating colour of avocado piece.
7 a New substance made (bubbles of gas).
b Most active C, then B, A, D.
c He will probably see nothing.
8 a Any two in group 7.   **b** Any two in group 1.
c Any two in group 8.

d Elements in a group have similar chemical properties

9 Calcium, sodium, argon, xenon, silicon, oxygen.

10 Group 1. The properties are similar to an active alkali metal.

11 a Information must be added in the correct place in the correct column.

b He, group 8: Li, group 1: Be, group 2: B, group 3: C, group 4: N, group 5.

c The metals are Li, Be.

12 a

Elements	Compounds	Mixtures
iron carbon copper silver tin oxygen chlorine sodium	metal oxides iron oxide salt (sodium chloride)	air gunpowder paint

13 a The ions have a charge.

b Electrolysis

14 Drawing should show blue colour has moved towards the − electrode and orange colour towards the + electrode. Explain by referring to ions being attracted to the opposite charge.

15 a Radiation is energy given out from (unstable) atoms.

b Background radiation is radiation that is always with us. It comes from sources like rocks, radiation (cosmic rays) from space, results of accidents, fallout from bomb tests etc.

c Judge the passage according to the results of the Talkabout exercises in class.

16 a Compare volume of foam produced, *or* count the bubbles.

b Same size of metal piece, same amount of vinegar, same temperature, same concentration of vinegar, same apparatus.

17 In all cases the rate is increased. A—Smaller size of reactant piece. B—Yeast contains an enzyme catalyst. C—Size of solid pieces are reduced. D and E—Heat increases rate.

18 a copper, iron, carbon

b silver oxide, tin oxide, carbon dioxide

19 a Group 1; the alkali metals.

b Melting points K (around 60°C) and Cs (less than 39°C); boiling point Na (around 900°C).

c Caesium.

d It will react even more violently in water (actually explodes) and always go on fire. The remaining solution will be alkaline.

20 Gold and copper are much less active metals than aluminium and magnesium. They can be extracted from ores without great energy. Aluminium and magnesium can only be extracted by using a lot of energy (as in electrolysis) and the Romans did not have access to it.

21 a Check scale is sensible and points are accurately plotted.

b Line should begin at the same point (5 g) and drop more gently. (The end point is not important.)

True/false 6

Each statement is marked as either true or false by the pupil. This gives a rapid assessment of a pupil's grasp of the Attainment Targets covered in the unit. The following list gives the Attainment Targets covered by each set of statements.

1	AT 6–6c	7	AT 7–7b
2	AT 6–6d	8	AT 8–6c
3	AT 6–7c	9	AT 8–7b
4	AT 7–6b	10	AT 8–7d
5	AT 7–6c	11	AT 17–7a
6	AT 7–7a		

Name _____

1 Write the meaning of each word in the space provided. The figures in brackets are references to *Understanding Science*, Books 1 and 2 (**book number**, page number). Use the references to *check* your answers.

- an element (**2**, 30)
- the periodic table (**2**, 30)
- a compound (**2**, 32)
- a mixture (**1**, 48)
- energy (**1**, 54)
- a hypothesis (**2**, 92)
- an atom (**2**, 159)
- a particle (**2**, 87)
- a molecule (**2**, 159)
- a chemical reaction (**2**, 38)
- a word equation (**2**, 33).

2 The meanings of many scientific words are connected together. Explain what the connection is between

- *element* and *periodic table*
- *element* and *compound*
- *compound* and *molecule*
- *atom* and *particle*
- *molecule* and *particle*
- *word equation* and *chemical reaction*
- *chemical reaction* and *energy*.

3 The spider diagram shows some of the connections between these terms. Complete the diagram with the correct words.

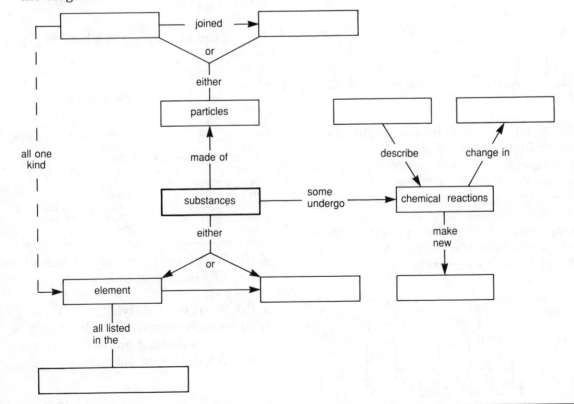

1 Examine the following pictures. They show examples of common chemical reactions.

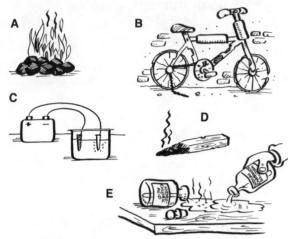

A

B

C

D

E

a For each picture name the type of chemical reaction.
b Choose three pictures. What evidence is there in each picture that a chemical reaction is taking place?

2 These pictures show several ways of trying to find out what affects the speed of a reaction.

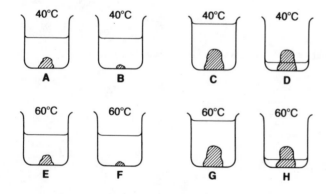

40°C 40°C 40°C 40°C
A B C D

60°C 60°C 60°C 60°C
E F G H

Which pairs of experiments would you use to find out the effect of
a temperature on the rate of reaction?
b amount of reactant on the rate of reaction?

3 You want to find out what effect temperature has on the rate of dissolving of two crystals.

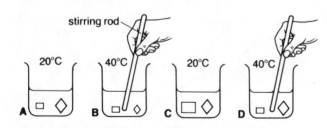

stirring rod

20°C 40°C 20°C 40°C
A B C D

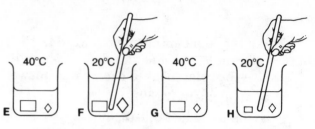

40°C 20°C 40°C 20°C
E F G H

a Which beakers should be compared to make the experiment fair?
b What variables are being controlled in this experiment?

4 Look at the drawings. Each drawing shows one way of reacting magnesium with acid.

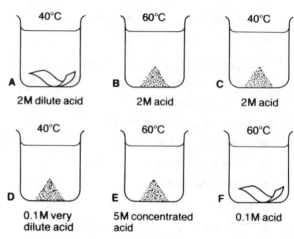

40°C 60°C 40°C
A B C
2M dilute acid 2M acid 2M acid

40°C 60°C 60°C
D E F
0.1M very dilute acid 5M concentrated acid 0.1M acid

Put the drawings in order of increasing rate of reaction.

5 Part of the index page of a book is given below.

a (i) Which pages would you look up to find out about industrial catalysts?
  (ii) What is a catalyst?
b (i) Which page would you look up to find out about enzymes?
  (ii) What does an enzyme do?

continued ▶

6 The flesh of an avocado pear blackens in the air within minutes. The following equipment can be used to find out if vinegar stops this blackening.

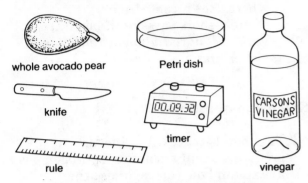

whole avocado pear

Petri dish

knife

timer

CARSONS VINEGAR

00.09.32

rule

vinegar

a Design this experiment. Draw a labelled sketch to show your design.
b Which variable will be changed in your experiment?
c Name three variables which you are going to try to control in the experiment.
d What will you measure during the experiment?

7 Alfredo adds three metals to a bucket of water. He writes down these observations.

METAL   OBSERVATIONS

A   Bubbles slowly. Metal still there after 60 minutes.

B   Metal disappears in 2 minutes. Loads of bubbles.

C   Metal buzzes and goes on fire.

D   A few bubbles appear during one hour.

a What evidence is there that the metals react with the water?
b Put the metals in order of reactivity, with the most reactive first.
c Alfredo is about to add another metal to fresh water. This metal is less reactive than the other four. Write down what he might observe.

8 The elements are arranged in the periodic table into groups. Collect a periodic table.
a Give the names of two elements in the same group as
    (i) fluorine
    (ii) potassium
    (iii) neon.

b Why are elements arranged in groups in the periodic table?

9 These symbols could represent chemical elements. Use a periodic table to list the names of the real elements from the list.

Ca, Ox, Ph, Na, Ar,
Xe, Fl, Si, O, A.

10 An element is shiny. It conducts electricity. It reacts very quickly with oxygen and it fizzes violently when put into water.
Is this element likely to be in group 1, 7 or 8?
Explain your answer.

11 Quazza looks up some information about several elements and notes it in a table.

Element	helium	lithium	beryllium	boron	carbon	nitrogen
Density kg m^{-3}	0.179		1850			1.25
Boiling point °C					4200	
Melting point °C		1.79	1230			
Group number	0			3		

a Copy the table and add the following information:

The density of lithium is 534 kg m^{-3}
The melting point of carbon is 3500°C
Boron boils at 2550°C
Beryllium boils at 1740 degrees above its melting point

b Use a periodic table and add the symbol and group number of each element to your table.
c Identify the metal elements in the table by putting a tick next to their name.

continued ▶

12 Read the following passage:

Elements and compounds are different types of substances. An element like iron contains only one kind of atom. In real life, pieces of iron are not pure. They usually have small amounts of other elements like carbon and copper mixed with the iron. A silver ring may contain other metals like copper and tin. Many metals corrode, joining with oxygen in the air to make metal oxides like iron oxide. Metals will also join with other reactive elements. Chlorine when mixed with sodium will join to make salt (sodium chloride). Substances can also mix together without joining. Gunpowder is one example. Paint is another.

a Copy the table. Put the names of the substances in the passage into the correct column in the table.

Elements	Compounds	Mixtures

b Add three further examples to each column of the table.

13 Look at the following chemical symbols.

$$H_2 \quad SiO_2 \quad Na \quad Cl^-$$

$$K^+ \quad Ag \quad Ni^{3+} \quad SO_4^{2-}$$

a Which ones represent ions?
b Electricity causes ions to move. What is this process called?

14 The following drawing shows an experiment with coloured ions.

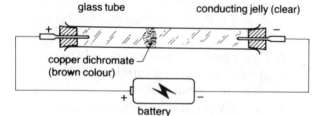

glass tube — conducting jelly (clear)
copper dichromate (brown colour)
battery

The copper ion is blue. The dichromate ion is orange.
The electricity is left on for 20 minutes.
Draw the experiment to show what will happen. Explain this result.

15 You have already prepared and given a talk about radiation.
a What is radiation?
b What is background radiation and where does it come from?
c Write a short passage titled either *good uses of radiation* or *radiation can be harmful.*

Extension questions

16 Two metals react with vinegar and produce a small amount of hydrogen gas.
a Explain how you could use the following apparatus to decide which metal was more reactive.

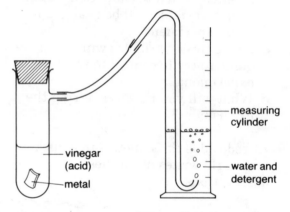

measuring cylinder
vinegar (acid)
metal
water and detergent

b Suggest three steps you would take to make sure that the comparison was fair.

17 The following drawings illustrate how a chemical reaction can be speeded up. Choose three drawings and explain why the rate of reaction is fast.

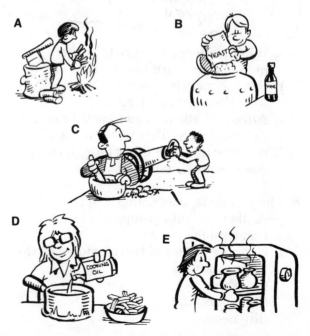

18 a Copy the following word equations. Underline the reactant which is undergoing oxidation.

copper + oxygen → copper oxide
copper oxide + iron → iron oxide + copper
lead oxide + carbon → carbon dioxide + lead

b Copy the following word equations. Underline the reactant which is undergoing reduction.

silver oxide → silver + oxygen
carbon + tin oxide → tin + carbon dioxide
carbon dioxide (CO_2) + carbon → carbon monoxide (CO)

19 The table shows some facts about one group in the periodic table.

Name	Symbol	Melting point °C	Boiling point °C
Lithium	Li	179	1330
Sodium	Na	98	—
Potassium	K	—	774
Rubidium	Rb	39	688
Caesium	Cs	—	690

a What is this group called?
b Look at the pattern of figures in the table. Predict the missing figures.
c Sodium is a more reactive metal than lithium. Which metal will probably be the most reactive in this group?
d Sodium reacts violently with water. It gives off hydrogen, gets very hot and sometimes goes on fire. The remaining solution is alkaline. Predict what caesium will do in water.

20 Explain by referring to the reactivity of metals why the Romans made objects from gold and copper but not from aluminium and magnesium.

21 The table shows how a sample of zinc disappears during the reaction with hydrochloric acid.

Time in minutes	0	2	4	6	8	10	12
Weight of zinc in grams	5	4.1	3.5	2.9	2.6	2.5	2.5

a Collect a piece of graph paper (which has the axes marked) and draw an accurate graph of these results.
b Add a line to represent the reaction of an identical sample of the less active metal iron with the same amount of acid.

Unit 6 Ideas of substance

Name_____

Put a tick after the statements that are true.
Put a cross after the statements that are false.

1 a This drawing represents the particles in a mixture. ☐

b This drawing represents the particles in a mixture. ☐

c A compound has the same properties as the elements in it. ☐

d A mixture of elements has the same properties as the elements in it. ☐

e An element is either a metal or a non-metal. ☐

f A substance which can be separated into two elements by using a magnet is a compound. ☐

g A substance which can be separated into two elements by filtering is a mixture. ☐

2 a The reactivity series of metals is useful for making predictions. ☐

b Silver is higher in the reactivity series than iron. ☐

c Sodium is near the top of the reactivity series so it will corrode quickly in air. ☐

d Iron will stop rusting if it is moved down the reactivity series. ☐

e If metal X is more active than metal Y then metal Y will fizz more in acid. ☐

3 a The periodic table groups together elements with similar properties. ☐

b The elements in group 1 are all non-metals. ☐

c Argon is an unreactive gas so neon is likely to be an unreactive solid. ☐

d Group 7 is called the alkali metals. ☐

e The elements in group 7 are all reactive non-metals. ☐

4 a During electrolysis electricity is used to break up compounds. ☐

b An ion is a particle with a charge. ☐

c An ion will be attracted to the electrode with the same charge as itself. ☐

d A metal ion always has a positive charge. ☐

e A metal ion will always be attracted to a negative electrode. ☐

5 a Electrolysis is a chemical reaction. ☐

b A chemical reaction can occur without energy being changed from one form to another. ☐

c Corrosion is not a chemical reaction because no heat is given out. ☐

d A chemical reaction can cause the surrounding air to cool down. ☐

e Most chemical reactions do not transfer energy to the surroundings. ☐

6 a The rate of reaction is a measurement of how fast/slow the reaction is. ☐

b When food is cooked, heat is added to increase the rate of a reaction. ☐

c In a fridge, heat is added to slow down the rate of a reaction. ☐

d In a chemical reaction, small pieces of substance will have a faster rate of reaction than larger pieces. ☐

e Medicine is powdered to make it last longer in the body. ☐

f Dilute acid reacts faster with magnesium than concentrated acid. ☐

g A catalyst is a booklet that a vet uses. ☐

h A catalyst increases the rate of a chemical reaction. ☐

i Enzymes are catalysts. ☐

j A fair amount of catalyst is used up in a reaction. ☐

k Enzymes are small molecules that are made in washing machines. ☐

7 a Reduction is a gain of oxygen. ☐

b Antioxidants preserve food by stopping oxygen from reacting with it. ☐

continued ▶

Understanding Science 3

c Rusting of iron is an example of oxidation. ☐

d Smelting reduces copper compounds to copper metal. ☐

e When carbon is burned it is reduced to carbon dioxide. ☐

8 a The word equation for the combustion of carbon is carbon dioxide → carbon + oxygen. ☐

b The word equation for the electrolysis of molten sodium chloride is sodium chloride → sodium + chlorine ☐

c A word equation is a shorthand way of saying how fast a reaction proceeds. ☐

d bicycle chain + oxygen → rust describes a chemical reaction. ☐

e water + heat → steam describes a chemical reaction. ☐

9 a Elements are made of ions. ☐

b These formulae all represent compounds: $NaCl$, K_2CO_3, CCl_4, O_2, KI. ☐

c These formulae all represent molecules: H_2O, CBr_4, CH_4, Cl_2. ☐

d These formulae all represent ions: Na^+, Ag^+, I^-, Fe^{2+}. ☐

e Ionic compounds contain charged ions that are attracted together. ☐

10 a Radioactive substances are all highly explosive. ☐

b Radioactive substances are unstable and give out energy in the form of radiation. ☐

c Radiation is only present in scientific establishments. ☐

d Radiation is used in medicine and to generate electricity. ☐

e Radiation is harmful and can cause damage to health. ☐

f A small dose of radiation will leave a person feeling bright and cheery. ☐

11 a The nuclear theory is a known fact of life. ☐

b We know more about the atom nowadays because we are smarter than people who lived long ago. ☐

c Scientific theories only affect the lives of people who are scientists. ☐

d The idea of the atom was invented in 1940. ☐

e People disagree about the dangers of nuclear energy. ☐

Unit 6 Ideas of substance

Name _____ ▶

Complete each sentence. Put the correct word(s) in each blank space.

1 When iron rusts it joins with _____ in the air and changes into a

new substance called _____ . This is an example of a chemical

_____ which gives out heat _____ into the

surroundings. The reaction can be described by a word equation:

iron + _____ → _____ .

2 Three other names of types of chemical reaction are

(a) _____ (b) _____ (c) _____ .

3 In any chemical reaction two things happen:

(a) a new _____ is formed and (b) an _____ change

occurs.

4 Some reactions happen slowly and some quickly: the speed is measured by the

_____ of reaction.

5 The rate of a chemical reaction can be changed by changing these variables:

(a) _____ (b) _____ (c) _____ .

6 To measure the effect of a variable on the rate of reaction you change this variable

and _____ the others. This makes any comparison fair.

7 A catalyst _____ the rate of reaction and yet it is

_____ at the end of the reaction. One example of a catalyst is

_____ .

8 Your body contains hundreds of catalysts called _____ .

9 Substances react in different ways but we can find patterns to help us predict future
reactions.

(a) One pattern is the _____ series of _____ . Metals

at the top of the series react _____ than metals at the bottom.

For example _____ is more active than _____ .

continued ▶

Name _____

(b) Another pattern is the _____ of elements in the periodic table.

Elements in the same group have _____ chemical properties.

For example the three elements _____ , _____

and _____ are all similar chemically.

The names of two groups in the table are _____ and

_____ .

10 A substance that contains atoms of the same type is called an

_____ . A substance made of two or more elements joined together

is called a _____ . A mixture contains two or more substances

which are not _____ together.

11

(a)   (b)   (c)

This is a drawing of particles in a(n)

(a) _____   (b) _____   (c) _____ .

12 Some substances are radioactive. They contain atoms that give out energy in the

form of _____ .

13 We are exposed to background radiation all the time. It comes from

_____ .

14 Two uses of radioactive substances are _____ and

_____ . Two examples of when radiation can be harmful

are _____

and _____ .

continued ▶

Name _____

15 Atoms can join together to form particles called _____ . Sometimes

charged particles called _____ are formed.

The charged particles can be moved apart by _____ energy. They

then form elements at the electrodes. This process is known as

_____ .

16 Electrolysis works because

(a) metal ions have a _____ charge and are therefore attracted to a

negative electrode

(b) non-metal ions have a _____ charge and are therefore attracted

to a positive electrode.

Activity 6

1 Set up the following apparatus.

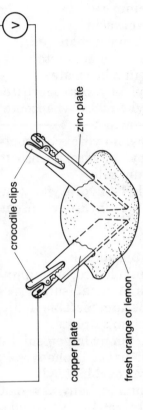

crocodile clips

copper plate

zinc plate

fresh orange or lemon

2 Replace the voltmeter with the little helicopter.

Activity 7

1 Put about 20 cm³ of copper sulphate solution in a small plastic beaker.
Measure the temperature of the solution.

2 Add 3 pieces of zinc foil.
Stir with a stirring rod.
Measure the temperature again.

Activity 8

1 Half fill a boiling tube with sodium silicate solution (water glass).

2 Sprinkle a few crystals of each of the coloured compounds onto the solution.

3 Wait for a few minutes.

Activity 3

1 Add 1 spatula-ful of ammonium chloride to a test tube.

2 Add a few cm³ of water and dissolve the solid.

3 Watch what happens.
Feel the bottom of the test tube.

4 Clean the test tube and repeat with
   ● sodium nitrate
   ● sodium chloride
   ● ammonium carbonate

Activity 4

1 Use the measuring cylinder labelled A.
Measure 20 cm³ of solution A and pour into the flask.

2 Use the measuring cylinder labelled B.
Measure 20 cm³ of solution B and add to the flask.

3 Watch carefully for about 2 minutes.

Activity 5

1 Mix a piece of Alka Seltzer tablet and water in a small test tube.

2 Mix sodium carbonate solution and hydrochloric acid in a clean test tube.

3 Mix lead nitrate solution and potassium iodide solution in a clean test tube.

Food additives

Colourings (E100–E199)

E100	Curcumin
E101	Riboflavin or Lactoflavin
E102	Tartrazine
E104	Quinoline Yellow
E110	Sunset Yellow FCF or Orange Yellow 5
E120	Cochineal or Carminic acid
E122	Carmoisine or Azorubine
E123	Amaranth
E124	Ponceau 4R or Cochineal Red A
E127	Erythrosine BS
E131	Patent Blue V
E132	Indigo Carmine or Indigotine
E140	Chlorophyll
E141	Copper complexes of chlorophyll and chlorophyllins
E142	Green S or Acid Brilliant Green BS or Lissamine Green
E150	Caramel
E151	Black PN or Brilliant Black BN
E153	Carbon Black or Vegetable Carbon
E160(a)	Alpha-carotene, Beta-carotene, Gamma-carotene
E160(b)	Annatto, Bixin, Norbixin
E160(c)	Capsanthin or Capsorubin
E160(d)	Lycopene
E160(e)	Beta-apo-8'-carotenal (C30)
E160(f)	Ethyl ester of Beta-apo-8'-carotenoic acid (C30)
E161(a)	Flavoxanthin
E161(b)	Lutein
E161(c)	Cryptoxanthin
E161(d)	Rubixanthin
E161(e)	Violaxanthin
E161(f)	Rhodoxanthin
E161(g)	Canthaxanthin
E162	Beetroot Red or Betanin
E163	Anthocyanins
E170	Calcium carbonate
E171	Titanium dioxide
E172	Iron oxide and hydroxides
E173	Aluminium
E174	Silver
E175	Gold
E180	Pigment Rubine or Lithol Rubine BK

Preservatives (E200–E299)

E200	Sorbic acid
E201	Sodium sorbate
E202	Potassium sorbate
E203	Calcium sorbate
E210	Benzoic acid
E211	Sodium benzoate
E212	Potassium benzoate
E213	Calcium benzoate
E214	Ethyl 4-hydroxybenzoate
E215	Ethyl 4-hydroxybenzoate sodium salt
E216	Propyl 4-hydroxybenzoate
E217	Propyl 4-hydroxybenzoate sodium salt
E218	Methyl 4-hydroxybenzoate
E219	Methyl 4-hydroxybenzoate sodium salt
E220	Sulphur dioxide
E221	Sodium sulphite
E222	Sodium hydrogen sulphite
E223	Sodium metabisulphite
E224	Potassium metabisulphite
E226	Calcium sulphite
E227	Calcium hydrogen sulphite
E230	Biphenyl or Diphenyl
E231	2-Hydroxybiphenyl
E232	Sodium biphenyl-2-yl oxide
E233	2-(Thiazol-4-yl)benzimidazole
E236	Formic acid
E237	Sodium formate
E238	Calcium formate
E239	Hexamine
E249	Potassium nitrite
E250	Sodium nitrite
E251	Sodium nitrate
E252	Potassium nitrate
E260	Acetic acid
E261	Potassium acetate
E262	Sodium hydrogen diacetate
E263	Calcium acetate
E270	Lactic acid
E280	Propionic acid
E281	Sodium propionate
E282	Calcium propionate
E283	Potassium propionate
E290	Carbon dioxide

Anti-oxidants (E300–E399)

E300	L-Ascorbic acid
E301	Sodium-L-ascorbate
E302	Calcium-L-ascorbate
E304	6-O-Palmitoyl-L-ascorbic acid
E306	Extracts of natural origin rich in tocopherols
E307	Synthetic alpha-tocopherol

1 of 2

Food additives *continued*

E308	Synthetic gamma-tocopherol	E407	Carrageenan
E309	Synthetic delta-tocopherol	E410	Locust bean gum
E310	Propylgallate	E412	Guat gum
E311	Octylgallate	E413	Tragacanth
E312	Dodecylgallate	E414	Acacia or gum Arabic
E320	Butylated hydroxyanisole	E415	Xanthan gum
E321	Butylated hydroxytoluene	E420(a)	Sorbitol
E322	Lecithins	E420(b)	Sorbitol syrup
E325	Sodium lactate	E421	Mannitol
E326	Potassium lactate	E422	Glycerol
E327	Calcium lactate	E440(a)	Pectin
E330	Citric acid	E440(b)	Pectin, amidated
E331	Sodium dihydrogen citrate	E450(a)	diSodium dihydrogen diphosphate
E331	diSodium citrate	E450(a)	tetraSodium diphosphate
E331	triSodium citrate	E450(a)	tetraPotassium diphosphate
E332	Potassium dihydrogen citrate	E450(a)	triSodium diphosphate
E332	triPotassium citrate	E450(b)	pentaSodium triphosphate
E333	Calcium citrate	E450(b)	pentaPotassium triphosphate
E333	diCalcium citrate	E450(c)	Sodium polyphosphates
E333	triCalcium citrate	E450(c)	Potassium polyphosphates
E334	Tartaric acid	E460(a)	Microcrystalline cellulose
E335	Sodium tartrate	E460(b)	Powdered cellulose
E336	Potassium tartrate	E461	Methylcellulose
E336	Potassium hydrogen tartrate	E463	Hydroxypropylcellulose
E337	Potassium sodium tartrate	E464	Hydroxypropylmethylcellulose
E338	Orthophosphoric acid	E465	Ethylmethylcellulose
E339(a)	Sodium dihydrogen orthophosphate	E466	Carboxymethylcellulose, sodium salt
E339(b)	diSodium hydrogen orthophosphate	E470	Sodium, potassium and calcium salts of fatty acids
E339(c)	triSodium orthophosphate	E471	Mono- and di-glycerides of fatty acids
E340(a)	Potassium dihydrogen orthophosphate	E472(a)	Acetic and esters of mono- and di-glycerides of fatty acids
E340(b)	diPotassium hydrogen orthophosphate	E472(b)	Lactic acid esters of mono- and di-glycerides of fatty acids
E340(c)	triPotassium orthophosphate	E472(c)	Citric acid esters of mono- and di-glycerides of fatty acids
E341(a)	Calcium tetrahydrogen diorthophosphate	E472(d)	Tartaric acid esters of mono- and di-glycerides of food fatty acids
E341(b)	Calcium hydrogen orthophosphate	E472(e)	Diacetyltartaric acid esters of mono- and di-glycerides of fatty acids
E341(c)	triCalcium diorthophosphate		

Texture modification agents (E400–E499)

E400	Alginic acid	E473	Sucrose esters of fatty acids
E401	Sodium alginate	E474	Sucroglycerides
E402	Potassium alginate	E475	Polyglycerol esters of fatty acids
E403	Ammonium alginate	E477	Propane-1,2-diol esters of fatty acids
E404	Calcium alginate		
E405	Propane-1,2-diol alginate	E481	Sodium stearoyl-2-lactylate
E406	Agar	E482	Calcium stearoyl-2-lactylate
		E483	Stearyl tartrate

Reactivity series data sheet

Reactivity series		Predictions	
Reactivity series		**Predictions**	
K Potassium	Most reactive	**A** *Metal*	*Date of discovery*
Na Sodium		K	1807
Li Lithium		Mg	1775
Ca Calcium		Fe	Prehistoric
Mg Magnesium		Au	Prehistoric
Al Aluminium		Na	_____
Zn Zinc		Zn	_____
Fe Iron		Sn	_____
Ni Nickel		Ag	_____
Sn Tin			
Pb Lead		**B** *Metals*	*Voltage*
Cu Copper		Cu + Zn	_____
Hg Mercury		Cu + Fe	_____
Ag Silver		Cu + Mg	_____
Pt Platinum		Cu + Pb	_____
Au Gold	Least reactive	Pb + Zn	_____
		Fe + Zn	_____

---- ✂ - ✂ - -

Reactivity series data sheet

Reactivity series		Predictions	
Reactivity series		**Predictions**	
K Potassium	Most reactive	**A** *Metal*	*Date of discovery*
Na Sodium		K	1807
Li Lithium		Mg	1775
Ca Calcium		Fe	Prehistoric
Mg Magnesium		Au	Prehistoric
Al Aluminium		Na	_____
Zn Zinc		Zn	_____
Fe Iron		Sn	_____
Ni Nickel		Ag	_____
Sn Tin			
Pb Lead		**B** *Metals*	*Voltage*
Cu Copper		Cu + Zn	_____
Hg Mercury		Cu + Fe	_____
Ag Silver		Cu + Mg	_____
Pt Platinum		Cu + Pb	_____
Au Gold	Least reactive	Pb + Zn	_____
		Fe + Zn	_____

Formulae card

$C_6 H_{12} O_6$	$Co\, Cl_2$
$Ca\, O$	H_2O
$Cu(NO_3)_2$	$C_2 H_5 OH$

Fold, stick and cut

Copper nitrate	Ethanol
Calcium oxide	Hydrogen oxide
Carbohydrate	Cobalt chloride

Communicating through electricity

This unit builds upon those aspects of unit 6 in Books 1 and 2 that introduced electricity and magnetism. The revision work therefore refers to basic properties of magnets and static charge, and to elements of electronic circuits. In the next four topics pupils investigate magnetic fields and electromagnetic machines such as motors and loudspeakers, dynamos, microphones and magnetic tape recorders. They examine ways of sending messages with analogue and digital electrical signals and with optical fibres. The ideas of electronic logic and control are introduced, leading to the automatic collection and recording of experimental data. A further topic studies the properties of electrostatic charge, and introduces the concept of electric charge and electric currents being the movement of electrons. The final three topics comprise a problem utilising magnetic tape recording, a discussion about the benefits and drawbacks of electrical power, and a reading exercise about geostationary communications satellites. This unit deals with Attainment Targets 11 and 12 of the 1989 National Curriculum. In addition to meeting the general requirements of Attainment Target 1, this unit deals specifically with AT1 levels 5a and 6.

Core and Reinforcement

7.0 Revision—Electricity and magnetism

> Revise background work.
> Complete a revision question sheet.
> Make a magnetic compass.   *page 104*

Revise earlier work.
Exercise manipulative skills.
Apply knowledge in an imaginative way.

7.1 Electromagnetic machines

AT11–6c, 7a, PoS

> Plot the magnetic fields of the Earth and of bar magnets.
> Investigate the magnetic effect of an electric current.
> Use an electromagnet to solve a physical problem.   *page 106*

Exercise manipulative skills.
Report experimental results.
Solve a technological problem and devise further applications.

7.2 Electric motors *AT11–6c, 7a, PoS; AT14–6c*

> Learn the parts of a d.c. motor.
> Construct a motor-driven machine.
> Understand the working of loudspeakers and experiment with one.
> Design a motor-driven cat flap.   *page 108*

Exercise constructional and manipulative skills.
Extract information from self sought sources.
Design a technological solution to a problem.
Experiment with apparatus and report findings.

Extension

AT11–7a; AT14–6c, 7a

> Learn how audio signals are recorded and stored on magnetic tape.
> Investigate the properties of audio-recording tape.
>   *page 164*

Follow instructions.
Exercise manipulative skills.
Report experimental results.

AT11–7a; AT14–6c

> Learn the dynamo principle.
> Construct a model lighthouse and a gravity-driven dynamo to power it.
> Use the voice and an oscilloscope to create sound-generated electrical signals.   *page 165*

Exercise constructional skills.
Experiment with apparatus and report findings.

Core and Reinforcement

7.3 Sending messages *AT12–6a,b, 7a; AT14–7a*

> Construct and use analogue communication devices employing sound and electricity, and analyse their qualities.
> Construct and use a digital communication device employing light.
> Draw a block diagram of a communication system. *page 110*

Design and make working devices and systems.
Relate scientific concept to everyday examples.

7.4 Electronic control *AT12–5b, 7b*

> Build and use simple electronic sensing circuits.
> Understand AND, OR and NOT logic gates.
> Build a simple memory circuit using an OR gate.
> Design logic circuits using NOT gates. *page 112*

Manipulate apparatus.
Design and make electronic logic circuits to solve problems.

7.5 Electrical energy *AT11–7c*

> Create small positive and negative electrostatic charges and observe their properties.
> Observe the effects of the very large charge on a Van de Graaff generator. *page 114*

Follow instructions and manipulate apparatus to conduct experiments.
Observe and report on self-performed experiments and demonstrations.
Draw conclusions from results.

7.6 Problem—Mystery tape *AT12–6b*

> Record 'mystery' sounds for a quiz.
> Make a 'mystery person' tape by recording clues.

Use technological equipment to fulfil a briefed task.

7.7 Talkabout—Quick, easy and clean
AT13–5b

> Discuss with a friend the benefits of electricity and the 'third world' issues it raises.

Extract relevant information from text and illustrations.
Explain and evaluate social and environmental implications.

Extension

AT12–7a

> Build a communication system using optical fibre.
> Design a portable version of the system and draw a block diagram analysis of it.
> *page 166*

Extract information from text.
Design and make a structure.
Report results using block diagrams.

AT12–7c

> Construct an experiment using an electronic stop clock to time an interval automatically.
> Study the use of a computer and interface to make and record rapid measurements.
> Use readings thus obtained. *page 167*

Select and use appropriate apparatus for computer assisted experiments.
Use data to plot a graph.

PoS

> Observe the movement along a thread of electrons generated as an electrostatic charge, demonstrating the equivalence of moving electrons and electric current. *page 168*

Observe and report on demonstrated phenomena.
Use observations to discuss scientific theory.

Core and Reinforcement

7.8 Readabout—Geostationary satellites

AT14–7a

> Read about a modern communications
> satellite in a geostationary orbit.

Extract relevant information from passage.

Equipment

required for each pupil group.

7.0—Revision—Electricity and magnetism

- Revision question sheet
- Strong bar magnet
- Thread
- Saucer or Petri dish
- Needle

7.1—Electromagnetic machines

- Plotting compass
- 2 bar magnets
- White paper
- Medium-sized compass
- Insulated copper wire (about 1 metre)
- Variable power supply
- Iron nail
- Switch
- Steel key
- Beaker of muddy water

Extension

- Musical instrument, e.g. guitar, electronic keyboard
- Old audio recording tape in a cassette
- Strong (ferrite) magnet
- Access to a cassette tape recorder

7.2—Electric motors

- 12 V or 6 V electric motor
- Switch
- Power supply
- Thread
- Rheostat
- Construction kit
- Connecting wires
- Old loudspeaker
- Dry cell
- Signal generator
- Mustard seeds or light polystyrene beads (as found in 'sag-bags')

Notes

Access to copies of *Understanding Science 1* and *2* will allow pupils to check their work and look for information they are unsure of.

A computer simulation for plotting magnetic fields on the BBC computer is available. The listing is on **R7.1**. This program and the one on **R3.4** can be obtained from Peter Warren, Acton High School, Gunnersbury Lane, London W3 8EY, by sending a blank disc and postage.

Any motor would do but Fischer or Meccano motors are easier to build into machines.

As an additional activity, **R7.2** gives instructions for making a working model motor from very simple components.

Equipment	Notes

Extension

- Dynamo/motor
- Light-emitting diode
- Three 1-newton masses on a mass hanger
- Thread
- Construction kit with axles, gears and pulley
- Old loudspeaker or cheap microphone
- Oscilloscope
- Connecting wires

Fischer motors work well, geared down with a pulley and axle as shown.

7.3—Sending messages

- Soft drink cans or similar with tops removed and holes in bases
- Strong thread
- Washers
- Old loudspeakers
- Connecting wires
- 12 V 24 W lamp in holder
- 12 V power supply
- Press switch

The Morse code is given on page 145 of the Pupils' Book.

Extension

- 1.5 V dry cell
- Press switch
- Lamp in holder
- Length of optical fibre
- Old box or container

7.4—Electronic control

- Electronic kit
- Connecting wires
- 1.5 V dry cell

The work on sensors and gates is very conveniently done with the Microelectronics For All (MFA) circuit boards. They also allow plenty of scope for extension studies.
A cheaper alternative is to use breadboards and separate components.

Extension

- Digital stop clock
- Aluminium foil
- Thick cardboard
- Scissors
- Stapler
- Clamp and stand
- Long connecting wires
- Metal ball (e.g. brass plumb-bob)
- Automatic timing switch sheet (RE7.4)
- Sound wave readings sheet (RE7.4B)
- Unilab (or similar) interface
- BBC computer
- Software
- Microphone and connecting wires
- Musical instrument
- Printer (if hard copy is wanted)

Digital stop clocks (e.g. Unilab) often have make-to-start, make-to-stop terminals. The home-made foil gates can be used to start and stop the clock automatically. Constructional details are shown on Resource sheet RE7.4

Equipment

7.5—Electrical energy

- Large metal tray
- Clean dry Plasticine
- Plastic rubbish sack

- 2 watch glasses
- 2 polythene rods
- Acetate rod
- Cloth

- Van de Graaff generator
- Thread
- Blu-Tack
- Paper
- Wig
- Insulated stool
- Bunsen burner
- Insulated clamp and stand

- Information sheet – sparks can be dangerous **(R7.5)**

Extension

- Van de Graaff generator
- Thread
- Microammeter
- Connecting wire

7.6—Problem—Mystery tape

- Portable cassette tape recorder
- Microphone
- Tape cassette
- Range of 'instruments' for making strange noises

7.7—Talkabout—Quick, easy and clean

No equipment required

7.8—Readabout—Geostationary satellites

- World map or access to globe
- Tennis ball

Notes

The purpose of 'rubbing the materials energetically together' is only a means of getting close contact between the surfaces.

One stroke may be enough provided the surfaces are pressed closely together. It is the separation of the surfaces that produces the energy and the opposite charges. This is shown when Sellotape is pulled off the reel. The sticky and non-sticky surfaces collect opposite charges, without any rubbing.

The polythene and acetate rods should be kept very dry for this experiment. It may be necessary to dry and re-charge the rods from time to time. They can be dried on a radiator or on a tripod over a light bulb.

Any moisture allows the charge to leak away because water acts as a good conductor at these voltages.

In dry air 3000 V produces a 1 cm spark. This can be used to estimate the voltage that builds up on the dome.

The charge that builds up is large in comparison to the charge on a balloon or plastic bag. It may be about 2 μC which would only give a small current if it were allowed to flow along a thread or escape as a spark.

The current would be too small to paralyse muscles and give an electric shock. The temperature of the spark however could cause burns or set light to flammable vapours.

The information sheet may be given out to pupils or discussed.

Assessment 7

The questions are designed to assess the skills and knowledge developed in the unit, as shown in the table. The Attainment Target assessed by each question is also shown. A selection of questions would be appropriate for a unit test.

Topic	Core	Attainment Target
7.1	1, 2, 3	AT11–6c, 7a
7.2	4	AT14–6c
7.3	5	AT12–6a, 7a
	6	AT12–6a
		AT14–7a
7.4	7	AT12–4b
	8	AT12–5b
	9	AT12–7b
7.5	10, 11	AT11–7c
Extension		
7.1	12	AT11–7a
7.2	13, 14	AT11–7a
	15	AT14–6c
7.3	16	AT15–7c
7.4	17	AT12–7c
7.5	18	AT11–7c

Answers

1 Electric current, magnetises, electromagnet.

2

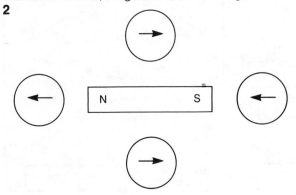

3

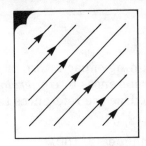

4 A force acts on the loudspeaker coil when a current passes through and it is drawn into (or pushed out of) the circular slot in the magnet.

5 a Digital
b B, A, D, C

6 a A, E; **b** C; **c** B; **d** D.

7 LDR, light
thermistor, temperature
probes, moisture

8 a Close both A and B.
b Close either C or D.

9 a The light will come on and stay on.
b The circuit has remembered that a light hit its sensor even after the event has ended.

10 A—spins anticlockwise, B—spins anticlockwise, C—spins anticlockwise.

11 The pieces of paper could fly off into the air, the threads could stand out from the dome, a spark could jump to the Bunsen burner and light the gas.

12 By stroking the tape with one end of the magnet a number of times.

13 See text.

14 Turns, turn it, dynamo.

15 Sound or vibrations, alternating voltage, microphone.

16 Security and speed.

17 a A—microphone, B—interface, C—computer, D—monitor/screen.
b A computer can take readings very rapidly, it can take readings over a very long period of time, it avoids human errors such as parallex and reaction times, it can automatically process the readings.

18 a It takes time for charge (electrons) to build up on the dome and then travel down the thread.
b Even after the belt has stopped, electrons continue to move down the thread until the dome is discharged.
c The damp thread is a better conductor than when dry and so the current of electrons is larger.

True/false 7

Each statement is marked as either true or false by the pupil. This gives a rapid assessment of a pupil's grasp of the Attainment Targets covered in the unit. The following list gives the Attainment Targets covered by each set of statements.

1	AT 11–6c	6	AT 12–6b
2	AT 11–7a	7	AT 12–7a
3	AT 11–7c	8	AT 12–7b
4	AT 12–5b	9	AT 14–6c
5	AT 12–6a	10	AT 14–7a
		11	AT 12–7c

Unit 7 Smart ideas

Name _____

1 Write the meaning of each word or phrase in the space provided. The figures in brackets are references to *Understanding Science*, Books 1 and 2 (**book number**, page number). Use the references to *check* your answers.

- magnetism (**2**, 67)
- an electromagnet (**2**, 150)
- electric (or electrostatic) charge (**1**, 86; **2**, 66)
- electronic system (**2**, 105)
- switch (**1**, 80; **2**, 105)
- resistor (**2**, 105)
- diode (**2**, 105)

2 The spider diagram shows some connections between these terms. Complete the diagram with the correct words.

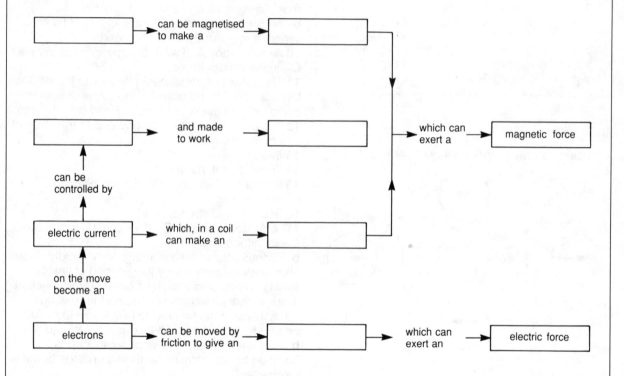

Understanding Science 3

1 Write down the words that go in the gaps.

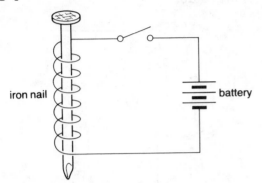

iron nail

battery

When the switch is closed, an _____

_____ flows around the coil of

wire. This _____ the iron nail.

The iron, wrapped in a coil of insulated wire, is called

an _____ .

2 The circles in the drawing below are small compasses placed near a bar magnet. Copy the picture and draw in the compass needles.

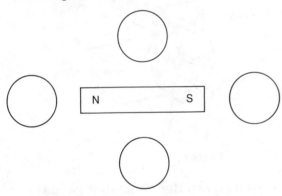

N   S

3 The picture below shows a compass and a piece of paper on a bench. Copy the picture and draw lines to show the magnetic field on the paper.

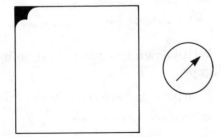

4 Use the picture of a loudspeaker to explain how it works.

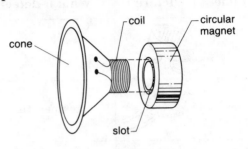

cone — coil — circular magnet

slot

5 Two prisoners communicate by tapping a pipe that runs between their cells.
  a Do they use an analogue or digital signal?
  b The block diagram of their 'communication system' is shown in this picture. Copy and complete this key for their system.

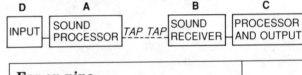

D	A		B	C
INPUT	SOUND PROCESSOR	TAP TAP	SOUND RECEIVER	PROCESSOR AND OUTPUT

Ear on pipe	
Finger on pipe	
Brain of sender	
Brain of listener	

6 A baby is trying to send a message to her dad through an intercom. Name the points in the system where the message is
  a a vibration in the air
  b an electrical analogue signal
  c being converted into an electrical signal
  d being converted from an electrical signal into a sound wave.

continued ▶

7 Copy and complete this table about electronic sensors.

Name	Picture	What it detects
	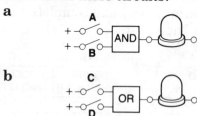	
		temperature
probes		

8 What must you do to make the lights come on in these circuits?

a

b

9 a The light is off. What will happen if the light from a torch hits the sensor for a second?

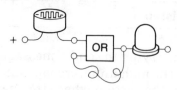

b Why could you say that this circuit has a simple memory?

10 The pictures show plastic rods charged with electricity. In each picture one of the rods is balanced on a watch glass so that it can spin. Describe the movement, if any, of the rods that can spin.

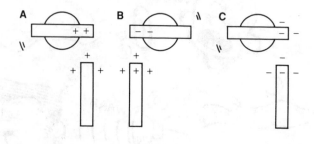

11 Describe and explain three things that could happen when the dome of the Van de Graaff machine shown below is charged up.

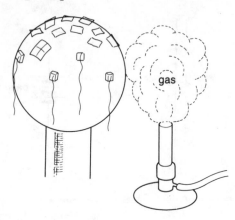

Extension questions

12 How can you erase music from an audio tape using a magnet?

13 Use the picture of a simple electric motor to explain how it works.

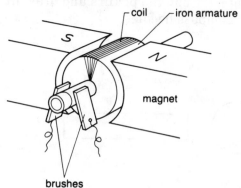

14 Write down the words that go in the gaps.

If you put electric current into an electric motor it

_____ .

You can make an electric motor generate electricity if you _____ .

It is then acting like a _____ .

15 Write down the words that go in the gaps.

If you put a rapidly changing current into a loudspeaker, it will produce

_____ .

If you make a loudspeaker cone vibrate it will produce a _____ .

It is then acting as a _____ .

continued ▶

16 An optical fibre is used to carry a signal made up of rapid flashes of light. The fibre carries the light from one room in a house to another.
Name two advantages of using optical fibre to carry the light message.

17 a The picture shows a computer set up to take automatic readings of sound signals. Name the parts A, B, C, D.

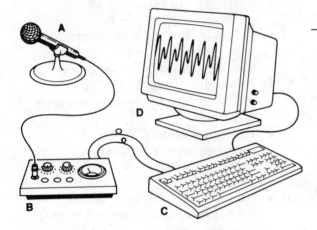

b Give two advantages of a computer taking measurements like this.

18 Explain these observations.

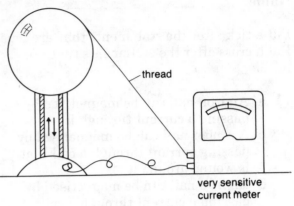

thread

very sensitive current meter

a The needle on the current meter doesn't deflect until a short time after the belt has started.
b The needle on the meter goes down slowly to zero some time after the belt has stopped.
c The meter deflects more if the thread is wet.

Unit 7 Smart ideas

Name_____

Put a tick after the statements that are true. Put a cross after the statements that are false.

1 a An iron nail can be magnetised by passing a current through it. ☐

b A copper nail can be magnetised by passing current through a coil that is wound around it. ☐

c An iron nail can be magnetised by passing a current through a coil that is wound around it. ☐

d An electromagnet has magnetism that can be switched on and off. ☐

2 a An electric current has got a magnetic field around it. ☐

b An electric current has no effect on a compass placed nearby. ☐

c Electricity can be made from mechanical energy by turning an electric motor by hand. ☐

3 a A comb that has been rubbed by a cloth can pick up pieces of paper because it is charged with electricity. ☐

b There are three types of electric charge: positive, negative and neutral. ☐

c Negative electric charges attract each other. ☐

d If you take negative charge away from an insulator, you leave it with a positive charge. ☐

4 a Logic gates have two inputs and one output. ☐

b Three types of logic gate are AND, OR and DON'T. ☐

c An AND gate needs two high inputs to give an output. ☐

d An OR gate needs two high inputs to give an output. ☐

e Logic gates can be used to make simple decisions. ☐

5 a The Morse code is an example of a digital signal. ☐

b A person who speaks to you across the room uses an analogue signal. ☐

c The wires between a radio and its loudspeaker carry a digital signal. ☐

6 a A microphone converts electrical energy into sound. ☐

b An amplifier increases the size of analogue signals. ☐

c A tape recorder stores sound as magnetic patterns on plastic tape. ☐

d A computer can store information in electronic memories. ☐

e The computer loses this information if the power and batteries are switched off. ☐

7 a Systems that transfer information usually have an input, an output and a processor, in that order. ☐

b Examples of inputs are microphones, keyboards and tape recorders. ☐

c Examples of outputs are loudspeakers, VDU screens, printers and sensors. ☐

8 a An electronic circuit that stays on, once it has been triggered, is called a 'latch'. ☐

b A 'latch' circuit is a simple memory because it can remember that it has been triggered. ☐

c A 'latch' circuit is stable in two states, on and off. ☐

9 a A loudspeaker has three main parts: a cone, a coil and a magnet. ☐

b A microphone generates electricity when its coil is made to move near to a magnet. ☐

c A telephone handset has a microphone at each end. ☐

10 a A telephone system converts sound to electrical signals and then back to sound again. ☐

b Optical fibres carry the electrical signals in a modern telephone system. ☐

c Radio waves can be used to carry the signals in a telephone system from one place to another. ☐

Extension

11 a A computer can be made to take measurements automatically. ☐

b The advantages are that the computer can be very fast and does not need to be programmed. ☐

c Computers can be used to control machines automatically. ☐

Name _____

Complete each sentence. Put the correct word(s) in each blank space.

1 An electric current has a _____ effect.

   An electromagnet can be made by winding _____ wire on an

   _____ core.

2 The magnetic field of a bar magnet looks like this (draw in the field lines):

   The magnetic field of the Earth across my table looks like this (draw in the field lines):

3 Electric motors convert _____ energy into movement (kinetic)

   energy or other forms of energy. Examples of machines at home that have electric

   motors are ● _____ ● _____ ● _____ .

   They contain a _____ that can spin and a _____ .

4 Another device that uses the force between an electric current and a magnet to

   produce sound is the _____ . A loudspeaker used 'in reverse' to

   generate current is acting like a _____ . A motor used 'in reverse' to

   make electric current is a _____ .

5 A message signal that is a string of ON's and OFF's is called _____ .

   A signal that changes continuously is called _____ .

6 A light dependent resistor is an electronic _____ . It responds to

   _____ .

   A thermistor senses _____ .

   Two wire probes can be used to sense _____ .

continued ▶

Name _____

7 Logic gates are electronic components that can make simple _____ .

They usually have _____ inputs and _____ output.

An AND gate comes on if _____ its inputs are switched on. An OR

gate comes on if one _____ other of its inputs are switched on.

A NOT gate can be used to 'reverse' a sensor and make a light detector into a

_____ detector. An _____ gate with a feed-back wire

makes a simple electronic memory. It 'latches' on and remembers an event once it

has been triggered.

8 You can charge an _____ with electricity by _____

it. There are _____ types of electric charge, called

_____ and _____ . Electric charges can make your

_____ stand on end and cause _____ . Sparks are hot

and can _____ gases.

9 An electric current is the _____ of electric charge.

Plotting magnetic fields

This program allows you to plot the magnetic fields of magnets (with and without the Earth's field) on the screen and print them out on paper.

```
10 REM Magnetic Field Demonstrator
20 MODE7:REM MODE135 on Master
30 PROCinst
40 MODE7
50 PROCquest
60 MODE1:REM MODE129 on Master
70 PROCgo
80 PROCquit
90 IF Y$="Y" OR Y$="y" GOTO 40
100 END
110 :
120 DEFPROCquest
130 FOR D=3 TO 4
140   PRINTTAB(15,D)CHR$141;"MAGNETS"
150 NEXT D
160 PRINTTAB(0,20)CHR$(130)"Do you
    want an Earth Field (Y/N) ?"
170 REM *FX4,1
180 REM Disable Cursor EDIT keys
190 A=GET
200 IF A=89 THEN H=-0.00001
210 IF A<>89 THEN H=0
220 IF A<>89 AND A<>78 GOTO190
230 PRINT"One magnet              "CHR
    $(133)"        1"
240 PRINT"Two magnets in line N to N"CH
    R$(133)"        2"
250 PRINT"Two magnets in line N to S"CH
    R$(133)"        3"
260 PRINT"Two magnets parallel N to N"C
    HR$(133)"      4"
270 PRINT"Two magnets parallel N to S"C
    HR$(133)"      5"
280 A=GET
290 ENDPROC
300 :
310 DEFPROCgo
320 IF A=49 PROCein
330 IF A=50 PROCzwei
340 IF A=51 PROCdrei
350 IF A=52 PROCvier
360 IF A=53 PROCfunf
370 IF H>=0 PROChr
380 IF H<0 PROChl
390 PROCcross
400 IF INKEY(-17) ENDPROC
410 REPEAT
420   PROCink
430 UNTIL INKEY(-17)
440 ENDPROC
450 :
460 DEFPROCein
470 D=0
480 PROCalone
490 ENDPROC
500 :
510 DEFPROCzwei
520 C=1
530 D=0
540 L=300
550 PROCinline
560 PROCpoles(360,510,80,510)
570 PROCpoles(900,510,1180,510)
580 ENDPROC
590 :
600 DEFPROCdrei
610 C=-1
620 D=0
630 L=300
640 PROCinline
650 PROCpoles(360,510,80,510)
660 PROCpoles(1180,510,900,510)
670 ENDPROC
680 :
690 DEFPROCvier
700 C=1
710 D=300
720 L=0
730 flog=2
740 P=150
750 Q=700
760 PROCside(P,Q)
770 PROCside(P+820,Q)
780 PROCpoles(140,690,140,420)
790 PROCpoles(945,690,945,420)
800 ENDPROC
810 :
820 DEFPROCfunf
830 C=-1
840 D=300
850 L=0
860 flog=2
870 P=150
880 Q=700
890 PROCside(P,Q)
900 PROCside(P+820,Q)
910 PROCpoles(140,690,140,420)
920 PROCpoles(945,420,945,690)
930 ENDPROC
940 :
950 DEFPROChr
960 VDU5
970 GCOL0,2
980 MOVE600,1000
990 PRINT"---->"
1000 ENDPROC
1010 :
1020 DEFPROChl
1030 VDU5
1040 GCOL0,2
1050 MOVE600,1000
1060 PRINT"<----"
1070 ENDPROC
1080 :
```

```
1090 DEFPROCink                        1600 :
1100 IF INKEY(-58) PROCcross:Y1=Y1+5:PRO   1610 DEFPROCspot2
     Ccross:REM UP                     1620 GCOL0,2
1110 IF INKEY(-42) PROCcross:Y1=Y1-5:PRO   1630 flag=0
     Ccross:REM DOWN                   1640 x%=X1:y%=Y1
1120 IF INKEY(-122) PROCcross:X1=X1+5:PR   1650 dot2=0
     OCcross:REM RIGHT                 1660 F1X=FNmag(0,L,1,0)
1130 IF INKEY(-26) PROCcross:X1=X1-5:PRO   1670 F2X=FNmag(0,0,-1,D)
     Ccross:REM LEFT                   1680 F3X=FNmag(820,0,C,0)
1140 IF INKEY(-99) AND flog=1 PROCspot1(   1690 F4X=FNmag(820,L,-C,D)
     H):REM SPACE                      1700 IF ERR=22 SOUND 1,-15,165,5:ON ERRO
1150 IF INKEY(-99) AND flog=2 PROCspot2        R OFF:ENDPROC
1160 IF INKEY(-51) PROCdump:REM D          1710 I=F1X+F2X+F3X+F4X+H
1170 ON ERROR CLS:REPORT:PRINT''"Program   1720 F1Y=FNmog(0,L,1,0)
     Aborted":END                      1730 F2Y=FNmog(0,0,-1,D)
1180 IF INKEY(-17) ENDPROC:REM Q           1740 F3Y=FNmog(820,0,C,0)
1190 ENDPROC                           1750 F4Y=FNmog(820,L,-C,D)
1200 :                                 1760 J=F1Y+F2Y+F3Y+F4Y
1210 DEFPROCcross                      1770 IF ERR=22 SOUND 1,-15,185,5:ON ERRO
1220 MOVE X1-20,Y1-20:PLOT 6,X1+20,Y1+20       R OFF:ENDPROC
                                       1780 PROCmargin:IF flag=1 THEN ENDPROC
1230 MOVE X1+20,Y1-20:PLOT 6,X1-20,Y1+20   1790 IF I<0 GOTO 1870
                                       1800 IF dot2=F1X SOUND 1,-10,135,3:ENDPR
1240 ENDPROC                                    OC
1250 :                                 1810 dot2=F1X
1260 DEFPROCquit                       1820 IF I=0 GOTO 1660
1270 CLS                               1830 x%=x%+30*COS(ATN(J/I))
1280 *FX15                             1840 y%=y%+30*SIN(ATN(J/I))
1290 PRINTTAB(12,24)"Another Go?"      1850 SOUND 0,-10,5,1
1300 Y$=GET$                           1860 GOTO 1900
1310 IF Y$="Y" OR Y$="y" ENDPROC       1870 x%=x%-30*COS(ATN(J/I))
1320 PRINTTAB(8,26)"Goodbye - until next   1880 y%=y%-30*SIN(ATN(J/I))
     time"                             1890 SOUND 0,-10,6,1
1330 VDU4                              1900 PLOT69,x%,y%
1340 *FX4,0                            1910 IF D=0 THEN PLOT69,x%,2*Q-y%
1350 END                               1920 GOTO 1660
1360 ENDPROC                           1930 ENDPROC
1370 :                                 1940 :
1380 DEFPROCtwo(P,Q)                   1950 DEF PROCmargin
1390 GCOL0,1                           1960 IF x%>1280 OR x%<0 OR y%<0 OR y%>10
1400 MOVE P-10,Q+40                         00 THEN flag=1:SOUND 1,-10,35,3:END
1410 PLOT13,P+320,Q+40                      PROC
1420 PLOT85,P+320,Q-40                 1970 IF D<>0 GOTO 2010
1430 DRAW P-10,Q-40                    1980 IF x%>P-10 AND x%<P+310 AND y%<Q+10
1440 PLOT85,P-10,Q+40                       AND y%>Q-90 THEN flag=1:SOUND 1,-1
1450 VDU5                                   0,55,3:ENDPROC
1460 MOVE P+10,Q                       1990 IF flog=1 ENDPROC
1470 PRINT"S"                          2000 IF x%>P+810 AND x%<P+1130 AND y%<Q+
1480 MOVE P+290,Q                           10 AND y%>Q-90 THEN flag=1:SOUND 1,
1490 PRINT"N"                               -10,75,3:ENDPROC
1500 MOVEP+820,Q                       2010 IF x%>P-40 AND x%<P+40 AND y%>Q-320
1510 PRINT"N"                               AND y%<Q+10 THEN flag=1:SOUND 1,-1
1520 MOVE P+1110,Q                          0,95,3:ENDPROC
1530 PRINT"S"                          2020 IF x%>P+780 AND x%<P+860 AND y%>Q-3
1540 X1=515:Y1=400                          20 AND y%<Q+10 THEN flag=1:SOUND 1,
1550 ENDPROC                                -10,115,3:ENDPROC
1560 :                                 2030 ENDPROC
1570 DEFFNmag (A,L,r,D)=r*(x%-(A+P+L))/(   2040 :
     ((x%-(A+P+L)) 2+(y%-Q+D) 2) 1.5)   2050 DEFPROCdump
1580 :                                 2060 *LOAD MDUMP3 0900
1590 DEFFNmog (A,L,r,D)=r*(y%-Q+D)/(((x%   2070 VDU2
     -(A+P+L)) 2+(y%-Q+D) 2) 1.5)      2080 CALL &0900
```

```
2090 VDU3
2100 ENDPROC
2110 :
2120 DEFPROCspot1(H)
2130 *FX15
2140 flag=0
2150 x%=X1:y%=Y1
2160 dot1=0
2170 F1X=FNmag(0,300,1,0)
2180 F2X=FNmag(0,0,-1,0)
2190 I=F1X+F2X +H
2200 F1Y=FNmog(0,300,1,0)
2210 F2Y=FNmog(0,0,-1,0)
2220 J=F1Y+F2Y
2230 IF dot1=F1Y SOUND  1,-10,-155,3:END
     PROC
2240 dot1=F1Y
2250 PROCmargin:IF flag=1 THEN ENDPROC
2260 IF I<0 THEN 2310
2270 x%=x%+30*COS(ATN(J/I))
2280 y%=y%+30*SIN(ATN(J/I))
2290 SOUND 0,-10,4,3
2300 GOTO 2340
2310 x%=x%-30*COS(ATN(J/I))
2320 y%=y%-30*SIN(ATN(J/I))
2330 SOUND 0,-10,7,3
2340 PLOT 69,x%,y%
2350 PLOT 69,x%,2*Q-y%
2360 GOTO 2170
2370 *FX21,0
2380 ENDPROC
2390 :
2400 DEFPROCinline
2410 P=80:Q=500:PROCtwo(P+820,Q)
2420 PROCtwo(P,Q)
2430 flog=2
2440 ENDPROC
2450 :
2460 DEFPROCalone
2470 P=500:Q=500:PROCtwo(P,Q)
2480 PROCpoles(780,510,500,510)
2490 flog=1
2500 ENDPROC
2510 :
2520 DEFPROCside(P,Q)
2530 GCOL0,1
2540 MOVE P-40,Q+10
2550 PLOT13,P+40,Q+10
2560 PLOT85,P+40,Q-320
2570 DRAW P-40,Q-320
2580 PLOT85,P-40,Q+10
2590 X1=200:Y1=500
2600 ENDPROC
2610 :
2620 DEFPROCpoles(a,b,c,d)
2630 GCOL0,0:VDU5
2640 MOVE a,b:PRINT"N"
2650 MOVE c,d:PRINT"S"
2660 GCOL0,1
2670 ENDPROC
2680 :
```

```
2690 DEFPROCinst
2700 CLS
2710 FOR D=3TO4
2720   PRINTTAB(15,D)CHR$141;"MAGNETS"
2730 NEXT D
2740 PRINTTAB(0,6)"This program simulate
     s the plotting of"
2750 PRINTTAB(0,7)"points along magnetic
      field lines.  The"
2760 PRINTTAB(0,8)"compass position is s
     hown on the screen"
2770 PRINTTAB(0,9)"by a cross.  It can b
     e moved around by"
2780 PRINTTAB(0,10)"the arrow keys.  Pre
     ssing the SPACE bar"
2790 PRINTTAB(0,11)"causes dots to appea
     r which show the"
2800 PRINTTAB(0,12)"path of a magnetic f
     ield line from"
2810 PRINTTAB(0,13)"the cross to the mag
     net - generally"
2820 PRINTTAB(0,14)"from N to S.  In som
     e places, two"
2830 PRINTTAB(0,15)"matching sets of lin
     es are produced."
2840 PRINTTAB(0,17)"If this computer is
     connected to an"
2850 PRINTTAB(0,18)"Epson compatible pri
     nter, a hard copy"
2860 PRINTTAB(0,19)"of the field plots c
     an be printed."
2870 PRINTTAB(0,22)"Press any key for th
     e instructions."
2880 N$=GET$
2890 CLS
2900 FOR D=3TO4
2910   PRINTTAB(10,D)CHR$141;"INSTRUCTION
     S"
2920 NEXT
2930 PRINTTAB(2,6)"ARROW keys    Move the
      cross"
2940 PRINTTAB(2,8)"SPACE         Starts a
      plot"
2950 PRINTTAB(2,10)" D           Starts
     the printer"
2960 PRINTTAB(2,12)" Q           Exit fr
     om current screen"
2970 PRINTTAB(2,14)"             Then ch
     oose..... "
2980 PRINTTAB(2,16)"             More or
      Program EXIT"
2990 PRINTTAB(0,22)"Press any key to sta
     rt program."
3000   M$=GET$
3010 CLS
3020 ENDPROC
3030:
3040 REM Original by Peter Warren
3050 REM Revised by Wilf James 6/1/91
```

continued ▶

3 of 4

Disassembler listing of MDUMP
This is a screen dump routine
for the MAGNET simulation
program.

Hexadecimal memory dump

```
0900 A9 FF       LDA #&FF
0902 85 72       STA &72
0904 A9 03       LDA #&03
0906 85 73       STA &73
0908 A9 00       LDA #&00
090A 85 77       STA &77
090C A9 04       LDA #&04
090E 85 78       STA &78
0910 A9 87       LDA #&87
0912 20 F4 FF    JSR &FFF4
0915 98          TYA
0916 D0 04       BNE &091C
0918 E6 77       INC &77
091A 46 78       LSR &78
091C A9 1B       LDA #&1B
091E 20 BF 09    JSR &09BF
0921 A9 41       LDA #&41
0923 20 BF 09    JSR &09BF
0926 A9 08       LDA #&08
0928 20 BF 09    JSR &09BF
092B A9 00       LDA #&00
092D 85 70       STA &70
092F 85 71       STA &71
0931 A9 1B       LDA #&1B
0933 20 BF 09    JSR &09BF
0936 A5 77       LDA &77
0938 F0 11       BEQ &094B
093A A9 4C       LDA #&4C
093C 20 BF 09    JSR &09BF
093F A9 80       LDA #&80
0941 20 BF 09    JSR &09BF
0944 A9 02       LDA #&02
0946 20 BF 09    JSR &09BF
0949 D0 0F       BNE &095A
094B A9 4B       LDA #&4B
094D 20 BF 09    JSR &09BF
0950 A9 40       LDA #&40
0952 20 BF 09    JSR &09BF
0955 A9 01       LDA #&01
0957 20 BF 09    JSR &09BF
095A A9 08       LDA #&08
095C 85 76       STA &76
095E A2 70       LDX #&70
0960 A0 00       LDY #&00
0962 A9 09       LDA #&09
0964 20 F1 FF    JSR &FFF1
0967 18          CLC
0968 A5 74       LDA &74
096A F0 01       BEQ &096D
096C 38          SEC
096D 26 75       ROL &75
096F A5 72       LDA &72
0971 38          SEC
0972 E9 04       SBC #&04
0974 85 72       STA &72
0976 B0 02       BCS &097A
0978 C6 73       DEC &73
097A C6 76       DEC &76
```

```
097C A5 76       LDA &76
097E D0 DE       BNE &095E
0980 A5 75       LDA &75
0982 20 BF 09    JSR &09BF
0985 18          CLC
0986 A5 78       LDA &78
0988 65 70       ADC &70
098A 85 70       STA &70
098C 90 02       BCC &0990
098E E6 71       INC &71
0990 A5 71       LDA &71
0992 C9 05       CMP #&05
0994 F0 0D       BEQ &09A3
0996 A9 20       LDA #&20
0998 18          CLC
0999 65 72       ADC &72
099B 85 72       STA &72
099D 90 BB       BCC &095A
099F E6 73       INC &73
09A1 B0 B7       BCS &095A
09A3 A9 0A       LDA #&0A
09A5 20 BF 09    JSR &09BF
09A8 A5 73       LDA &73
09AA 30 03       BMI &09AF
09AC 4C 2B 09    JMP &092B
09AF A9 0C       LDA #&0C
09B1 20 BF 09    JSR &09BF
09B4 A9 1B       LDA #&1B
09B6 20 BF 09    JSR &09BF
09B9 A9 40       LDA #&40
09BB 20 BF 09    JSR &09BF
09BE 60          RTS
09BF 48          PHA
09C0 A9 01       LDA #&01
09C2 20 EE FF    JSR &FFEE
09C5 68          PLA
09C6 20 EE FF    JSR &FFEE
09C9 60          RTS
```

End of listing.

```
0900  A9 FF 85 72 A9 03 85 73
0908  A9 00 85 77 A9 04 85 78
0910  A9 87 20 F4 FF 98 D0 04
0918  E6 77 46 78 A9 1B 20 BF
0920  09 A9 41 20 BF 09 A9 08
0928  20 BF 09 A9 00 85 70 85
0930  71 A9 1B 20 BF 09 A5 77
0938  F0 11 A9 4C 20 BF 09 A9
0940  80 20 BF 09 A9 02 20 BF
0948  09 D0 0F A9 4B 20 BF 09
0950  A9 40 20 BF 09 A9 01 20
0958  BF 09 A9 08 85 76 A2 70
0960  A0 00 A9 09 20 F1 FF 18
0968  A5 74 F0 01 38 26 75 A5
0970  72 38 E9 04 85 72 B0 02
0978  C6 73 C6 76 A5 76 D0 DE
0980  A5 75 20 BF 09 18 A5 78
0988  65 70 85 70 90 02 E6 71
0990  A5 71 C9 05 F0 0D A9 20
0998  18 65 72 85 72 90 BB E6
09A0  73 B0 B7 A9 0A 20 BF 09
09A8  A5 73 30 03 4C 2B 09 A9
09B0  0C 20 BF 09 A9 1B 20 BF
09B8  09 A9 40 20 BF 09 60 48
09C0  A9 01 20 EE FF 68 20 EE
09C8  FF 60 00 00 00 00 00 00
```

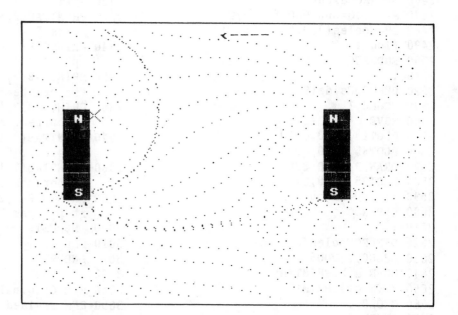

4 of 4

Fact sheet—Tape recording

The tape

Early tape recorders used steel wire but modern machines use plastic tape coated with an extremely fine magnetic powder. Ferrite (an oxide of iron) and chromium oxide are typical examples. The tape is made from thin, but very strong, non-stretch plastic so that it can be wound into a compact spool.

The record/play-back head

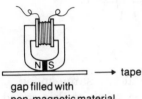

gap filled with
non-magnetic material

tape

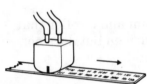

The 'head' is made from a coil of fine wire wound on a ferrite or iron core. The core is an almost-closed loop with a narrow gap where it touches the tape. When current passes through the coil, it produces a strong magnetic field which travels round the core and the strip of tape that crosses the gap. This strip then becomes magnetised with a strength and direction that depends on the size and direction of the current.

A sound is recorded by using a microphone and amplifier to convert its vibrations into a varying voltage. This is fed to the head which prints a magnetic pattern on the passing tape.

On play-back, the patterns on the moving tape induce small changing voltages in the coil of the head. These are amplified and fed to a loudspeaker. The diagram shows how the same amplifier and head can be used for recording and playing-back. The amplifier has to be able to increase the output from the head (a few microvolts) to the few volts needed to magnetise the tape or work the loudspeaker.

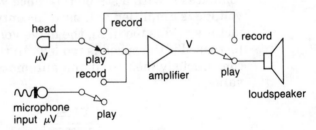

Stereo and mono

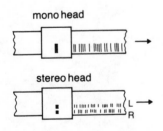

mono head

stereo head

A mono cassette recorder has a single head that records on the lower half of the tape. The tape can then be turned over for the head to record on the upper half. A stereo cassette recorder has two smaller heads that record and read separate right and left tracks. The two tracks are designed to cover the same width of track as a mono track so that a mono recorder can play stereo recordings.

Ultrasonic bias

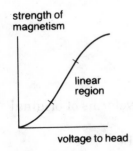

strength of
magnetism

linear
region

voltage to head

The simple tape-recorder design shown would unfortunately sound dreadful. This is due to the magnetic properties of the tape. The strength of its magnetism does not go up linearly with voltage. An a.c. audio signal goes from + to − through zero where the magnetising curve is far from straight. The magnetic patterns in this region would be distorted and would not faithfully follow the voltage changes.

continued ▶

1 of 2

The problem is overcome by mixing a high frequency ultrasonic wave (40 kHz) with the sound signal. Its amplitude is designed to make the peaks of the ultrasonic wave always lie in the straight region of the magnetising curve.

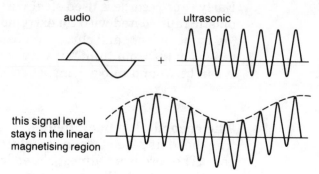

this signal level stays in the linear magnetising region

Tape speed

For accurate reproduction, the tape must move at the same speed for record and play-back. All tape recorders must work at this speed and it should not vary as the battery voltage drops or as tape drag alters.

The tape is moved by pinching it between a drum and a roller that is driven by a motor. The take-up spool is also driven but does not pull the tape along.

Electronic speed control

The picture shows a feedback system that keeps the motor speed constant. A generator fitted to the motor produces a voltage proportional to its speed. This is fed to an electronic chip that compares it with a stable reference voltage. The difference in voltage is amplified and used to control the drive voltage. If the motor speed is too high, the drive voltage is reduced, and it is increased if the speed is too low. In this way the motor speed is continuously measured and automatically adjusted to the correct value.

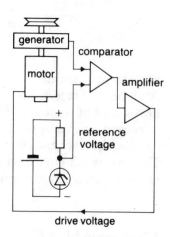

Ideas for investigations

- The breaking strength of audio tape.
- Its magnetic properties.
- The quality of the recordings – comparing waveforms of original and recorded sound on an oscilloscope.
- An experiment to measure the speed of the tape.

2 of 2

How to make a simple electric motor

1 Wind a coil from insulated single-core copper wire. Leave the two bared ends sticking out.

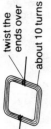

twist the ends over

about 10 turns

2 Bend two paper clips like this.

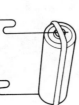

3 Fix the paper clips to the terminals of a cell with a wide rubber band.

4 Lay a magnet on the cell, with one of its poles uppermost.
Slab 'ferrite' magnets work well.

5 Rest the coil on the paper clips and give it a flick. It should spin merrily – until the battery goes flat.

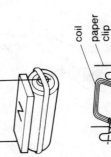

coil
paper clip
(ferrite) magnet
rubber band
dry cell

How to make a simple electric motor

1 Wind a coil from insulated single-core copper wire. Leave the two bared ends sticking out.

twist the ends over

about 10 turns

2 Bend two paper clips like this.

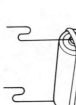

3 Fix the paper clips to the terminals of a cell with a wide rubber band.

4 Lay a magnet on the cell, with one of its poles uppermost.
Slab 'ferrite' magnets work well.

5 Rest the coil on the paper clips and give it a flick. It should spin merrily – until the battery goes flat.

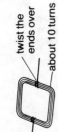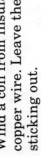

coil
paper clip
(ferrite) magnet
rubber band
dry cell

How to make switches for automatic timing

Top switch (starts the clock)
The metal ball connects the two aluminium strips as it passes through the hole.

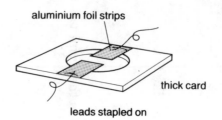

aluminium foil strips

thick card

leads stapled on

Bottom switch (stops the clock)
Staple the foil squares to the top and bottom of the frame. Staple a wire to each square.

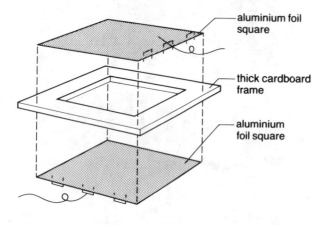

aluminium foil square

thick cardboard frame

aluminium foil square

Make sure the squares do not touch and that the staples do not connect them.

the ball presses the top square onto the bottom one

How to make switches for automatic timing

Top switch (starts the clock)
The metal ball connects the two aluminium strips as it passes through the hole.

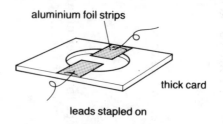

aluminium foil strips

thick card

leads stapled on

Bottom switch (stops the clock)
Staple the foil squares to the top and bottom of the frame. Staple a wire to each square.

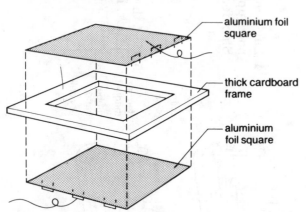

aluminium foil square

thick cardboard frame

aluminium foil square

Make sure the squares do not touch and that the staples do not connect them.

the ball presses the top square onto the bottom one

Sound wave readings

Three sound waves were sampled and measured automatically by a computer. Each set of 256 readings was taken in 1.3 ms.

The sounds were made by a

- low pipe
- tuning fork
- whistle.

Use some of the readings to plot each wave. Can you tell which is which?

Read the figures from left to right, starting at the top row.

a

156	152	136	108	97	101	117	135
159	173	178	168	144	121	101	88
83	93	110	129	147	162	171	166
153	139	121	108	101	97	103	112
119	124	131	135	134	128	120	104
91	84	83	87	133	119	132	146
158	160	156	149	141	131	125	125
126	127	128	126	123	120	121	122
121	121	124	124	121	112	105	105
107	108	114	125	133	134	131	126
120	115	112	114	118	123	129	137
146	155	158	156	147	131	114	98
88	83	87	97	111	123	135	139
136	130	123	116	112	112	115	121
127	133	140	145	146	139	130	122
112	103	98	101	111	127	138	145
148	141	128	112	101	94	94	103
114	125	133	136	136	133	130	126
123	124	128	132	134	133	132	132
131	130	131	133	136	135	130	123
114	104	99	98	102	111	119	126
129	128	125	123	123	122	121	121
123	124	126	127	129	130	132	131
129	128	127	128	129	132	135	139
142	144	145	144	141	135	128	120
114	111	110	112	117	122	127	130
131	130	130	129	129	130	131	131
133	137	140	141	140	136	132	129
127	127	129	133	136	135	132	125
116	108	107	111	119	131	143	150
149	143	132	120	110	101	100	104
115	127	0	0	0	0	0	0

b

159	157	153	152	156	158	160	154
147	140	138	136	136	133	128	128
126	114	106	106	111	110	106	104
101	104	102	99	101	98	96	95
105	114	123	127	124	130	131	130
135	138	140	144	150	152	157	159
157	158	157	154	152	156	160	154
147	140	137	138	136	130	127	124
117	113	109	112	114	112	108	97
98	100	101	100	102	101	101	106
103	114	119	124	125	129	136	136
140	144	142	143	149	152	156	159
158	157	159	159	158	158	156	149
140	137	139	139	135	131	128	122
114	108	103	109	110	106	105	104
104	102	103	96	93	97	100	107
117	124	125	124	127	130	134	134
133	137	145	151	156	159	159	156
156	155	153	153	156	156	153	151
144	137	133	132	131	128	121	112
114	113	110	108	108	104	97	97
101	106	104	96	95	100	104	103
111	121	125	125	130	134	137	139
137	141	145	150	152	154	160	159
154	152	154	156	157	152	146	144
142	136	132	129	126	122	119	112
105	108	109	110	107	100	98	95
98	97	95	95	97	103	106	109
119	124	125	122	124	130	137	138
137	145	148	150	151	153	157	156
155	151	154	159	155	149	143	140
137	135	0	0	0	0	0	0

c

159	164	167	169	170	168	165	163
158	154	153	151	150	148	147	146
140	136	132	127	122	119	116	113
109	106	103	101	98	95	93	91
90	90	92	96	102	110	117	125
129	134	138	141	145	148	153	159
163	167	169	171	170	168	166	162
157	154	152	151	158	148	146	143
138	134	130	125	120	117	113	111
108	105	102	99	95	92	90	90
89	91	95	99	105	112	120	127
130	134	138	141	145	150	155	160
163	167	169	169	167	163	160	157
153	151	150	148	146	144	141	139
133	129	125	120	117	113	109	108
104	101	97	93	90	88	88	87
87	91	95	101	107	114	120	125
130	134	136	140	144	149	154	159
162	166	166	164	161	158	154	151
148	147	145	143	140	138	134	132
127	123	118	114	111	108	106	103
98	95	91	87	83	82	82	83
87	91	95	101	107	115	120	125
127	132	136	140	145	150	155	160
162	163	162	160	157	154	152	149
146	144	143	140	138	134	132	127
124	120	116	112	108	105	102	99
95	91	87	84	81	80	81	85
88	93	99	105	111	116	121	127
129	133	137	143	147	153	159	162
163	163	161	158	153	150	148	147
145	144	0	0	0	0	0	0

Sparks can be dangerous

Sparks from static electricity are hot enough to make a mixture of gas and air burst into a flame. If you make sparks jump from a charged Van de Graaff dome to the nozzle of a gas burner, the gas from it may light. A tiny spark can produce a frightening burst of flame.

butane

Dangerous situations

The flame from a gas burner burns steadily but some mixtures of gas and air do not burn. They explode violently. Examples of these explosive mixtures are petrol vapour and air and some anaesthetics. A small spark can trigger off a large explosion of these mixtures.

a Petrol and oil tankers.

The movement of petrol and oil as it is being transported in tankers can build up an electric charge. A spark from this charge could make petrol vapour explode. An escape route for the charge has to be provided to prevent any possibility of sparking. A chain to the ground, or tyres made from special conducting rubber, are used to allow the charge to escape to 'earth'.

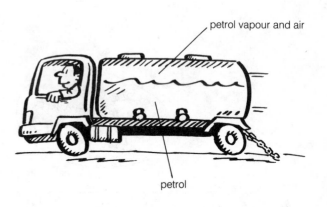

petrol vapour and air

petrol

b The operating theatre.

Sudden movement of blankets, apparatus or clothes in operating theatres can cause sparks to fly. Careful precautions are taken to make conducting paths to the ground so that static charges do not build up. Sparks are especially dangerous because of the flammable gases used to anaesthetize the patient and the large amount of oxygen present in the air of the theatre.

cotton (not nylon) gowns

the patient's skin is earthed

anaesthetic machines connected to the ground by a chain

floor made from conducting tiles

antistatic conducting shoes

trolley wheels made of antistatic rubber

Understanding Science 3

Problem solving with materials

This unit builds upon those aspects of unit 6 in Book 2 that introduced the uses of science in materials technology. The revision work therefore refers to the different sources of raw materials and to the methods of purifying these and subsequently manufacturing useful products. However the five topics which follow stress an investigative approach to the useful properties of a wide range of everyday materials. Hence the work is presented in real contexts, such as how to insulate a pet's hutch, how to choose a material for a baby's mitts, how to test a smoke alarm and so on. The principles of good scientific design of investigations are thoroughly encouraged throughout and linked with examples of good consumer 'research'. Basic knowledge concerning the main types of materials, their important properties and therefore uses, rusting and its reduction, the importance of neutralisation reactions giving salts and the industrial uses of thermal and electrolytic decomposition is also presented. The final three topics comprise an investigation to discover the 'best' kitchen tile, a group discussion activity about graphs and tables and a reading exercise about industrial methods of electrolysis. This unit deals with Attainment Targets 6 and 7 of the 1989 National Curriculum. In addition to meeting the general demands of Attainment Target 1, this unit deals specifically with AT1 levels 5d, 6 and most aspects of 7.

Core and Reinforcement

8.0 Revision—The material world

> Complete a revision question sheet.
> Write a short story that names many materials and their uses. *page 120*

Revise the essential prerequisite concepts.

8.1 Types of materials   *AT6–7a*

> Use a key to identify types of materials.
> Investigate materials for insulating a guinea pig hutch. *page 122*

Observe systematically.
Devise and carry out tests of given properties.
Understand how to use a key.

8.2 The property pages   *AT6–6a, 7b*

> Test and compare the appropriate properties of different baby wools or disposable nappy fillings.
> Write an advert to highlight an appropriate property of a material used in a manufactured article. *page 124*

Devise and carry out experiments to test self-selected properties of a material.
Record results in a suitable form.
Draw conclusions from experimental results.
Communicate in appropriate written form.

Extension

    AT6–6a, 7b

> Compare and contrast the properties of different types of building materials. *page 169*

Observe systematically.
Extract information relevant to a given context.

    AT6–6a, 7b

> Read consumer magazine reports and use information from them to design appropriate tests to investigate cloth for wear and tear. *page 170*

Extract, from given information, data relevant to a given context.
Devise and carry out experiments to test a property of a range of materials.
Communicate the method, results and conclusion of a scientific investigation in appropriate written form.

Core and Reinforcement

8.3 Destroyed by fire *AT6–7b*

> Examine a smoke alarm, find out how it works
> and design a safe test of its operation.
> Compare flameproofed and non-flameproofed
> material.   *page 126*

Extract, from given information, data relevant to a
given context.
Follow instructions.
Devise and carry out a safe experiment to test the
operation of a piece of equipment.
Communicate the method, results and conclusion of
a scientific experiment in appropriate written form.

8.4 Damaged by the weather *AT7–7d*

> Compare weathered with unweathered
> materials.
> Investigate methods of slowing down
> corrosion.   *page 128*

Observe accurately and systematically.
Extract from a variety of resources, information
relevant to a given context.
Devise and carry out an experiment to investigate a
given question.

8.5 Changeable materials *AT6–5b; AT7–6a*

> Temper steel and neutralise acidic water.
> Make a given salt from acid and neutraliser.
>   *page 130*

Follow instructions.
Communicate the method of an experiment in
written form using given terms correctly.
Draw conclusions from observations.

8.6 Problem—Piles of tiles *AT6–6a, 7b*

> Find out which one of a range of floor tiles
> would be best for a kitchen floor.   *page 132*

Devise and carry out a series of experiments to test
the properties of a range of materials.
Manipulate an independent variable whilst
controlling others.
Select appropriate methods of measurement.
Record data.
Communicate the method, results and conclusions
of the investigation in appropriate written form.

8.7 Talkabout—Every picture tells a story
AT7–4b; AT13–5b

> Extract information from bar graphs, pie
> charts, a diagram and a complex table.
>   *page 133*

Extract information from a variety of data.
Translate from bar graphs, pie charts and tables
into oral communications.
Draw conclusions from data.

Extension

AT7–5c, 7c

> Investigate the thermal decomposition of
> carbonates.
>   *page 171*

Given the equipment, devise an experiment to test
a hypothesis.
Communicate the method, results and conclusion of
a scientific experiment in appropriate written form.
Translate from an observation into a word equation.

AT6–7b

> Use the alloy solder to make a shape.
>   *page 172*

Follow instructions.
Translate information from a written passage to a
table.
Communicate the method and result of a practical
activity.

AT5–5a, 6c

> Measure the amount of dissolved solid in a
> sample of water (in grams per 20 cm^3 sample).
>   *page 173*

Follow instructions.
Measure accurately and systematically.
Calculate a weight by subtraction.

Core and Reinforcement

8.8 Readabout—Breaking up substances with electricity
AT7–6b, 7c; AT11–7b

> Find, collate and summarise information about the uses of electricity in industry using a range of resource material. *page 134*

Extract and collate self-sought information from a variety of resources.
Translate information from written form to a spider diagram.

Equipment	**Notes**

Equipment
required for each pupil group

8.0—Revision—The material world
- Revision question sheet

Access to copies of *Understanding Science 1* and *2* will allow pupils to check their work and look for information they are unsure of.

8.1—Types of materials
- Battery, bulb and connecting wires
- Sharp nail
- Access to hot water (kettle)
- Microscope (or hand lens)
- Bunsen burner and heatproof mat

Plastics should be burned in a fume cupboard.

- Set of material samples, to include metal foil, metal chunk, clear glass, coloured glass, wool, woven cloth, thermoplastic plastic (polythene), thermosetting plastic (piece of electric plug), pot fragment, ceramic tile.
- Materials key **(R8.1)**

The key does not work perfectly with every material. It is only a guide to a rough and ready classification; that of the National Curriculum. A good teaching point is to identify modern materials which are exceptions to the classification (e.g. glass fibre, semi-conductors, epoxy-carbons and other composites – see Extension 8.1).

- Handful-sized samples of straw, paper, woven cloth, polythene sheeting, metal foil, jiffy post bags.
- Thermometer

- Small cardboard box or similar

Represents the hutch.

- Metal tin or similar

Represents the guinea pig.

- Access to hot water
- Poster paper, coloured pencils etc.

Represents the animal's body heat. However give pupils time to design their own test without guidance (possible homework exercise).

Extension
- Access to a dictionary

8.2—The property pages
- 3 types of white wool

Include baby wool, which is soft but is also very easy to break; hence it does not damage tiny digits.

- 3 types of disposable nappy
- Access to testing equipment: e.g. weights, newton meter or similar, balance, ruler, filter paper etc.

Most modern disposable nappies are filled with a gel which absorbs water and swells. Older and cheaper nappies may contain absorbent fibre. A good nappy should absorb a lot of water and yet remain dry to the skin.

- Advert cards **(R8.2)**
- Poster paper (or unlined A4)
- Coloured pencils

Different coloured paper is useful.

Equipment

Notes

Extension

- Copies of *Which?* magazine (or similar)
- 5 pieces of cloth; e.g. hard-wearing synthetic, light cotton fabric, wool-based cloth, nylon or similar, linen or other synthetic
- Access to testing equipment; e.g. pins, mass carrier and masses, paint roller, 2 newton meters, block of wood and coarse sandpaper, wood with rough surface (e.g. painted with textured surface like Artex, or covered in mortar and then pebble-dashed)
- Hints page **(RE8.2D)**

Alternatively use the sample report **(RE8.2A)** that refers to carpet tests (*Which?* March 1983). This has the advantage of describing tests which were done on a piece of fabric and some of these will be relevant to the required investigation. The other two sample reports **(RE8.2B** and **C)** refer to tests performed on adhesives and on video recorders (*Which?* May 1981 and February 1984).

8.3—Destroyed by fire

- Smoke alarm (one from a DIY superstore, with an instruction booklet)
- Access to a fume cupboard if possible
- Bunsen burner and heatproof mat
- Wooden splints or something else that is safe to burn

- Flameproofed cotton fabric
- Normal cotton fabric
- Other fabrics as available
- Safety glasses
- Bunsen burner and heatproof mat
- Tongs
- Clamp stand
- Paper strips (about 6 cm by 2 cm)
- Small piece of wire
- Access to a stapler
- Access to clock or timer

The design is often quite ingenious. Some, for example, contain a radioisotope: the smoke stops the radioactivity being picked up by a sensor and the alarm goes off. However, the instruction with the alarm will not reveal the design, hence the pupils are merely being asked here to find out how the alarm operates, not why it operates.

Divide one piece of cotton fabric (about 20 cm by 20 cm) into halves. Flameproof one half by dipping into a solution of 43.5 g of borax and 18.5 g of boric acid dissolved in 500 cm^3 of water (heat to dissolve). This treatment is effective with cotton and viscose rayon (but not acetate rayon). The treated material scorches but does not catch fire. All other materials do catch fire. Treated samples can be dried in an oven at about 100°C or left overnight. Treat the other fabrics in the same way as the cotton.

Extension

- Basic glassware

One possible set up is:

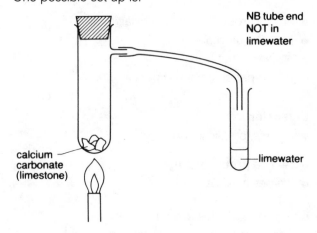

Warn pupils about 'suckback' if necessary.

- Limewater
- Limestone pieces (often sold as 'marble')
- Magnesium carbonate (chunks if possible)
- Bunsen burner and heatproof mat
- Safety glasses

Magnesium carbonate does decompose to give magnesium oxide and carbon dioxide.

Equipment	Notes

Equipment

8.4—Damaged by the weather

- Samples of weathered artifacts, e.g. metal (rusty tool, etc.), stone (split), brick (crumbled), wood (wet rot)
- Samples of unweathered artifacts for comparison
- Access to binocular microscope (or hand lens)
- Equipment to test flexibility, hardness and strength.
- Access to books containing information about dry rot, wet rot and woodworm

Investigation cards **(R8.4)**

- Rust indicator

Card 1

- 2 small iron nails
- Battery (or d.c. power pack)
- Connecting leads
- Petri dish of salt water

Card 2

- Tin-plated iron
- Sharp point
- Petri dish of salt water

Card 3

- Partly galvanised iron nail (either DIY or commercial)
- Petri dish of salt water

Card 4

- Partly electroplated iron nail
- Petri dish of salt water

Card 5

- Strips of metal foil: Mg, Zn, Al, Sn, Pb, Cu
- Small iron nails

Notes

Use inexpensive manufactured items if possible.

See Pupils' book for details.

DIY manuals are useful sources here. Check the index of any intended resource for the given key words.

Dissolve a spatula-ful of potassium hexacyanoferrate in 50 cm³ of salty water. Put in small dropper bottles. Colour change is from pale yellow/green to dark blue/green.

The nail is protected by connecting it to the *negative* terminal.

Exposed iron will rust faster.

Pupils can do this by dipping the nail into molten zinc prepared by the teacher. Using a fume cupboard, melt zinc granules in a crucible (with a lid) over a Bunsen burner. The zinc will melt and form a thin layer of zinc oxide on top. Keep the zinc molten. To galvanise a nail, hold it with tongs and push the point through the oxide layer into the molten zinc. Remove and leave on a mat to cool. The galvanised part of the nail will not corrode. It will also protect the ungalvanised part.

Electroplate by making the nail the *negative* electrode in an electrolysis. Use a solution of zinc sulphate (about 0.5M), a power pack with about 6 V d.c. and connecting leads with crocodile clips. Iron will corrode faster if partly covered with a less active metal (like copper or tin). It will not corrode if partly covered with a more active metal like zinc.

Make up a solution of agar (3 g/100 cm³) in salt water. Add a dropperful of rust-indicator solution. When the pupils have set up nails with metals attached and laid them out in their Petri dish, pour the agar on top. The agar will set quickly and the colour of the indicator can then be left to develop slowly by diffusion. Those metals lower in the

Equipment	Notes

<table>
<tr><td></td><td>reactivity series will cause iron to corrode faster whilst the metals above iron will protect it from corrosion.</td></tr>
</table>

Fact-finder
- Access to a camera

Extension
- 10 thin wires
- Small pliers
- Solder (with flux)
- Soldering iron and stand
- Heatproof mat
- Continuity tester
- Safety glasses

Demonstrate the soldering technique to the pupils, stressing safety.

Wires, battery and bulb.

8.5—Changeable materials
- Steel wire
- Tongs
- Bunsen burner and heatproof mat
- Safety glasses
- Glass beaker
- Dilute hydrochloric acid (about 0.05M) labelled 'acidified water'
- Sodium hydroxide (0.1M)
- Universal indicator in dropper bottle
- Access to a burette
- Conical flask
- White tile
- Sulphuric acid (1M)
- Copper carbonate solid
- Filter funnel and paper
- Crystallising dish (or Petri dish)
- Heatproof mat (to contain spillages)

With this concentration, the end point should be easy to spot (the indicator goes green).

Demonstrate the correct procedure for using a burette if this is necessary. If the concentrations are fairly accurate then it should only require 10 cm³ of alkali to neutralise the acid. Thus one burette refilled as necessary will serve the whole class.

The practice of liming acidified lakes and streams was introduced in the early 1970s. However, while this may be beneficial in certain circumstances, evidence has accumulated suggesting that it is often itself ecologically harmful. (See *New Scientist* 10 March 1990.)

Extension
- 20 cm³ pipette
- Evaporating basin (or beaker)
- Watch glass
- Desiccator
- Sample A (distilled water)
- Sample B (sodium chloride solution)
- Bunsen burner and heatproof mat
- Access to an electronic balance
- Safety glasses
- Hard and soft water supplement **(RE8.5A)**
- Hard water information sheet **(RE8.5B)**

Cover the evaporating basin with the watch glass to prevent spurting.

Containing 5 g per 100 cm³: this will give an answer of 1 g.

These resources are provided especially for pupils in Northern Ireland to address the requirements of AT10–7e, f of the Science Curriculum.

Equipment

8.6—Problem—Piles of tiles

- Samples of different tiles, e.g. cork, vinyl, lino, wood, carpet etc.
- Hints sheet **(R8.6)**
- Filter paper
- Blackcurrant juice in dropper bottles
- Tongs
- Bunsen burner and heatproof mat
- Timer
- 1 m length of plastic pipe
- Rubber stopper with large nail or large dissection pin in it
- Plasticine
- Sandpaper
- Hand lens
- Mud
- Cloth
- Sharp knife
- Hinged tiltboard
- Polished stone weight or sole

8.7—Talkabout—Every picture tells a story

No equipment required

8.8—Readabout—Breaking up substances with electricity

- Range of resource material that allows pupils to use the given keywords, viz. booklets from industry, textbooks, video material, dictionaries.

Notes

Pupils should be encouraged to design their own tests. The equipment needs are thus difficult to predict. These ones are based on the hints sheet.

Use concentrated solution of Ribena.

This is a good opportunity to use Campus 2000 or a similar online database system to search for information.

Assessment 8

The questions are designed to assess the skills and knowledge developed in the unit, as shown in the table. The Attainment Target assessed by each question is also shown. A selection of questions would be appropriate for a unit test.

Topic	Core	Attainment Target
8.1	1	AT6–7a
8.2	2	AT6–7b
8.3	3, 4, 5	AT6–7b
8.4	6	AT7–7d
8.5	7	AT7–6a
	Extension	
8.1	8	AT6–6a
	9	AT6–7b
8.2	10	AT6–7b
8.3	11	AT7–7c
8.5	12	AT5–5a; AT6–5b
	13	AT5–5a
	14	AT5–6a
	15	AT5–5a

Answers

1 a A—metal, B—plastic, C—metal.
b (i) Ceramic: non-conductor, hard, not see through, does not soften in hard water, musical sound when struck, does not burn.
(ii) Fibre: non-conductor, soft, tears easily, thread-like in microscope.
2 a Glass—see through, does not shatter into sharp pieces, shaped, strong.
Steel—strong, shaped, hard.
Fabric—soft, strong, hard wearing, can be coloured.
b Suitable experiment. Answer should mention each of the four points given. At least two variables should be controlled in the comparison.
3 a Smoke and poisonous gases produced in the fire can kill.
b Any two sensible precautions, e.g. smoke alarm, blanket.
4 a Material A.
b Bar chart showing temperature drop for each material.
c Use same flask and same amount of covering. Begin at the same temperature.
5 Any suitable drawing and description. Safety important. At least two variables controlled.

Flammability measured (qualitative measurement acceptable). Results recorded on paper.

6 a Nail B; **b** Nail A; **c** Oxygen and water;
d Painting, greasing, oiling, electroplating, galvanising etc.

7 Suitable explanations which each include idea that the acid present is being neutralised by the other substance so that the problem/source of irritation is removed.

8 A suitable experimental design that controls at least two variables, measure the amount of rotting/corrosion, records change over a reasonable time period, incorporates a logic for reaching a conclusion.

9 A—Strong, flexible, corrosion-proof, easily sharpened etc.
B—High melting point, non-flammable, insulator, strong etc.
C—Strong, light, easily cut, absorbs force etc.

10 a How well adhesives stick plastics together.
b Amount of push; setting time of glue; area of joint; type of plastic.
c Weight needed to pull joint apart.
d Reduce times for setting; use weights to measure the breaking point; use smaller cross-section to reduce weight needed; bend rather than pull joint apart.

11 a Chlorine, hydrogen, sodium hydroxide.

b Salt → sodium + chlorine
c

Product of electrolysis	One use of product
sodium	indigo dye (titanium extraction)
chlorine	solvents (pesticides, swimming pools)

d Sodium hydroxide and chlorine.
e Hydrogen + chlorine → hydrochloric acid
f Hydrogen, hydrochloric acid, sodium hydroxide (also salt).
g Chlorine.

12 a Factories, power stations, vehicles.
b They dissolve.
c Use an indicator to show the pH (colour matching).
d Add a neutraliser (like lime).

13 a Sulphur dioxide, nitrogen oxides.
b Water (H_2O) and oxygen (O_2).
c Sulphuric acid and nitric acid.

14 a Sulphur dioxide—power stations; nitrogen oxide—vehicles.
b Check that pupils have drawn sensible and correct bar charts.

15 C → E → B → A → F → D

True/false 8
Each statement is marked as either true or false by the pupil. This gives a rapid assessment of a pupil's grasp of the Attainment Targets covered in the unit. The following list gives the Attainment Targets covered by each set of statements.

1	AT 6–6a	5	AT 7–6b
2	AT 6–7a	6	AT 7–7c
3	AT 6–7b	7	AT 7–7d
4	AT 7–6a	8	AT 11–7b

Unit 8 Make and break

Name_____

1 Write the meaning of each word or phrase in the space provided. The figures in brackets are references to *Understanding Science*, Books 1 and 2 (**book number**, page number). Use the references to *check* your answers.

- material (**2**, 116)
- filtration (**1**, 48)
- distillation (**1**, 48/121)
- chemical reaction (**2**, 38)
- manufacture of new products (**2**, 42/117)
- strength (**2**, 116)
- flexibility (**2**, 116)
- hardness (**2**, 116)
- solubility (**1**, 42)
- the three states of matter (**2**, 96)
- the mass of a substance (**1**, 66)
- the volume of a substance (**1**, 66).

2 Give **three** examples of each of the following:

- natural materials
- synthetic materials
- sources of raw material
- methods of separation
- chemical reactions
- manufactured products
- properties of materials.

3 The spider diagram shows some of the connections in this revision section. Complete the diagram with the correct words.

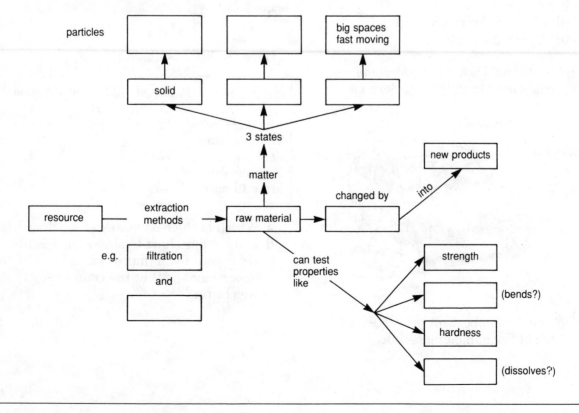

Unit 8 Make and break

1 a Use the key to classify each of the materials (A, B, C) in the table.

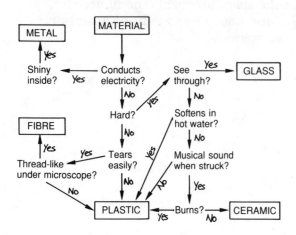

Material	A	B	C
Is it hard?	yes	no	no
Thread-like?	no	yes	no
Conducts electricity?	yes	no	yes
Shiny?	yes	no	yes
Tears easily?	no	no	yes

b Use the key to describe four likely properties of
   (i) a ceramic material
   (ii) a fibre material.

2 The following drawing shows some materials used to build a modern car.

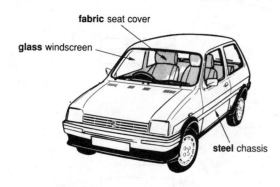

fabric seat cover
glass windscreen
steel chassis

a Name two important properties for each of the named materials.

b An engineer suggests that the car body should be made from plastic. You are given two types of plastic. Describe how you would investigate the strength of these two plastics. Your answer must mention how you would
   ● control the variables
   ● measure strength
   ● record your results
   ● decide which plastic was strongest.

3 a Heat can change materials. Why is this dangerous in a house fire?
   b Give two precautions people should take to protect themselves against fire in the home.

4 A young investigator wants to find out which of three materials is best for keeping a person warm. She uses warm water to represent a person and sets up the following experiments.

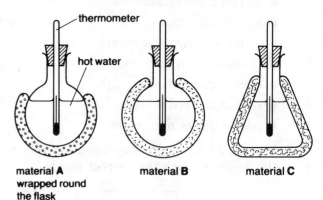

thermometer
hot water

material **A** wrapped round the flask   material **B**   material **C**

Here are her results.

	Material A	Material B	Material C
Temperature at start	85	85	90
Temperature after 10 min	73	71	71

a Which is the best material for the job?
d Draw a bar chart to shows the results.
c How would you improve this experiment so that the comparison was fairer?

continued ▶

5 Two identical small pieces of wood are painted with the same gloss paint. One piece of wood has had undercoat applied first. Describe (with the aid of a drawing) a safe laboratory experiment to find out whether undercoat reduces the flammability of the wood.
Your answer must mention how you would
- make the experiment safe
- control the variables
- measure flammability
- record your results.

6 The drawings show the results of an experiment about corrosion.

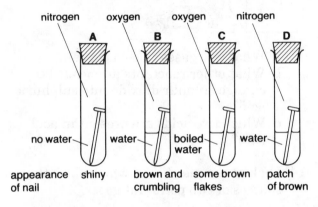

nitrogen   oxygen   oxygen   nitrogen

A   B   C   D

no water   water   boiled water   water

appearance of nail: shiny / brown and crumbling / some brown flakes / patch of brown

a Which nail has corroded most?
b Which nail has not corroded?
c From the experiment, what substances are needed before iron will corrode?
d Give three ways of slowing down or stopping corrosion of iron.

7 Use the idea of *neutralisation* to describe and explain what is happening in each of the following cartoons.

a

b

c

Extension questions

8 Choose **one** of the following questions and describe how you would investigate it. Mention what equipment or materials you need and what method you would use.

 A Does a dent in iron change the rate of rusting?
 B Do all woods rot at the same speed?
 C Does metal corrode faster in sea water?

9 The material in these objects has been chosen to do a particular job. In each case think about the use of the object and describe three properties which the material must have.

a   b   c

titanium surgical instrument   plastic cover for oven-ready food   polystyrene packing case

10 Read this consumer report.

> **Plastics**
> We made butt joints with these, using polystyrene, ABS and cellulose acetate; and kept the joints pushed firmly together for 24 hours. We then stored them for a further six days before pulling them apart. For a joint with a cross-sectional area of 50 mm² (about the cross-sectional area of a pencil) an adhesive rated ● ● ● ● ● would take a straight pull of more than 30 kg (66 lb) to pull it apart, for an adhesive rated ● ● it will take about a tenth or less of this weight. This may still sound quite adequate, but the area of the joint will often be a lot less than this – and, because of the leverage, bending it apart will be a lot easier than pulling it apart. For all the adhesives, the plastic was always stronger than the joint, but for many repairs, strength will not be important.

a What property of the item was tested?
b Which variables were controlled?
c Which variable was measured?
d Describe how you would adapt this test to use in your laboratory.

continued ▶

11 The flow diagram shows how salt is a raw material for the manufacture of a number of other substances.

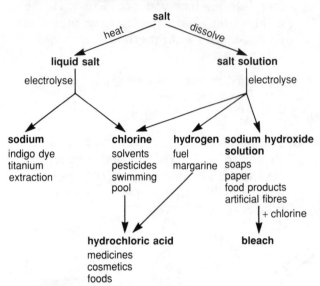

From the diagram

a What are the three products when salt solution is electrolysed?

b Write a word equation for the electrolysis of molten salt.

c Make a table to show *product of electrolysis* and *one use of product* for molten salt.

d Which two products of electrolysis can be combined together to make bleach?

e Write a word equation for the production of hydrochloric acid.

f Which products are used to manufacture foods?

g Which product is used to kill microbes?

12 The diagram shows how acid rain is formed.

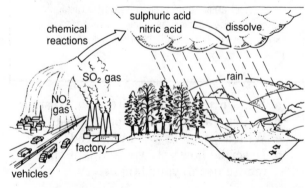

a Where do the chemical pollutants that cause acid rain come from?

b How do the pollutant gases come to be in the rain?

c How could you show in the laboratory that the rain was acid?

d What methods might be used to neutralise acid rain?

13 The flow diagram summarises some of the chemical changes which cause acid rain.

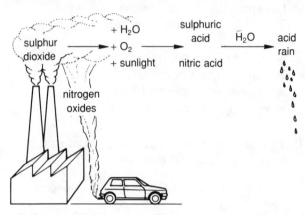

a What two gases cause acid rain?

b What other reactants are needed to change sulphur dioxide into sulphuric acid?

c Which two acids are present in acid rain?

14 Look at the pie charts, which show the sources of two pollutant gases.

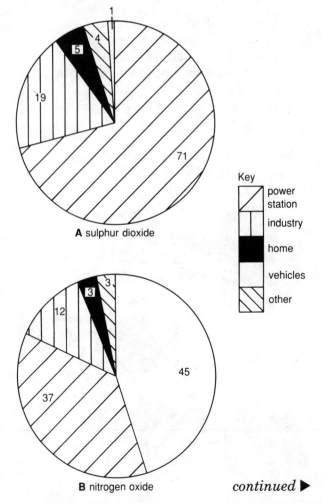

A sulphur dioxide

B nitrogen oxide

Key
- power station
- industry
- home
- vehicles
- other

continued ▶

A refers to sulphur dioxide and **B** to nitrogen oxide. The figures are percentages.

a What is the major source of each of the pollutant gases?

b Draw **one** bar chart to show the information on **both** pie charts.

15 A young scientist is trying to find out exactly how much solid is dissolved in a sample of river water. The pictures show the stages in the method of his experiment but they have been jumbled up. Write the stages in the correct order.

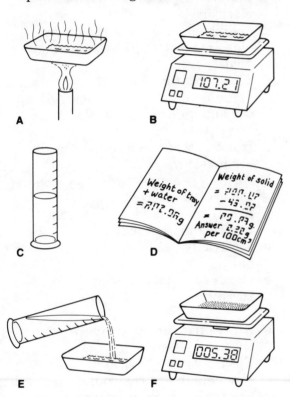

A

B

C

D

E

F

Unit 8 Make and break

Name_____

Put a tick after the statements that are true.
Put a cross after the statements that are false.

1 a An elastic material can spring back into shape. ☐
b An elastic material keeps the same shape when force is exerted on it. ☐
c Thermal conductivity is a measure of how hot an object is. ☐
d A metal will have a high electrical conductivity. ☐
e Density measures the intelligence of a material. ☐
f Ice is more dense than water. ☐

2 a A material which conducts heat well is likely to be a ceramic. ☐
b Fibre materials usually tear easily unless the fibres are twisted together. ☐
c Glass materials are see-through. ☐
d Metals conduct electricity. ☐
e An object which is hard until it is put in hot water could be made of ceramic. ☐
f Materials are difficult to classify. ☐

3 a Ceramic is used on the space shuttle because it can withstand great heat. ☐
b Metals are used to make wire because they are shiny. ☐
c Plastic items are cheap and they rot easily. ☐
d Glass bottles are good for keeping liquids in because glass is insoluble. ☐

4 a An acid will react with a salt to produce a substance called an alkali. ☐
b An alkali is an example of a neutraliser. ☐
c When an acid is neutralised a compound called a salt is formed. ☐
d Sodium chloride and sodium hydroxide are examples of salts. ☐

5 a In electrolysis electricity is used to break up compounds. ☐
b All compounds can be electrolysed. ☐
c Electricity can separate the ions in an ionic compound. ☐
d A positive ion is attracted to a positive electrode. ☐

6 a Bauxite contains aluminium. ☐
b When bauxite is heated a metal boils off. ☐
c Impure copper can be purified by electrolysis. ☐
d Sodium chloride is separated into elements by using electricity and heat. ☐
e These substances are all manufactured by using heat: glass, cement, quicklime, petrol. ☐

7 a Iron corrodes when water and air are present. ☐
b Rusting is not expensive because the iron can be replaced. ☐
c A nail which is covered by paint will rust more slowly. ☐
d Electricity can be used to slow down rusting. ☐
e Heat can be used to slow down rusting. ☐

8 a An electric current can have chemical effects. ☐
b Electricity can separate the elements in any compound. ☐
c Electricity makes free ions move. ☐
d In a molten substance metal ions will form metal at the negative electrode. ☐
e Water is split up into hydrogen and oxygen by electrolysis. ☐

Unit 8 Make and break

Name _____

Complete each sentence. Put the correct word(s) in each blank space.

1 A material is a substance that can be used to _____ and to

_____ .

2 The five main types of materials are

Type	Two important properties
● metal	conducts and _____
● _____	_____
● _____	_____
● _____	_____
● _____	_____ .

3 The usefulness of a material depends upon its _____ . Three

important properties of the material used to make a child's toy are

_____ and _____ and _____ .

4 Many materials are flammable which means that

_____ .

5 A material which burns can be dangerous in several ways. It will give out

_____ energy, it may release _____ which can

suffocate a person and it may also give out poisonous gases like

_____ .

6 Substances which burn to release a lot of heat energy are called

_____ . The fuel joins with _____ from the air when

it burns.

7 Weather factors such as _____ and _____ can also

destroy materials, causing stone to _____ and metal to

_____ .

continued ▶

Name_____

8 Corrosion of iron is called _____ . It causes great expense because

the iron loses its strength. Three ways of slowing down the corrosion of iron are

(a) _____

(b) _____

(c) _____ .

9 The properties of a material can be changed by chemical reactions. Acid is

neutralised by adding _____ . This reaction forms a compound

called a _____ . Two examples of salts are

(a) _____ used for _____ , and

(b) _____ used for _____ .

10 Heat is used to change materials.

An example of this is _____ .

11 Electricity is used to change materials.

An example of this is _____ .

12 Electricity can split up _____ compounds. When the ions are free to

move they are _____ to electrodes with the opposite charge. So

positive metal ions go to the _____ electrode and

_____ non-metal ions go to the positive electrode. This process is

called _____ .

Materials key

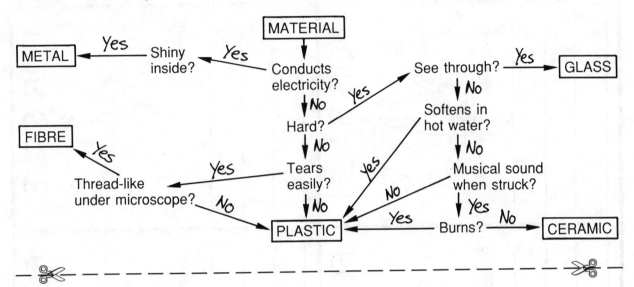

- - - ✂ - ✂ - - -

Materials key

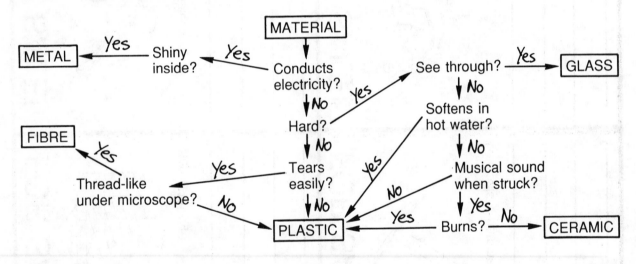

- - ✂ - ✂ - -

Materials key

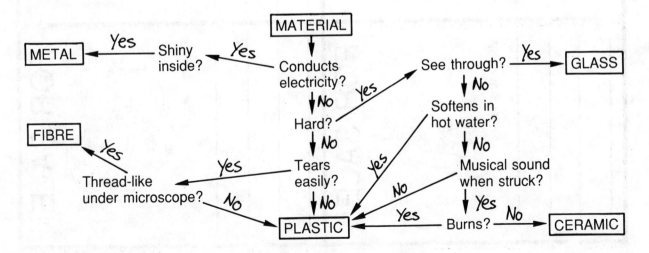

Advert cards

FOR SALE!

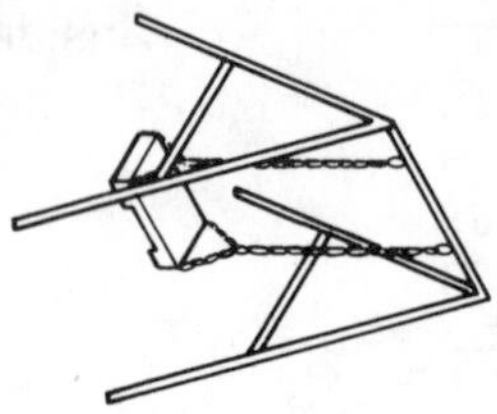

Swing

FOR SALE!

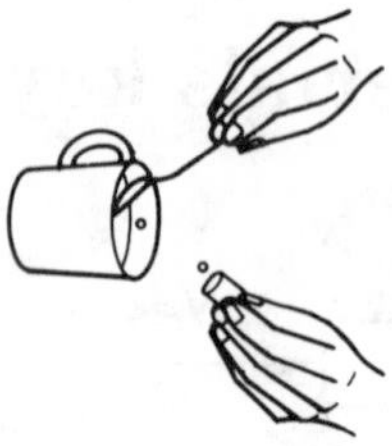

Sweetner tablets

FOR SALE!

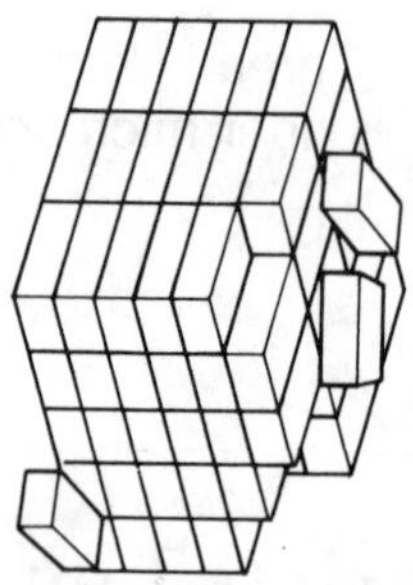

House bricks

FOR SALE!

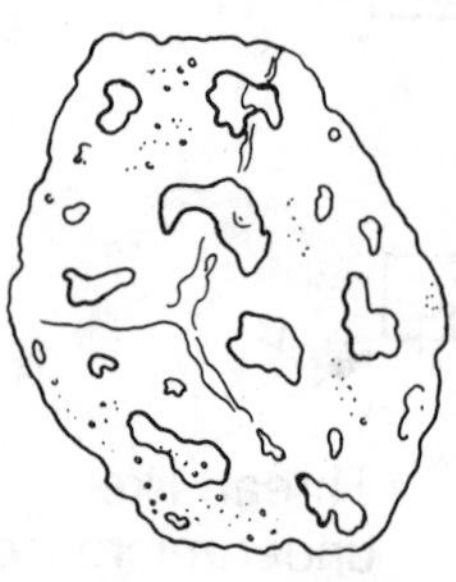

Bath sponges

FOR SALE!

Toy snakes

FOR SALE!

Toy boats

FOR SALE!

Geologist's hammer

FOR SALE!

Mackintoshes

Advert cards

FOR SALE!

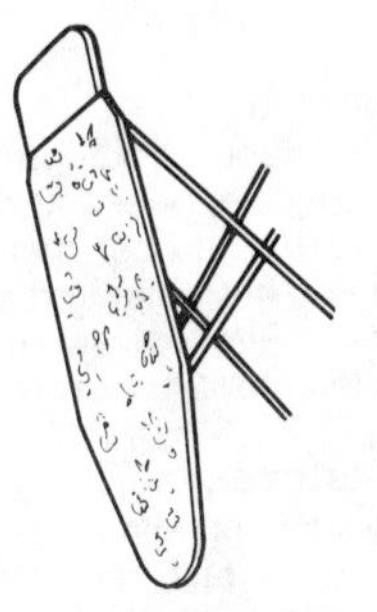

Ironing boards

_____
_____
_____
_____

FOR SALE!

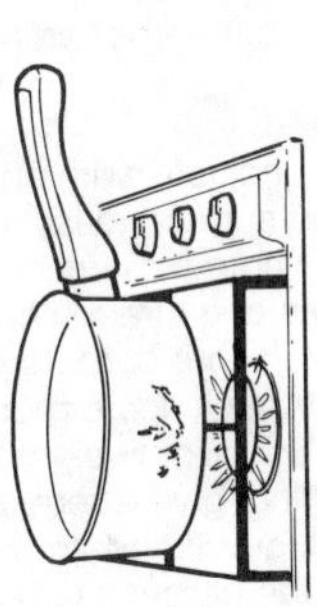

Shelf units

_____
_____
_____
_____

FOR SALE!

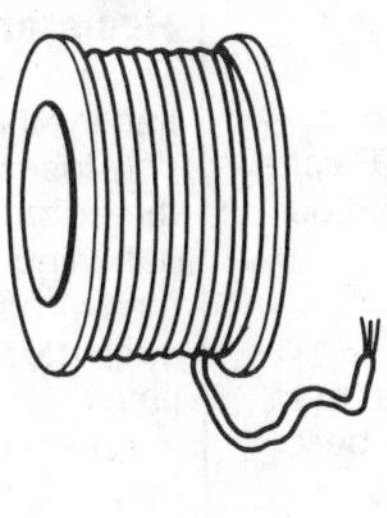

Saucepans

_____
_____
_____
_____

FOR SALE!

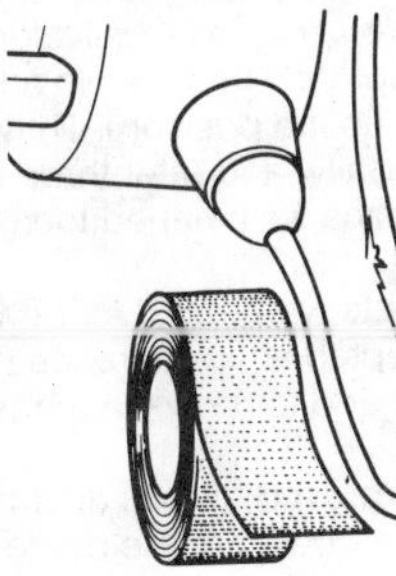

Electric cable

_____
_____
_____
_____

FOR SALE!

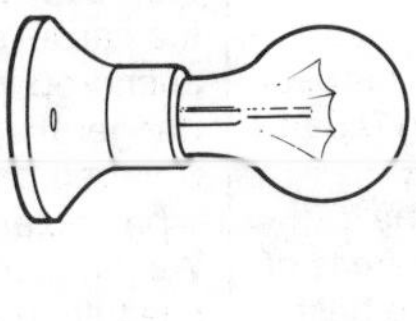

Insulation tape

_____
_____
_____
_____

FOR SALE!

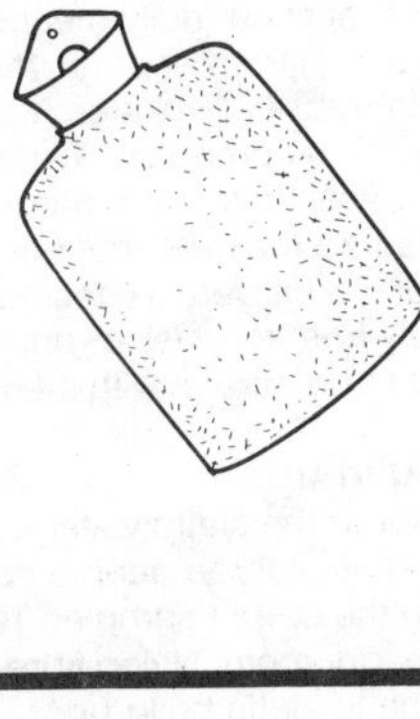

Light fittings

_____
_____
_____
_____

FOR SALE!

Hot-water bottles

_____
_____
_____
_____

FOR SALE!

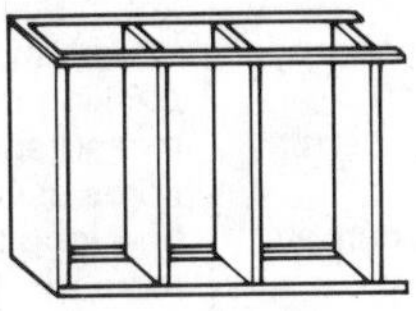

Elastic cords

_____
_____
_____
_____

2 of 2

Testing carpets

Which brand of carpet?
People tend to buy carpet by looks and type rather than by brand. In any case a particular brand and quality may come in a range of patterns and colours; these change regularly and many of our carpet samples are even now no longer available in the same colour or pattern. So use the results carefully (and generally), to guide you towards carpets of the same type.

Plain tufteds – velours
Very little to choose between our five samples; any of them would survive reasonable wear in a medium traffic area. Courts Regal looks like the best bargain.

Plain tufteds – semi-shags
The two most expensive carpets in this group – Lancaster Cachet and Lancaster Bliss – were best.

Plain tufteds – shags
Two samples only in our tests, little to choose between them. Abingdon Palette was the cheaper and came through our walking trials looking a little better.

Patterned tufteds – cut-pile
Harris Trio was considerably better than the other three – in fact one of the best carpets we tested (but it was more expensive). It was suitable for almost anywhere in the house for reasonable service, barring heavy traffic areas.

Patterned tufteds – loop-pile
All should wear reasonably well and continue to look good in most rooms. Once again the best carpet was the most expensive in its group – Allied Inca, also one of the best carpets we tested.

Short loop-pile carpets
In general a good group of tough carpets which should be fairly long lasting (apart from the Gilt Edge Endurance).

Not much to choose between the others; all could be used in most areas of the home. Co-op Chieftain was the best of the plain carpets and reasonably cheap. Both the patterned carpets – Harris Majestic and Kosset Debonair – did well, and their patterns might help them to keep their looks longer.

OUR TESTS

Construction
We measured the number of pile tufts (or loops) and the weight of pile above the backing over a given area. These two measurements, together with type of fibres used, give a good indication of how long the pile should last in use: the more pile tufts and the heavier the pile, the longer the carpet should last. And nylon, for example, is a more durable fibre than viscose.

We also measured the pile density, which is the combination of weight of pile over a given area, divided by the pile thickness. It is one of the most important single factors in carpet life. The rating in the Table for 'construction' takes all these factors into account.

Resistance to crushing
Once a carpet pile has been badly flattened by heavy traffic over it, it not only loses its looks but it may begin to get threadbare. Using a test to simulate this flattening under repeated treading, we measured the final thickness of the pile of each carpet, after being pounded 1000 times.

Another thing that can damage a carpet is heavy furniture standing on it for a long time, and leaving a permanent mark.

We tested this, in much the same way, by measuring the thickness of the pile after being heavily loaded for 24 hours, and then being allowed to recover for another 24 hours.

We've combined these two results in a single rating in the Table.

Resistance to tuft pulling
If a carpet's pile hasn't been securely anchored into the backing, there is a danger that individual tufts may pull out. Children and pets can be an extra hazard – particularly cats which claw at the pile. We measured the force needed to pull pile tufts out.

Resistance to pilling
When the pile of a carpet gets scuffed, fibres tend to break loose and roll up into small balls which stick to the carpet surface. Pilling may well spoil the looks of a carpet; a lot of pilling means that the pile itself is being weakened.

We rubbed all our carpets on a machine to simulate this abrasion.

Resistance to wear
Eventually all carpets begin to show bare patches. We simulated the effect of this on the abrasion machine, too. The Table shows how well the carpets resisted this sort of wear.

Keeping appearance
Heavy traffic over a carpet will affect the colour and texture of the pile, before the pile starts to wear away completely.

We simulated the effect of this on each carpet; then at the end of the test, we graded for loss of colour and texture.

Stain removal
We dropped spots of orange juice, blackcurrant juice, beer and sugary white coffee on to each carpet, then used a detergent and hot water to remove the stains (one lot after only five minutes, another after a full 24 hours).

Colour fastness
If you spill liquid on to a carpet in which the dyes are not 'fast', the colours will come out on to anything damp that might come into contact with the carpet – a baby in a damp nappy for instance. Or, in a multi-coloured carpet, you may find that if the colours get wet they run into each other, spoiling the appearance.

Backings
It is always sensible, with any carpet, to have a good surface to lay it on – generally using a separate underlay (unless it has one already built in).

All but two of our carpets had synthetic rubber foam backings bonded to them. However, a very lightweight foam backing will not give adequate support for a carpet; or if the foam is not fixed properly to the carpet it is likely to come loose or even tear away.

The Table shows which of our carpets had the densest backings and those which were most likely to resist peeling; most were rather poor.

Walking trials
We laid the carpet samples in a busy corridor for six months (equivalent to between two and five years in a house, depending on the position). They were vacuumed daily, and after three months and six months we cleaned them more thoroughly.

The carpets were rated for how well they had kept their appearance (texture and colour) and for how clean they had stayed.

The trials proved, above anything else, that cheap carpets can be made to last for a reasonable length of time. None of our samples had gone into holes or worn bare. They were, however, fairly heavily soiled, and most had lost colour and texture, and become dull and flat.

Resistance to fire
A hot coal from an open fire or a dropped cigarette almost certainly means, at the very least, a charred spot on your carpet. Fixed foam rubber backings add to the risk of the burn spreading. We dropped a hot bit of metal on to each carpet sample, and measured the area that got burnt.

None of the carpets we tested was completely free from risk of burning, so you need to be careful with them.

Static build-up
We measured the static voltage built up on the bodies of three people pacing up and down the carpet samples 100 times in a warm, dry room. Nylon fibre was the most prone to static build-up.

From 'Cheap carpet', Which? March 1983 (Consumers' Association)

Testing adhesives

Our tests – by material

Wood
We used beech (as specified in the relevant British Standard) and made double lap joints (see drawing) following the manufacturers' instructions for each adhesive. After one week, we pulled the joints apart and measured how much force was needed to do this. The joint strength ratings are based on these results.

For wood, ratings ● and ●● would be sufficient only for jobs that will not have to carry any load – for example, sticking down a laminate veneer or a decorative trim. For these sorts of jobs, many people use contact adhesives because they are cheap and convenient and you don't *have* to clamp them down. For load-bearing – the joints of a chair, for example, adhesives rated ●●●● or ●●●●● should be used – in our tests, glues rated ●●●●● were as strong as or stronger than the wood, and those rated ●●●● were only just weaker.

In our *Glues for wood* report in 1976, we tested several of the adhesives that we have tested here – including Araldite, Bostik 1, Seccotine and Unibond Universal. Some of the specialist wood glues were stronger and cheaper than the best in these tests – Borden Wood Glue and Dunlop Woodworker were our recommendations then for glues that didn't have to stand up to wet conditions. Some oily woods, like teak, need a special glue. However, if you're just doing the occasional wood repair and want an adhesive that can do other jobs, one with either of the top two ratings will do.

Steel
We used mild steel to make a single lap joint (see drawing) which we pulled apart after allowing the adhesives a week to harden. The results we got on steel were about twice as strong as those we got on wood – as a very rough guide an adhesive with a ●●●●● rating would have twice the strength as a piece of wood: this is, of course, still weaker than the metal, so even the strongest adhesives – Araldite, or any of the two-part acrylics – are no substitute for bolting, rivetting or welding.

Glass
We carefully broke and rejoined ten glass rods – 8mm ($\frac{5}{16}$in) diameter – for each brand. After a week, we bent apart the samples – but, where the manufacturer specifically said that an adhesive was suitable for washing, we first washed half of them ten times on the 'delicate' cycle of a dishwasher. In the Table, we have given two ratings – the first for unwashed strength and the second, where appropriate, for strength after washing. Where there is a dash for the second rating, the brand was not recommended for washing.

Loctite Glass Bond did very well; any others were not as strong or were rather more conspicuous.

Ceramics
We broke the handles off teacups and then stuck them back on again. We waited a week, then tested half, and washed half (this time on

a 'normal' programme) before testing. Again we didn't wash the brands where the manufacturers specially warned against it. To test these joints, we broke the handles off again and carefully examined how the joint had fared – for adhesives rated ●●●●● the handle nearly always broke in a new place; for those rated ● the adhesive always gave way. An adhesive rated ●●●● will usually have about the same strength as the ceramic it is joining – this is the minimum acceptable strength for something that you're going to use. For something that you're going to wash, don't use adhesives where this isn't recommended and avoid an adhesive where the washed strength is more than one blob lower than the unwashed strength – this really means that Araldite is the only commonly available contender for this job. (Devcon '2-ton' was the runner-up.)

Plastics
We made butt joints (see drawing) with these, using polystyrene, ABS and cellulose acetate; and kept the joints pushed firmly together for 24 hours. We then stored them for a further six days before pulling them apart.

For a joint with a cross-sectional area of 50sq mm (about the cross-sectional area of a pencil) an adhesive rated ●●●●● would take a straight pull of more than 30kg (66lb) to pull it apart, for an adhesive rated ●● it will take about a tenth or less of this weight. This may still sound quite adequate, but the area of the joint will often be a lot less than this – and, because of the leverage, bending it apart will be a lot easier than pulling it apart. For all the adhesives, the plastic was always stronger than the joint, but for many repairs, strength will not be important.

Because it can be difficult to tell polystyrene and ABS apart, we think that you should pick an adhesive that will stick both well. For strong joints, your choice comes down to Araldite, Araldite Rapid, Borden Superfast, Bostik 10 Hyperbond, Evo-Stik 60 Fix, Loctite Super Glue 3, UHU Supalok, or Ultrabond. If you're certain you're repairing polystyrene, you could try polystyrene cement which actually dissolves a small amount of the mating surfaces.

For cellulose acetate, Araldite and Rawlplug Durofix were the best. If you're repairing spectacle frames (which usually break at the bridge), you'll need some kind of reinforcement to support the joint.

Flexible PVC
We joined strips together and kept them under pressure for 24 hours, before storing them for six days. Because flexible PVC is used for things like airbeds and beach balls, we then immersed our joint strips in water at room temperature for seven days and any that survived this period were then peeled apart. Even for the best adhesive, this didn't take a particularly strong pull. Three of the 'universals' – Bostik 1, Evo-Stik Clear & Clean and Gloy Clear – worked better than any of the specialist PVC adhesives. However, for repairing splits – in furniture, say – only the specialist solutions are suitable.

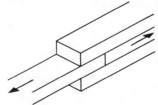

double lap joint – wood

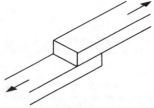

single lap joint – steel

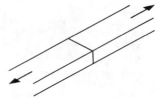

butt joint – plastics

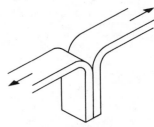

peel testing – flexible pvc

From 'Adhesives', *Handyman Which?* May 1981 (Consumers' Association)

Testing video recorders

HOW WE DID OUR TESTS

This time our lab tested a total of 26 video recorders – the ones for this issue, plus others tested for our partner consumer organisations in Belgium and the Netherlands. By working together like this, we can reduce testing costs, and sometimes bring you details of very new models which could be bought on the Continent before they were on sale here.

There's more to our simple 'picture quality' and 'sound quality' ratings than you might think. On this page there are details of some of the many tests which are taken into consideration in arriving at these verdicts. We thought these pictures might give you an idea of the months of painstaking testing and checking which precede a report like this one.

And there's more besides – we haven't room to show you the ergonomics assessment, the 50-hour running test for faults or breakdowns, the electrical safety checks and all the other work that goes into a *Which?* report.

A LOOK INSIDE CONSUMERS' ASSOCIATION'S LABORATORY

Every recorder undergoes a series of technical measurements which can tell us how well it will perform in practice. These tests measure video noise – which may show up as a grainy, snowy picture, or a streaky effect in large areas of colour

The measurements are backed up by practical tests. Special patterns, similar to the BBC and IBA test cards, are recorded and played back on each video, and assessed by a panel of experienced engineers. We also make copies of high-quality video recordings and compare the copies with the originals.

The detailed questionnaires filled in by our panel are computer analysed and then compared and combined with our laboratory measurements to give us our final rating for picture quality

Here, the sound quality of each recorder is being rated by our listening panel. They'll also check whether there's any annoying noise from the recorder itself. The equipment is behind the special curtain which lets sound through while preventing the panel from knowing which model they're judging. The results are analysed in the same way as the viewing tests, and again there will be lab measurements, this time to check bass and treble reproduction, background hiss, and speed variations which could show up as a wavering of the pitch of recorded music

This test tells us whether the colours in the recorded picture will be too intense, or weak and washed-out, or even slightly the wrong colour

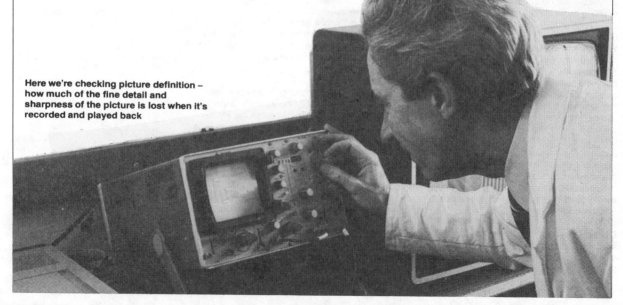

Here we're checking picture definition – how much of the fine detail and sharpness of the picture is lost when it's recorded and played back

From 'Video recorders', *Which?* February 1984 (Consumers' Association)

Cloth testing hints

Wear and **Tear**
Give each cloth the **same** treatment

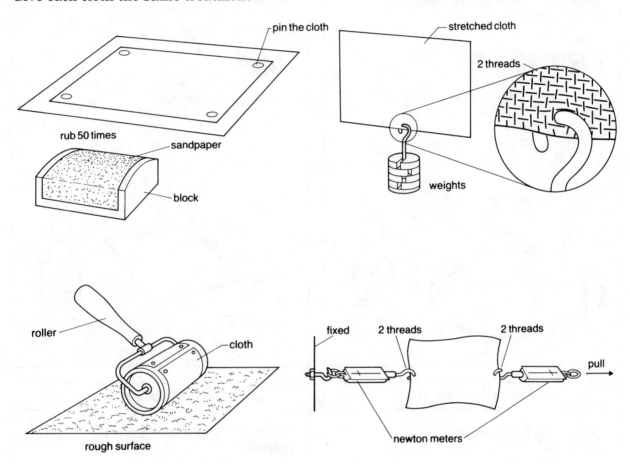

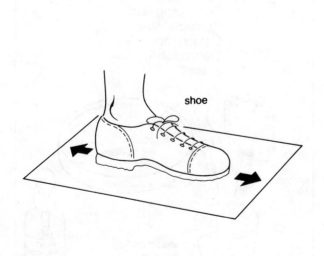

Investigation 1

Is an iron nail protected from corrosion by connecting it to the positive or the negative terminal of a battery?

Collect
Rust indicator
Salt water
Petri dish
2 small iron nails
Battery (or d.c. power pack)
Connecting leads

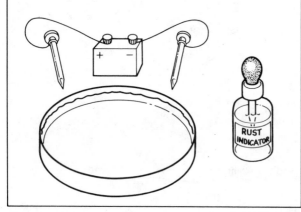

Investigation 2

Does scratching or bending a piece of tin-plated iron alter the rate of corrosion?

Collect
Rust indicator
Salt water
Petri dish
Sharp point
Tin-plated iron

Investigation 3

Will a partly galvanised iron nail corrode?

Collect
Rust indicator
Salt water
Petri dish
Iron nail
Tongs
Heatproof mat

FUME CUPBOARD

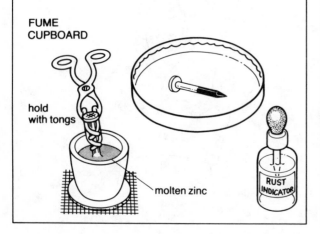

hold with tongs

molten zinc

Investigation 4

Will a partly electroplated nail corrode?

Collect
Rust indicator
Salt water
Petri dish
Iron nail
Power pack
Connecting leads
Crocodile clips
Carbon rod
Electroplating solution

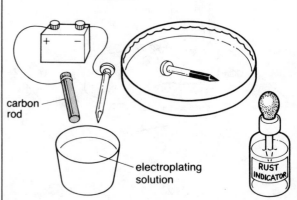

carbon rod

electroplating solution

1 of 2

Resource 8.4

Investigation 5

Which metals between magnesium and copper in the reactivity series can protect iron from corrosion?

Collect Petri dish
Small iron nails
Strips of metal foil:
Mg, Zn, Al, Sn, Pb, Cu
(Your teacher will add the rust-indicating liquid, which will set)

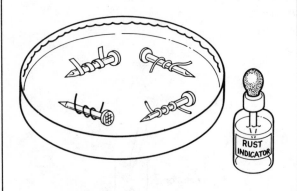

Investigation 5

Which metals between magnesium and copper in the reactivity series can protect iron from corrosion?

Collect Petri dish
Small iron nails
Strips of metal foil:
Mg, Zn, Al, Sn, Pb, Cu
(Your teacher will add the rust-indicating liquid, which will set)

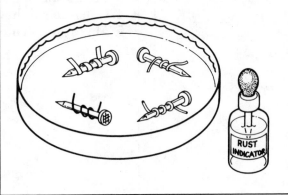

Investigation 5

Which metals between magnesium and copper in the reactivity series can protect iron from corrosion?

Collect Petri dish
Small iron nails
Strips of metal foil:
Mg, Zn, Al, Sn, Pb, Cu
(Your teacher will add the rust-indicating liquid, which will set)

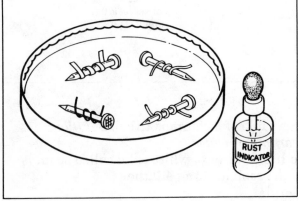

Investigation 5

Which metals between magnesium and copper in the reactivity series can protect iron from corrosion?

Collect Petri dish
Small iron nails
Strips of metal foil:
Mg, Zn, Al, Sn, Pb, Cu
(Your teacher will add the rust-indicating liquid, which will set)

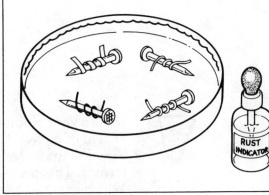

2 of 2

Understanding Science 3

193

Hard and soft water

Water has a remarkable ability to dissolve substances. Raindrops dissolve gases from the air; rainwater dissolves all sorts of substances from the soil; river water slowly dissolves away the rocks it runs over. All these substances eventually end up in the sea. Some of these substances cause hard water.

Collect

Ruler
Test-tube and cork
Measuring cylinder
Dropper
100 cm³ beaker

Test the following samples for hardness, as shown in the diagrams. Wash the glassware in distilled water before **each** test.

1 Distilled water.
2 Tap water.
3 Potassium sulphate solution.
4 Calcium sulphate solution.
5 Magnesium chloride solution.

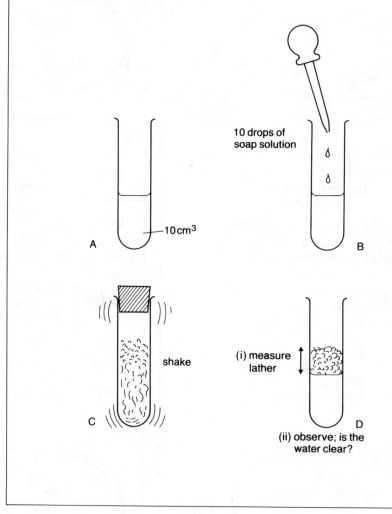

1 Record your results in a table of 3 columns titled: *Solution, Height of lather, Appearance of water*.
2 When soap is added to **hard** water, a white solid called scum is formed. This prevents the soap forming a lather.
   Which samples were hard?
3 From your results, what do you think causes hard water?
4 **Collect** and read the information sheet on hard water. Write a revision summary of this sheet.

Information—hard water

How does hardness get into water?

Rain water contains some dissolved carbon dioxide which forms carbonic acid. This makes natural rain slightly acidic (pH 5). There are no calcium or magnesium compounds present in rain water and rain water is therefore completely soft.

When rain water trickles through the ground it will dissolve any soluble rocks. The most important rocks which dissolve are *gypsum* (calcium sulphate) and *limestone* or *chalk* (calcium carbonate). Calcium sulphate is only very slightly soluble. Calcium carbonate is insoluble in pure water but is soluble in rain water because of its acidity. When calcium carbonate dissolves in rainwater the unstable compound *calcium hydrogen carbonate* is formed.

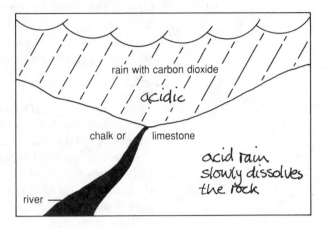

In some limestone areas the rock dissolves to form large underground caverns.

$$\underset{\text{(rock)}}{\underset{\text{carbonate}}{\text{calcium}}} + \underset{\substack{\text{(rain} \\ \text{and} \\ \text{rivers)}}}{water} + \underset{\text{dioxide}}{\underset{}{\text{carbon}}} \rightarrow \underset{\text{(tap water)}}{\underset{\text{carbonate}}{\underset{\text{hydrogen}}{\text{calcium}}}}$$

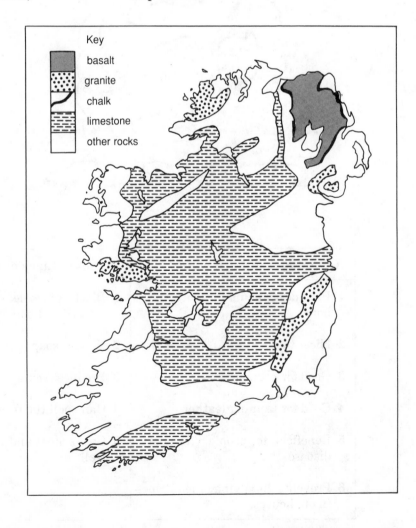

continued ▶

Advantages and disadvantages of hard water

One of the most important effects of hardness in water is that it forms a dirty white substance with soap. This white substance is called *scum*.

soap + hardness in water → scum

This scum is the grey ring that is left round the sink or bath after washing. The substances that cause the hardness join with the soap. The soap cannot produce a good lather. Soap can be used to test for hardness. If there is a lot of hardness the soap will give a poor lather and a lot of scum. If there is little hardness the soap will give a good lather and little scum.

Advantages of hard water	Disadvantages of hard water
1 Provides calcium for teeth and bones	1 Blocks pipes, leaves scale in kettles and boilers
2 Nicer taste	2 Wastes soap
3 Good for brewing	3 Produces scum
4 Good for tanning leather	4 Can spoil the finish of fabrics
5 Beneficial for people with heart disease	5 Cooks meat and vegetables less well.
6 Prevents dissolving of lead pipes in old houses.	

2 of 2

Tile tests hints sheet

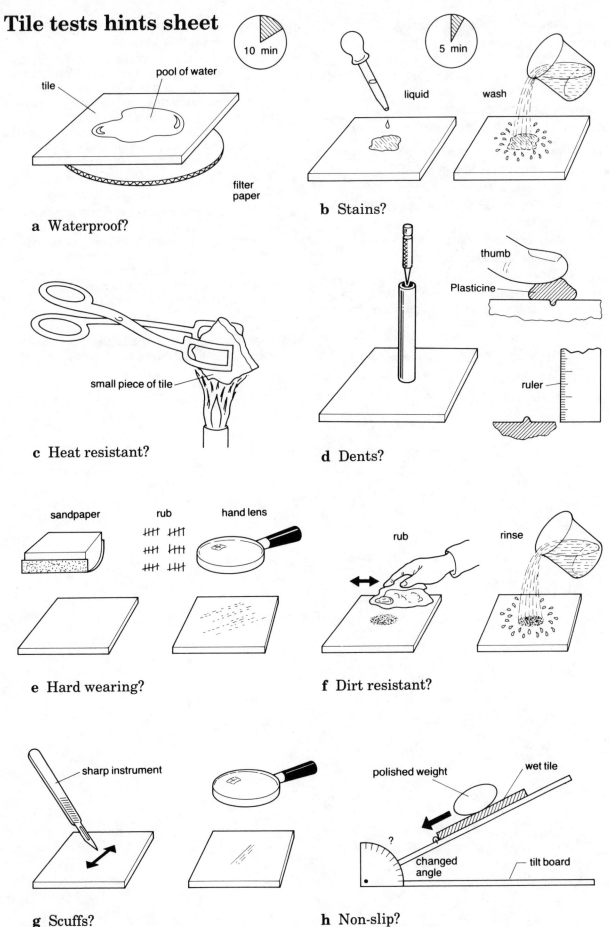

10 min

tile
pool of water

filter paper

a Waterproof?

5 min

liquid
wash

b Stains?

small piece of tile

c Heat resistant?

thumb
Plasticine
ruler

d Dents?

sandpaper
rub
hand lens

e Hard wearing?

rub
rinse

f Dirt resistant?

sharp instrument

g Scuffs?

polished weight
wet tile
?
changed angle
tilt board

h Non-slip?

Skills sheets

The following skills sheets are intended to:

- make pupils aware of the need to plan their revision
- enable pupils to assess their level of knowledge across the Attainment Targets
- provide targetted extension material
- provide material that is largely self-corrected.

They cover several categories of skills. These are:

- planning revision (skills sheets 1–5)
- making a revision summary (skills sheets 6–9)
- reading skills (based on the Nature of Science) (skills sheets 10–13)
- preparing for examinations (skills sheets 14, 15)
- using revision checklists (skills sheets 16–30).

At the time of going to press the proposed changes to the National Curriculum have not been agreed. The revision checklists are based on the original Statements of Attainment.

The skills sheets offer a valuable resource bank that can be used in a variety of ways:

- *As additional extension material:* the sheets (1–15) would be arranged in booklet form in the order suggested. Each individual pupil can then work through the booklet during those odd free times during, or at the end of, a lesson. Questions are answered at the back of the pupil's notebook and work can be self-marked from a prepared marked copy of the sheets.
- *As targeted extension material for specific lessons:* revision, reading tasks and so on.
- *As the central material for a series of lessons where the aim is to prepare for national examinations. Exercises 16–30 are consumable revision checklists. They present the content of Key Stage 3 in a way that involves the pupil in active revision. (The teacher may wish to photoreduce these skills sheets.)*
- *As homework.*

The sheets also provide a model that could be used to generate additional material.

Revision skills—Using study time

People learn in many different ways. It is difficult to know how you learn best unless you try different ways. The profile below shows how Jackie usually studies: *quite early in the morning, lots of background noise, an hour at a time, one subject at a time, anywhere, writing a few notes, always alone.*

Early in the morning   Late at night

Complete silence   Noisy background

Study for hours   Study for minutes

One subject   All subjects

Favourite place   Any place

Write everything   Write nothing

Study alone   Study in large group

1 **Collect** a blank study profile.
Complete the profile for your **usual** study habits.

2 Compare your profile with a friend's profile.
Talk to your friend about differences between the way each of you studies.
Is there anything you would like to do differently next time?

Skills sheet 1

Study profile

Early in the morning	Late at night
Complete silence	Noisy background
Study for hours	Study for minutes
One subject	All subjects
Favourite place	Any place
Write everything	Write nothing
Study alone	Study in large group

✂ - ✂

Study profile

Early in the morning	Late at night
Complete silence	Noisy background
Study for hours	Study for minutes
One subject	All subjects
Favourite place	Any place
Write everything	Write nothing
Study alone	Study in large group

Revision skills—Getting organised

It is sensible to organise your work. If you don't everything tends to pile up. You always feel under pressure but you seldom get things done. The first step in getting organised is to get a notebook or a diary. This acts as a planner and a homework diary.

Here is a sample page from Robin's diary.

Week 5	Planned		Homework due	
Monday 21st	Maths homework	Material for Science Project		
Tuesday 22nd	Revise Geog test Geog homework	English homework	Maths French	P 52 Q 3–12 vocab.
Wednesday 23rd		Science homework		
Thursday 24th	Revise geog test		Science	Skills 15, 16
Friday 25th	FREE		Geog Eng	P113 + test Chapter 2 (read)
Weekend 26th/27th	Revise science test	Maths homework FREE.		

Collect two blank diary pages.
Complete one for this week and begin one for next week.
Keep the diary pages handy. Fill in next week's homework for all your subjects as soon as you get it.

If you find the diary useful you can collect more blank pages from your teacher and staple them together inside a cover of your own design.

Skills sheet 2

Diary page

Week	Planned	Homework due
Monday		
Tuesday		
Wednesday		
Thursday		
Friday		
Weekend		

Diary page

Week	Planned	Homework due
Monday		
Tuesday		
Wednesday		
Thursday		
Friday		
Weekend		

Revision skills—Concentrating on revision

Revision is important but it is easy to avoid. You may recognise some of these common ways of pretending to do home study. They may fool other people at home but they shouldn't fool you. Try to guess what the person in the following cartoons is doing instead of working.

 Which of these excuses have you used? Do you have your own special ways of avoiding work?

Draw a labelled diagram/cartoon to show a method that you have used to avoid study.

Revision skills—Test, check, retest

When you revise for an exam you try to remember what you have learned about an entire topic. One way of helping your memory is the *test, check, retest* method.

To use this revision method, follow the instructions:

Test   Write down what you remember about the topic.
Try to write it in the form of a revision summary or a spider diagram.

Check **a** Skim the topic.
Check that you have included each main idea.
Add any that you missed to your revision summary *in red ink.*
  b Scan the topic.
Add any important details that you missed *in red ink.*
Change any details that you got wrong, again in *red.*

Retest Read these revision notes for 10 minutes then put them aside. Make a new revision summary or spider diagram.

Try the *test, check, retest* method with the first topic of this year's science course.

Revision skills—A summary

Look at the diagram below. These are some of the skills that are useful during revision. Discuss the diagram with a friend. Talk about the revision methods that you find useful.

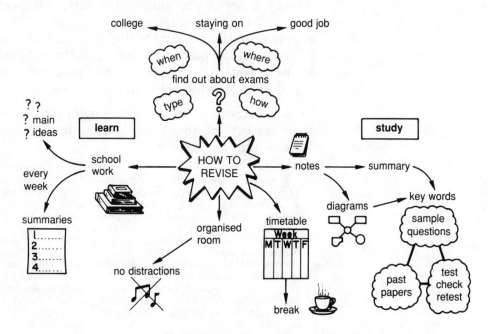

You can practise some of these skills again by using the following skills sheets from *Understanding Science* Books 1, 2 and 3.

Skill	Where practised Book: *Skills sheet*
A Revising work during term time (*learning*)	
1 Read your work at the end of each week. Find the main ideas.	1: *14, 15, 17* 2: *3, 10*
2 Make short notes of your weekly work.	2: *2, 6, 13, 23*
3 Make short summary diagrams.	2: *30, 31, 38, 41*
B Revising before a test/exam (*studying*)	
1 Get organised.	2: *18* 3: *2*
2 Make a revision summary.	2: *32, 40, 45* 3: *6, 7, 8, 9*
3 Remember what you read.	2: *12, 27* 3: *4*

Revision skills—Making a revision summary 1

You have probably forgotten some of the work you completed last year and the year before on human influences on the Earth. This work must be revised and relearned. It helps to be an active learner. When you revise you could make notes. To revise the ideas described in the passage below:

- first skim the passage to find the main ideas
- next read the passage more carefully and make notes as you read
- finally cover up the passage and your notes and check how much you know by answering the questions.

Human activity makes an ever bigger impact on the environment. Some predictions about changes in climate and the effect of this are described in the passage.

Agreement among the world's top scientists has concluded that the climate will become hotter than at any time in the past two million years – unless urgent steps are taken to combat the greenhouse effect. The scientists warn that harvests are likely to fail, nearly a quarter of a million miles of coastline could be submerged, tens of millions of people could be made homeless and tropical diseases could spread into temperate countries. They add that the changing climate could spring unpleasant 'surprises' that no one can predict.

The panel's findings have been checked by scores of experts to ensure an unusual level of agreement. The eagerly awaited report puts an end to serious debate over whether pollution by carbon dioxide and other 'greenhouse gases' does threaten to heat up the world.

The report says: 'The scientific community agrees on the climate changes that could occur if the present build-up of greenhouse gas emissions continues into the next century.' It adds: 'It is obvious that we are facing a very difficult issue, with no simple solutions.'

If nothing is done to curb the pollution, the report estimates that the climate will change faster during the next century than at any time since the ending of the last Ice Age. By 2025, the world would, on average, be one degree Centigrade warmer than today, before the end of the century it would be three degrees hotter – warmer than at any time in the past two million years.

As the world warmed up, the report continues, the seas would rise, on average, by two-and-a-half inches a decade. They could swell by as much as three feet by the year 2100, affecting 224,000 miles of the world's coastline. It adds: 'In the absence of any adaptive measures this could render some island countries uninhabitable, displace tens of millions of people, seriously threaten low-lying urban areas, flood productive land, contaminate fresh water supplies and destroy many coastal wetlands.'

There would also be important effects on food supplies. The report names some areas at risk, including southern Europe and 'central North America', the world's bread basket. In both areas, temperatures could rise faster than the global average and summer rainfall would diminish and harvests fall. And it predicts 'severe effects' in Brazil, Peru, the Sahel, South-East Asia, Soviet Asia and China, though it warns that precise regional predictions cannot yet be made.

Wildlife species and ecosystems would be devastated, and tropical diseases could move to temperate areas 'putting large populations at risk'. 'Furthermore,' the report continues, 'we must recognise that our imperfect understanding could make us vulnerable to surprises.' The report also discredits specific objections from a handful of American scientists who claim that climatic 'feedback' mechanisms would counteract global warming. The report shows that feedbacks would worsen the effect.

It also warns that, even if all the pollution stopped at once, the warming would continue.

Adapted from Geoffrey Lean in the *Observer*, 19 August 1990

1 Copy a sentence that shows that:
   a the effects of a change in climate are being *predicted* in the passage;
   b some scientists do not agree with these predictions.

2 What substances are causing the air pollution described? What are the sources of this pollution?

3 There are connections between the main ideas in the passage and what you studied last year and the year before on human influences on the Earth.
   Collect a worksheet and complete the table and diagram. It links together some of the main ideas about the environment.

Skills sheet 6

Pollution

Type of pollution	Source of pollution	Effect of pollution

Complete the diagram below by adding examples to each category.

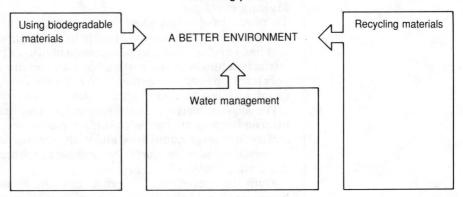

Preventing pollution

Using biodegradable materials → A BETTER ENVIRONMENT ← Recycling materials

Water management

Pollution

Type of pollution	Source of pollution	Effect of pollution

Complete the diagram below by adding examples to each category.

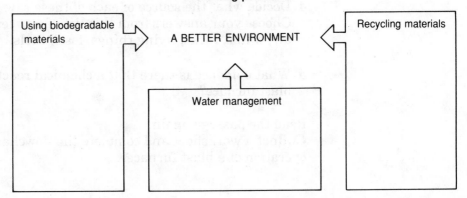

Preventing pollution

Using biodegradable materials → A BETTER ENVIRONMENT ← Recycling materials

Water management

Revision skills—Making a revision summary 2

You have probably forgotten some of the work which you completed last year and the year before on making new materials. This work must be revised and relearned. It helps to be an active learner. When you revise you could make notes. To revise the passage below:
- first skim the passage to find the main ideas
- next read the passage more carefully and make notes as you read
- finally cover up the passage and your notes and check how much you know by answering the questions.

Making steel

To understand what steel is, it is important first of all to know something of iron, because steel is in fact iron which has been refined and had carefully measured amounts of other elements added to it.

Iron is common in the earth's crust and occurs in many forms, but the only form we need to consider here is where it occurs in large quantities, usually as iron oxide in rocks, which we call iron ore.

The modern world's great demand for steel has meant an increasing need for large quantities of rich, high quality ore, and this only occurs in sufficiently large quantities (and with reasonable accessibility) in a few scattered areas of the world, for most part in Scandinavia, the Americas, Australia, North Africa, and Russia.

From these orefields the ore is brought by sea in huge carriers to harbours close to the steelworks where it is unloaded and stored in the ore stockyard. The ore is graded and crushed and some of the finer ore ('fines' in the industry) is taken to the sinter plant where it is mixed with coke (and sometimes limestone) and heated to form an iron-rich clinker known as 'sinter'.

This sinter is fed into the top of the blast furnace together with more iron ore, coke and limestone in controlled proportions, and the whole is fired. Great heat is generated, and fanned to white hot intensity by blasts of superheated air from which the furnace derives its name. The iron in the sinter and ore melts to form a pool of molten metal at the foot of the furnace. The limestone combines with impurities in the iron ore, forming a liquid 'slag' which, being lighter than the metal, floats on top of it.

Adapted from *Making Steel*, British Steel PLC (1990)

---

1 What is steel made from?

2 What happens in a 'sinter' plant?

3 What materials go into a blast furnace?

4 Decide what the source of each of these raw materials is. Choose your answers from this list of sources:
air, water, rocks, living things, fossil fuels.

5 What evidence is there that a chemical reaction occurs in the blast furnace?

Read the passage again.
Collect a worksheet and complete the flowchart to show the operation of a blast furnace.

Skills sheet 7

The operation of a blast furnace

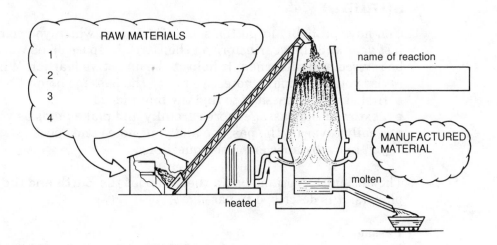

The operation of a blast furnace

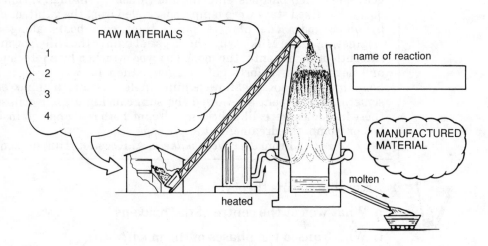

The operation of a blast furnace

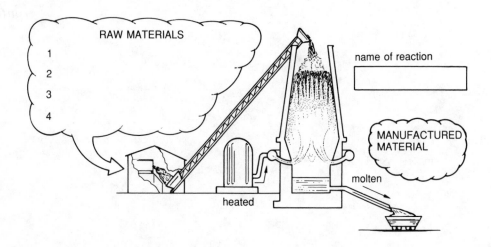

Revision skills—Making a revision summary 3

You have probably forgotten some of the work which you completed last year and the year before on the Earth in space. This work must be revised and relearned. It helps to be an active learner. When you revise you could make notes. To revise the passage below:
- first skim the passage to find the main ideas
- next read the passage more carefully and make notes as you read
- finally cover up the passage and your notes and check how much you know by answering the questions.

The ancient Egyptians had a theory about the Earth and the planets. It is described in passage A.

Passage A

> The universe of the Egyptians was a more rectangular oyster or box; the earth was its floor, the sky was either a cow whose feet rested on the four corners of the earth, or a woman supporting herself on her elbows and knees; later, a vaulted metal lid. Around the inner walls of the box, on a kind of elevated gallery, flowed a river on which the sun and moon gods sailed their barques, entering and vanishing through various stage doors. The fixed stars were lamps, suspended from the vault, or carried by other gods. The planets sailed their own boats along canals originating in the Milky Way, the celestial twin of the Nile. Towards the fifteenth of each month, the moon god was attacked by a ferocious sow, and devoured in a fortnight of agony; then he was re-born again. Sometimes the sow swallowed him whole, causing a lunar eclipse; sometimes a serpent swallowed the sun, causing a solar eclipse. But these tragedies were, like those in a dream, both real and not; inside his box or womb, the dreamer felt fairly safe.
>
> From *The Sleepwalkers*, A. Koestler (Hutchinson 1968)

1 According to this theory:

   a What was at the centre of the heavens?

   b What caused the phases of the moon?

   c What caused a solar eclipse?

   d What are the stars?

   e How do the planets move?

continued ▶

▶ *continued*

We also have a theory about the world and the planets. It is described in passage B.

Passage B

> We approach the planets of our system, largish worlds, captives of the Sun, gravitationally constrained to follow nearly circular orbits, heated mainly by sunlight. Pluto, covered with methane ice and accompanied by its solitary giant moon Charon, is illuminated by a distant Sun, which appears as no more than a bright point of light in a pitch-black sky. The giant gas worlds, Neptune, Uranus, Saturn—the jewel of the solar system—and Jupiter all have an entourage of icy moons. Interior to the region of gassy planets and orbiting icebergs are the warm, rocky provinces of the inner solar system. There is, for example, the red planet Mars, with soaring volcanoes, great rift valleys, enormous planet-wide sandstorms, and, just possibly, some simple forms of life. All the planets orbit the Sun, the nearest star, an inferno of hydrogen and helium gas engaged in thermonuclear reactions, flooding the solar system with light.
>
> Finally, at the end of all our wanderings, we return to our tiny, fragile, blue-white world, lost in a cosmic ocean vast beyond our most courageous imaginings. It is a world among an immensity of others. It may be significant only for us. The Earth is our home, our parent. Our kind of life arose and evolved here. The human species is coming of age here.
>
> From *Cosmos*, C. Sagan (Macdonald Futura 1981)

2 According to this theory:

  a What is at the centre of the solar system?

  b What causes the planets to follow their orbits?

  c What causes the Sun to give out energy?

  d What are the stars?

  e How do the planets move?

3 Write a revision summary of the passage that describes the modern theory.

Revision skills—Making a revision summary 4

You have probably forgotten some of the work you completed last year and the year before on the variety of life. This work must be revised and relearned. It helps to be an active learner. When you revise you could make notes. To revise the ideas described in the passage below:

● first skim the passage to find the main ideas
● next read the passage more carefully and make notes as you read
● finally cover up the passage and your notes and check how much you know by answering the questions.

The passage describes an animal that is well suited to its environment.

A man even on a reasonably warm day uses half his intake of food to keep his body warm. In really cold circumstances with inadequate clothing, he cannot replace the heat at the rate he loses it, no matter how much he eats. His brain and the other highly complex organs of his body cannot tolerate more than a few degrees variation in temperature, and if his body cools to a level that would make reptiles merely lethargic, he dies.

The characteristic birds of the Antarctic, which are often taken, indeed, as the very symbol of the far frozen south, are, of course, the penguins.

Penguins are superbly adapted to the swimming life . . . Swimming everywhere demands good insulation and the penguins have developed their feathers to provide it. They are very long and thin, with tips that turn downwards towards the body. The shaft not only has filaments along the blade but, at the base, fluffy tufts that mat together and form a layer that is virtually impenetrable to wind or water. This feather coat covers more of their body than does that of any other bird. It extends low down on the legs of most of them, and the little Adelie penguin, which is one of only two species that lives on Antarctica, even has feathers growing on its stubby beak. Underneath this feather coat is a layer of blubber. So effectively protected are penguins that, like the vicuna, they run a real risk of overheating. They deal with that when necessary by ruffling their feathers and by holding their flippers out from their body to increase their radiating surface.

With such efficient insulation penguins have been able to colonise most of the waters of the southern oceans and in places they flourish in astronomic numbers.

From *The Living Planet*, David Attenborough (BBC/Collins 1984)

---

1 Why can humans not survive easily in the Antarctic?

2 Make a detailed drawing of a penguin feather. Label the parts.

There are connections between the main ideas in the passage and what you studied last year and the year before on the variety of life. **Collect** a worksheet and complete the diagram. It links together some of the main ideas about living things.

Skills sheet 9

The variety of life

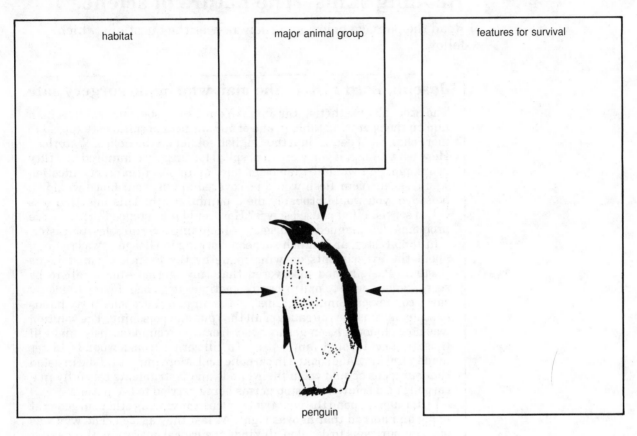

habitat | major animal group | features for survival

penguin

The variety of life

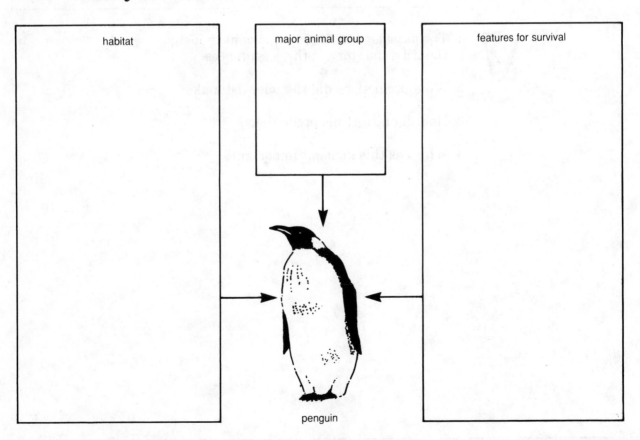

habitat | major animal group | features for survival

penguin

Reading skills—The nature of science 1

Read the passage below and then answer the questions which follow.

Joseph, Lord Lister—the man who made surgery safe

The Scottish anesthetist, Sir James Young Simpson, once said: 'A man laid on the operating table in one of our surgical hospitals is exposed to more chances of death than the English soldier on the field of Waterloo.' He wasn't joking. If you were in hospital for surgery a hundred and fifty years ago, you would be far from safe. More often than not, infection would set in. Your flesh would be covered in pus, your blood would be poisoned: you would probably die a painful death. This infection was called sepsis. What caused sepsis? How could it be stopped? These were problems that plagued all surgeons—including a certain Joseph Lister.

In 1865 Lister, an English surgeon working in Glasgow, was reading about the experiments on wine made by the French chemist Louis Pasteur. Pasteur had discovered that tiny 'germs'—too small to be seen—caused wine to mature and sometimes to go bad. Lister suddenly saw a connexion. Similar 'germs', in the air or on surgeons' dirty hands or scalpels, must be the cause of all that pus and poisoning. The solution was now obvious. Keep germs away from the wound (asepsis) and kill those that get through (antisepsis). To kill germs in open wounds, Lister made a lint bandage soaked in carbolic acid. More important, he insisted that surgeons should wash their hands and instruments carefully in a carbolic acid solution, to stop germs being carried to the patient.

Lister had to spend the next twelve years convincing other surgeons at home and abroad that he was right. At last they agreed. The way was open for surgeons to develop all kinds of surgical operation, things that would have been impossible in the bad old days before antiseptic surgery. Heart transplants, spare-part surgery and all the other complex surgical operations of today would not have been possible without Lord Lister's remarkable work.

From *Famous Names in Medicine*, G. De Stevens (Wayland 1979)

---

1 The passage describes an incident in history.
Describe the story in three sentences.

2 What predictions did the scientist make?

3 How did he test his predictions?

4 Why was this incident important?

Reading skills—The nature of science 2

Read the passage below and then try to answer the questions.

The day the lizards were stoned to death

THE DINOSAURS went out like a light. The end came like a bolt from the blue. About 65 million years ago the world was a hot, wet, leafy place and trees grew in the Antarctic and on Greenland and the huge, ferocious tyrannosaurus rex and the bland and bovine brontosaur, the megalosaur, pterosaur and icthyosaur contentedly plodded or paddled or swam in a cold-blooded sort of way over most of the globe.

Then one day, they were gone. If the scientists are right (and they don't agree among themselves) the end was so sudden it literally *was* a bolt from the blue: a huge, thumping asteroid from outer space that was five miles across, weighed 500 billion tons and hit our world at 25 miles a second with an earth-shaking splat.

How do we know? Geologists can read the Earth like a book. It is really a book, written by time. Chapter one is the oldest rocks we know, and sometimes the deepest, and most of us are actually standing on the last page to be written.

Just as one day future geologists will be able to reconstruct our lives from old cigarette packets, aluminium ring pulls and fossil chewing gum so geologists can put together a picture of the past at a particular time from the rocks themselves, the air trapped in them and the debris of ancient life – leaves, spiders, amber, dinosaur droppings, teeth, bones, pollen and so on – trapped in fossil form forever.

If it is a book, some of the pages are torn out and others are scrumpled and scribbled over so sometimes it's a matter of following the story as far as chapter five and then landing yourself in chapter seven and guessing what happened in between, or combing the world for another paragraph, or a torn half page.

When the geologists were reading the chapter called the Cretaceous, the last chapter of the dinosaurs, however, they found a last sentence. And then the chapter called the Tertiary began, with a completely different story with new characters in it: none of them dinosaurs. And right there in the last sentence they think they have found a very short account of what some of them have called the 'worst weekend in the history of the world'.

Bolts from the blue happen every day. Most meteorites are pretty small, and burn up in the atmosphere. At night we call them 'shooting stars'. But every now and then a bigger one lands with a thud somewhere. And every few million years there is a really big one.

So what happened at the end of the Cretaceous? When a visitor five miles across weighing 500 billion tons and travelling at 25 miles a second hits even something as thin as air, it's like a bomb exploding against a brick wall, only much worse.

At 20 miles up it would have heated the air to 2000 degrees and set the nitrogen and the oxygen aflame. This would have turned into a boiling sheet of millions of tons of nitric acid. Then the asteroid would have hit the sea – it must have been the sea because nobody has found a 65 million year old crater big enough – and boiled it, started a tidal wave five miles high then pulverised itself into dust which shot up 20 miles.

This dust would have circled round the stratosphere and blotted out the sun for three months. Dinosaurs were cold blooded. They had to have sun to keep alive. The plants they ate would have died, because plants need sun. The world would have turned terribly cold, so cold, so suddenly it freeze-dried all the trees. Which means that the next lightning storm would have set them aflame.

Geologists poking about in the debris of the meteorite, right there, everywhere in the world, at the last sentence of the Cretaceous, have found so much soot they think that 80 per cent of all the trees in the world would have burned in one vast planet-wide inferno.

So when it wasn't freezing it would have been burning, and when it wasn't burning, there would have been a deadly rain of corroding acid. Even more (this sounds like overkill!) the acid rain would have leached mercury, lead, cadmium and arsenic from the rocks and into the streams to poison the fresh water. And the asteroid would have blasted so much limestone into smithereens it would have increased the carbon dioxide content of the air. It also would have destroyed the ozone layer.

So think about it. First the dinosaurs near the asteroid would have been pulverised in the collision, or fried in the heat flash, or swept away by a tidal wave. The survivors would have frozen almost instantly to death. Or starved. Or they would have burned in forest fires or been gassed or poisoned by acid rain. And anything that crept out when the skies cleared would have suffocated in a greenhouse earth and got skin cancer from the ultraviolet light normally blocked by the ozone layer.

That last sentence turned into a death sentence, and for some animals, the world came, right there and then, to a full stop.

Tim Radford in *The Guardian*,
20 September 1989

1 What do some scientists think happened on 'the worst weekend in the history of the world'?

2 What effects did this have on the atmosphere?

3 a Why might the plants have burned?
   b Is there any evidence that plants did burn?

4 Read the last paragraph again and list five things which could have caused the death of dinosaurs.

5 What do you think about the scientific hypothesis given in the passage?

6 a Discuss with your classmates other possible reasons for the end of the dinosaurs. (Do not worry about your ideas being wrong. Many scientists think that the hypothesis of the meteorite is wrong.)
   b Write a short article about your best reason.

Reading skills—The nature of science 3

No one knows for certain how life began on the planet Earth, and it remains one of the great mysteries. Read the passage below and then answer the questions that follow.

To talk sensibly about the beginning of life we have to be very realistic. We have to ask a historical question. Four thousand million years ago, before life began, when the earth was very young, what was the surface of the earth, what was its atmosphere like?

Very well, we know a rough answer. The atmosphere was expelled from the interior of the earth, and was therefore somewhat like a volcanic neighbourhood anywhere – a cauldron of steam, nitrogen, methane, ammonia and other reducing gases, as well as some carbon dioxide. One gas was absent: there was no free oxygen. That is crucial, because oxygen is produced by the plants and did not exist in a free state before life existed.

These gases and their products, dissolved weakly in the oceans, formed a reducing atmosphere. How would they react next under the action of lightning, electric discharges, and particularly under the action of ultra-violet light – which is very important in every theory of life, because it can penetrate in the absence of oxygen? That question was answered in a beautiful experiment by Stanley Miller in America round about 1950. He put the atmosphere in a flask - the methane, the ammonia, the water, and so on – and went on, for day after day, and boiled and bubbled them up, put an electric discharge through them to simulate lightning and other violent forces. And visibly the mixture darkened. Why? Because on testing it was found that amino acids had been formed in it. That is a crucial step forward, since amino acids are the building blocks of life. From them the proteins are made, and proteins are the constituents of all living things.

We used to think, until a few years ago, that life had to begin in those sultry, electric conditions. And then it began to occur to a few scientists that there is another set of extreme conditions which may be as powerful: that is the presence of ice. It is a strange thought; but ice has two properties which make it very attractive in the formation of simple, basic molecules. First of all, the process of freezing concentrates the material, which at the beginning of time must have been very dilute in the oceans. And secondly, it may be that the crystalline structure of ice makes it possible for molecules to line up in a way which is certainly important at every stage of life.

At any rate, Leslie Orgel did a number of elegant experiments of which I will describe the simplest. He took some of the basic constituents which are sure to have been present in the atmosphere of the earth at any early time: hydrogen cyanide is one, ammonia is another. He made a dilute solution of them in water, and then froze the solution over a period of several days. As a result, the concentrated material is pushed into a sort of tiny iceberg to the top, and there the presence of a small amount of colour reveals that organic molecules have been formed. Some amino acids, no doubt; but, most important, Orgel found that he had formed one of the four fundamental constituents in the genetic alphabet which directs all life. He had made adenine, one of the four bases in DNA. It may indeed be that the alphabet of life in DNA was formed in these sorts of conditions, and not in tropical conditions.

From *The Ascent of Man*, J. Bronowski (BBC 1973)

1 Stanley Miller's experiment was based on a model of the Earth's early atmosphere.
   Describe this early atmosphere.
   What evidence is there to support this model?

2 Draw a labelled diagram of Miller's apparatus.
   List the substances he identified after a few days.
   Why were these important?

3 The results of Miller's experiments made other scientists think.
   They suggested a different model to explain how life began.
   What prediction did they make?
   Describe the new model.

4 These experiments must leave you with many unanswered questions.
   Write down some of your questions about how life began on planet Earth. Discuss them in a group.
   Write down any hypotheses that you think could be tested.

Reading skills—The nature of science 4

The work of Charles Darwin had a huge impact on the way people thought. In his own lifetime he was regarded as a great scientist and thinker by some people, but as a dangerous and downright foolish man by most.

Read the passage below about Darwin's theory of evolution.

In 1832 a young Englishman, Charles Darwin, twenty-four years old and naturalist on HMS *Beagle*, a brig sent by the Admiralty in London on a surveying voyage round the world, came to a forest outside Rio de Janeiro. In one day, in one small area, he collected sixty-eight different species of small beetle. That there should be such a variety of species of one kind of creature astounded him. He had not been searching specially for them so that, as he wrote in his journal, 'It is sufficient to disturb the composure of an entomologist's mind to look forward to the future dimensions of a complete catalogue'. The conventional view of his time was that all species were immutable and that each had been individually and separately created by God. Darwin was far from being an atheist – he had, after all, taken a degree in divinity in Cambridge – but he was deeply puzzled by this enormous multiplicity of forms.

The suspicion grew in Darwin's mind that species were not fixed for ever. Perhaps one could change into another. Maybe, thousands of years ago, birds and reptiles from continental South America had reached the Galapagos, ferried on the rafts of vegetation that float down the rivers and out to sea. Once there, they had changed, as generation succeeded generation, to suit new homes until they became their present species.

The differences between them and their mainland cousins were only small, but if such changes had taken place, was it not possible that over many millions of years, the cumulative effects on a dynasty of animals could be so great that they could bring about major transformations. Maybe fish had developed muscular fins and crawled on to land to become amphibians, maybe amphibians in their turn had developed water-tight skins and become reptiles; maybe, even, some ape-like creatures had stood upright and become the ancestors of man.

In truth the idea was not a wholly new one. Many others before Darwin had suggested that all life on earth was interrelated. Darwin's revolutionary insight was to perceive the mechanism that brought these changes about. By doing so he replaced a philosophical speculation with a detailed description of a process, supported by an abundance of evidence, that could be tested and verified; and the reality of evolution could no longer be denied.

Put briefly, his argument was this. All individuals of the same species are not identical. In one clutch of eggs from, for example, a giant tortoise, there will be some hatchlings which, because of their genetic constitution, will develop longer necks than others. In times of drought they will be able to reach leaves and so survive. Their brothers and sisters, with shorter necks, will starve and die. So those best fitted to their surroundings will be selected and be able to transmit their characteristics to their offspring. After a great number of generations, tortoises on the arid islands will have longer necks than those on the watered islands. And so one species will have given rise to another.

This concept did not become clear in Darwin's mind until long after he had left the Galapagos. For twenty-five years he painstakingly amassed evidence to support it. Not until 1859, when he was forty-eight years old, did he publish it and even then he was driven to do so only because another younger naturalist, Alfred Wallace, working in South-east Asia, had formulated the same idea. He called the book in which he set out his theory in detail, *The Origin of Species by Means of Natural Selection or the Preservation of Favoured Races in the Struggle for Life*.

Since that time, the theory of natural selection has been debated and tested, refined, qualified and elaborated. Later discoveries about genetics, molecular biology, population dynamics and behaviour have given it new dimensions. It remains the key to our understanding of the natural world and it enables us to recognise that life has a long and continuous history during which organisms, both plant and animal, have changed, generation by generation, as they colonised all parts of the world.

From *Life on Earth*, David Attenborough (BBC/Collins 1979)

continued ▶

► *continued*

Darwin's work shocked the many people who believed that all living things were created in their present form by God. To people who believed that the different human races were completely unrelated it was even more shocking to read that we are all descended from an apelike ancestor.

Today his theories are generally accepted and need not conflict with our religious beliefs. They give us a deeper understanding of our place in the living world, and encourage us to respect all living creatures.

1 Describe Darwin's theory of evolution.

2 What more recent evidence supports his theory?

3 Explain some of the ways in which the theory of evolution affected people's lives and thinking.

4 Do you believe Darwin's ideas?
What weaknesses are there in his theory?
What further evidence would you like to find?

Examination skills—Know your exam

You need to know your exam well. You should know what to expect. For example, in the national science examinations:

● How much time do you have?
● How many questions are there?
● Is there a choice of questions?
● What equipment (pens, ruler etc.) do you need?

One way of finding answers to such questions is to read and translate the instructions that are given to all examination candidates.

Read the sample instructions below.

SCIENCE

PAPER I

4th May—9.30 a.m. to 11.00 a.m.

Section A   1–8   24 marks
Section B   9–13   24 marks

All questions should be attempted. It should be noted, however, that some questions (4, 7, 10) contain a choice.

Necessary data will be found in the booklets of Mathematical Tables and Science Data.

Candidates are reminded that 2 marks are allocated for communication skills, assessed in section B of the paper.

Write legibly.

Use a calculator where appropriate.

Avoid the use of paper-correcting fluid.

---

1 How much time is allowed for this exam?

2 How many questions are in section A?

3 How many questions are in section B?

4 How much time would you give to each section?
Explain your answer.

5 Do you have a choice of question?

6 What other important advice is given?

Examination skills—Good practice

The list below suggests how you can cope with important exams. All these things have been shown to help people like you do their best in an exam.

Discuss the list with a friend and decide on a reason for each point. For example you should *revise every part of the course* because *this will give you great confidence.*

Weeks before exams
- Make a revision timetable.
- Revise every part of the course.
- Find out about the exam. (Number of questions, time allowed etc.)
- Buy extra pens, pencils etc.
- Eat proper meals and get enough sleep.
- Find out which room the exam is in.
- Find out when the exam starts.

The evening before an exam
- Do **not** plan to revise a lot of work.
- Read over revision summaries for a short while.
- Relax. Watch TV or read something you enjoy.
- Get your clothes and equipment ready for the next day.
- Go to bed early.
- Set an alarm clock to go off a little earlier than usual.

The day of the exam
- Get up early.
- Do **not** attempt to do any revision.
- Eat a full breakfast.
- Avoid conversations with friends about revision.

During the exam
- Set your watch to agree with the clock in the exam room.
- When you receive the paper, check that it is the right one.
- Write your name and any other details asked for on the answer sheets.
- Read all the questions.
- If you have a choice, tick the questions that you think you can do.
- Check the time regularly throughout the exam.
- Leave enough time to read over your answers.
- If you are likely to run out of time then write summary notes to answer the remaining questions.

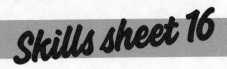

Examination skills—Knowing Attainment Target 2

The questions in your examination at the end of Key Stage 3 will test your knowledge and understanding of the National Curriculum in Science. You already know a great deal about this course.

The course is divided up into separate Attainment Targets at different Levels. Your teacher will discuss with you which Levels of Attainment you should concentrate on.

Attainment Target 2 is about *The Variety of Life*.

Level	What you need to know	Do you know it? (Tick for yes)	Read about it in Book	Page
4 a	Spot the important similarities/differences between groups of plants	____	1	112
	and groups of animals.	____	1	28
b	Know about the process of decay.	____	3	16
c	Know about how living things are preserved as fossils.	____	2	128
5 a	Know that different places with different climates	____	2	13
	and different weather	____	2	12
	offer habitats to different animals and plants.	____	2	13
b	Know the important details of the groups of animals	____	3	10
	and be able to use keys.	____	1	34, 35
c	Know about the good and bad points about the use of fertilisers and have a view about this.	____	2	24
d	Understand predator–prey relationships.	____	2	16
6 a	Know that the features of a living thing allow it to survive in its habitat.	____	3	12
b	Know that recycling keeps the correct balance of material in the environment	____	3	17
	and that humans can affect the recycling.	____	3	139
7 a	Know the role of microbes in the carbon and nitrogen cycles.	____	3	139
b	Know about biomass and pyramids of numbers.	____	3	14, 15

 Complete the checklist above by ticking **only** the things that you **know**. The book reference numbers will help you to look up the details of the more difficult things. You need to revise anything that you do not know **or** are unsure of. Your teacher will help you to plan this revision.

Examination skills—Knowing Attainment Target 3

The questions in your examination at the end of Key Stage 3 will test your knowledge and understanding of the National Curriculum in Science. You already know a great deal about this course.

The course is divided up into separate Attainment Targets at different Levels. Your teacher will discuss with you which Levels of Attainment you should concentrate on.

Attainment Target 3 is about *The Processes of Life.*

Level	What you need to know	Do you know it? *(Tick for yes)*	Read about it in Book	Page
4 a	Know the names of the main organs and systems in plants	____	2	132
	and animals.	____	2	44
b	Know that fitness and health depend on healthy teeth,	____	2	48, 49
	a balanced diet,	____	2	46, 47
	body defence systems	____	2	62
	and avoiding harmful substances.	____	2	56, 57
c	Understand how mammals reproduce.	____	1	139
d	Know the main stages of reproduction in flowering plants.	____	1	100
5 a	Know that living things are made up of different kinds of cells, each with a different job.	____	1	96
b	Understand what malnutrition is.	____	2	47
	Understand how diet, exercise, health and fitness affect the heart and circulation.	____	2	54, 146
c	Know that digestion makes food soluble so it can pass into the blood supply.	____	2	50
d	Understand how microbes and your way of life affect health.	____	2	62
e	Describe the functions of the main organ systems.	____	2	44
6 a	Know that in respiration energy is transferred from food for growth, repair and other life processes.	____	2	141
b	Know that photosynthesis uses light energy to change carbon dioxide and water into starch and sugars. Oxygen is a by-product.	____	2	132
c	Understand the conditions and experiences required for the full development of a very young child.	____	3	30, 31
d	Know about the physical and emotional changes that take place in a teenager, and about the need for responsible behaviour.	____	3	39
e	Understand why solvent and alcohol abuse and smoking are dangerous and how they affect the body.	____	2	56, 57
f	Understand how a human being is conceived.	____	1	139
7 a	Know that plants require nitrogen, phosphorus, potassium and magnesium for normal growth.	____	3	136
	Know that plants can change sugar made during photosynthesis into substances important for their survival such as starch and cellulose.	____	3	138
b	Understand the process of digestion.	____	3	32, 33
c	Describe a behaviour in terms of stimulus, receptor, co-ordinator and effector.	____	3	144

Complete the checklist above by ticking **only** the things that you **know**. The book reference numbers will help you to look up the details of the more difficult things. You need to revise anything that you do not know **or** are unsure of. Your teacher will help you to plan this revision.

Examination skills—Knowing Attainment Target 4

The questions in your examination at the end of Key Stage 3 will test your knowledge and understanding of the National Curriculum in Science. You already know a great deal about this course.

The course is divided up into separate Attainment Targets at different Levels. Your teacher will discuss with you which Levels of Attainment you should concentrate on.

Attainment Target 4 is about *Genetics and Evolution.*

Level	What you need to know	Do you know it? *(Tick for yes)*	Read about it in Book	Page
4 a	Know how to measure variation in living organisms.	_____	1	31, 68
5 a	Know that information is passed from parents to children in the form of genes.	_____	1	138
6 a	Know that there are two causes of variation—genetics and the environment.	_____	3	26–28
b	Know that some diseases such as a form of diabetes can be inherited.	_____	3	27
7 a	Understand how the sex of a baby is controlled by the sex chromosomes of each parent.	_____	3	141

Complete the checklist above by ticking **only** the things that you **know**. The book reference numbers will help you to look up the details of the more difficult things. You need to revise anything that you do not know **or** are unsure of. Your teacher will help you to plan this revision.

Examination skills—Knowing Attainment Target 5

The questions in your examination at the end of Key Stage 3 will test your knowledge and understanding of the National Curriculum in Science. You already know a great deal about this course.

The course is divided up into separate Attainment Targets at different Levels. Your teacher will discuss with you which Levels of Attainment you should concentrate on.

Attainment Target 5 is about *Human Influences on the Earth.*

Level	What you need to know	Do you know it? *(Tick for yes)*	Read about it in Book	Page
4 a	Know that some waste material can be recycled.	_____	2	172
5 a	Describe the sources, implications and possible ways of preventing pollution.	_____	2	18
b	Identify examples of biodegradable and non-biodegradable waste.	_____	2	172
c	Argue for and against particular planning proposals that might have an impact on the environment.	_____	2	22
6 a	Understand the processes which affect water purity.	_____	3	140
b	Understand the importance of good water management.	_____	3	19
c	Identify the good and bad effects of exploiting raw materials.	_____	3	22
7 a	Understand the balance of advantages and disadvantages of human activity on the environment.	_____	3	19
b	Know that human activity has had a recent impact on the environment.	_____	3	22
	Know that this is because of population size, economic factors and industrial requirements.	_____	3	21

Complete the checklist above by ticking **only** the things that you **know**. The book reference numbers will help you to look up the details of the more difficult things. You need to revise anything that you do not know **or** are unsure of. Your teacher will help you to plan this revision.

Examination skills—Knowing Attainment Target 6

The questions in your examination at the end of Key Stage 3 will test your knowledge and understanding of the National Curriculum in Science. You already know a great deal about this course.

The course is divided up into separate Attainment Targets at different Levels. Your teacher will discuss with you which Levels of Attainment you should concentrate on.

Attainment Target 6 is about *Types and Uses of Materials*.

Level	What you need to know	Do you know it? *(Tick for yes)*	Book	Page
4 a	Know how to compare materials': strength, hardness, flexibility	_____	2	116
	and solubility.	_____	1	43
b	Be able to work out which property of a material is useful for a particular job.	_____	2	76, 77
c	Know how to measure the weight	_____	1	66, 67, 126
	and volume of solids and liquids.	_____	1	66, 67, 126
d	Know that melting, freezing, evaporation and condensation are changes of state.	_____	1	40, 41
e	Classify materials as solid, liquid or gas	_____	2	95, 96
	and know the important properties of solid, liquid and gas.	_____	2	163
5 a	Know that gases have weight.	_____	3	85
b	Know that indicators can be used to classify solutions as acidic, alkaline or neutral.	_____	2	36, 37
c	Describe and explain the methods of separating and purifying mixtures.	_____	1	48
6 a	Understand the meaning of the properties: strength, hardness, elasticity	_____	3	124, 125
	solubility,	_____	1	42
	density,	_____	3	125
	melting point,	_____	2	26, 28
	electrical conductivity	_____	1	78, 133
	and thermal conductivity.	_____	3	72
b	Know the difference between mixtures and compounds.	_____	2	32
c	Know the difference between the properties of elements and compounds	_____	2	32
	and metal elements and non-metal elements.	_____	2	136
d	Make predictions using the reactivity series.	_____	3	96, 162
e	Know that the volume of a gas depends on the temperature and pressure.	_____	3	66, 86
7 a	Know the difference in properties between metals, ceramics, glass, plastics and fibres.	_____	3	122
b	Know that the use of a material depends on its properties.	_____	3	169
c	Know that elements in the same group of the periodic table have similar properties.	_____	3	97

Complete the checklist above by ticking **only** the things that you **know**. The book reference numbers will help you to look up the details of the more difficult things. You need to revise anything that you do not know **or** are unsure of. Your teacher will help you to plan this revision.

Examination skills—Knowing Attainment Target 7

The questions in your examination at the end of Key Stage 3 will test your knowledge and understanding of the National Curriculum in Science. You already know a great deal about this course.

The course is divided up into separate Attainment Targets at different Levels. Your teacher will discuss with you which Levels of Attainment you should concentrate on.

Attainment Target 7 is about *Making New Materials*.

Level	What you need to know	Do you know it? *(Tick for yes)*	Book	Page
4 a	Know that new substance(s) form(s) in a chemical reaction.	_____	2	38, 140
b	Know that raw materials are changed into useful products by chemical reactions.	_____	2	42, 117
5 a	Know that air, water, rocks, living things and fossil fuels are all sources of raw materials for use in manufacture.	_____	2	42, 120
b	Know how some manufacturing processes use microbes	_____	2	110
	and/or enzymes.	_____	2	111
c	Describe the processes of combustion	_____	2	134, 120
	and respiration.	_____	2	134, 112
6 a	Know the importance of making salts by neutralising acid and alkali.	_____	3	131
b	Explain electrolysis.	_____	3	98
c	Know that most reactions transfer energy to the surroundings.	_____	2	38
7 a	Know the effect on the rate of reaction of temperature, concentration and particle size	_____	3	92, 93
	and use of a catalyst.	_____	3	94
b	Know about oxidation/reduction in manufacturing.	_____	3	95, 161
c	Describe examples of the use of heat to break up compounds	_____	3	171
	and the use of electricity to break up compounds.	_____	3	134
d	Know the causes of rusting,	_____	2	34
	its cost	_____	3	128
	and ways of stopping it.	_____	3	129

 Complete the checklist above by ticking **only** the things that you **know**. The book reference numbers will help you to look up the details of the more difficult things. You need to revise anything that you do not know **or** are unsure of. Your teacher will help you to plan this revision.

Examination skills—Knowing Attainment Target 8

The questions in your examination at the end of Key Stage 3 will test your knowledge and understanding of the National Curriculum in Science. You already know a great deal about this course.

The course is divided up into separate Attainment Targets at different Levels. Your teacher will discuss with you which Levels of Attainment you should concentrate on.

Attainment Target 8 is about *Explaining How Materials Behave.*

Level	What you need to know	Do you know it? *(Tick for yes)*	Read about it in *Book*	*Page*
4 a	Know about particle theory	———	2	93
	and use it to explain solid, liquid and gas	———	2	95, 96
	and to explain dissolving.	———	2	90
5 a	Know that everything is made up of atoms.	———	2	159
6 a	Know about the spacing and movement of particles in solid, liquid and gas.	———	2	95, 96
b	Know how heat causes a change in state	———	2	96
	and expansion of an object.	———	2	97, 164
c	Write word equations for reactions.	———	2	33
7 a	By thinking about the energy of particles, explain how the state of matter can change	———	2	95
	and why liquids evaporate	———	2	96
	and how substances diffuse	———	2	161
	and why solutes dissolve.	———	2	90
b	Know about atoms and molecules	———	2	159
	and ions.	———	3	98, 163
c	Understand models and diagrams of atoms	———	3	102
	and molecules.	———	2	159
d	Know that radioactive substances give out radiation which can be harmful but also beneficial and that background radiation exists.	———	3	101

 Complete the checklist above by ticking **only** the things that you **know**. The book reference numbers will help you to look up the details of the more difficult things. You need to revise anything that you do not know **or** are unsure of. Your teacher will help you to plan this revision.

Examination skills—Knowing Attainment Target 9

The questions in your examination at the end of Key Stage 3 will test your knowledge and understanding of the National Curriculum in Science. You already know a great deal about this course.

The course is divided up into separate Attainment Targets at different Levels. Your teacher will discuss with you which Levels of Attainment you should concentrate on.

Attainment Target 9 is about the *Earth and Atmosphere*.

Level	What you need to know	Do you know it? *(Tick for yes)*	Book	Page
4 a	Know how to measure temperature, rainfall, wind speed and wind direction.	_____	2	10
	Understand that wind is moving air.	_____	2	130
b	Know that climate affects the success of farming. Understanding how very severe weather damages the environment.	_____	2	13
5 a	Know that the landscape is formed by earth movements, weathering, erosion, and deposition.	_____	2	23
	Know that the time each takes to cause an effect is different.	_____	3	65
b	Describe how an earthquake and a volcano can produce landforms.	_____	2	23
c	Describe and explain the stages of the water cycle.	_____	1	41
6 a	Describe the rock cycle and explain how igneous, sedimentary and metamorphic rocks are formed.	_____	3	60
b	Describe how the properties of rocks and minerals affect their use as raw materials.	_____	3	62, 63
c	Understand how different airstreams give different weather.	_____	2	130
7 a	Know how air pressure differences affect winds.	_____	3	151
b	Describe patterns in the distribution of surface features of the Earth and zones of active crust.	_____	3	152

Complete the checklist above by ticking **only** the things that you **know**. The book reference numbers will help you to look up the details of the more difficult things. You need to revise anything that you do not know **or** are unsure of. Your teacher will help you to plan this revision.

Examination skills—Knowing Attainment Target 10

The questions in your examination at the end of Key Stage 3 will test your knowledge and understanding of the National Curriculum in Science. You already know a great deal about this course.

The course is divided up into separate Attainment Targets at different Levels. Your teacher will discuss with you which Levels of Attainment you should concentrate on.

Attainment Target 10 is about *Forces*.

Level	What you need to know	Do you know it? *(Tick for yes)*	Book	Page
4 a	Understand that the size and direction of forces affects the movement of an object.	_____	2	64, 65
b	Understand that the faster an object is moving the greater the force and the longer the time it takes to stop. Understand the importance of this for road safety.	_____	2	151
c	Understand that gravity is a force that attracts objects to the centre of the Earth.	_____	2	66
d	Know that weight is a force and is measured in newtons.	_____	2	149
5 a	Understand balanced forces and recognise examples of this.	_____	2	68, 71
b	Describe an investigation into the strength of a structure.	_____	2	74
c	Describe how to measure forces and distance and time.	_____	2 / 3	149 / 77
d	Describe the effect of friction on a moving object.	_____	2	68, 69
6 a	Calculate speed from direct measurements of distance and time.	_____	3	156
b	Understand how force, area and pressure are related.	_____	3	79
c	Understand that the effect of a turning force depends on its distance from a pivot and its line of action.	_____	2	152, 153
7 a	Explain the effects of force, pressure, friction, mass, velocity and acceleration in familiar situations.	_____	3	76–81
b	Judge how good the design of a structure or object is by considering strength, choice of material and cost.	_____	3	78

Complete the checklist above by ticking **only** the things that you **know**. The book reference numbers will help you to look up the details of the more difficult things. You need to revise anything that you do not know **or** are unsure of. Your teacher will help you to plan this revision.

Examination skills—Knowing Attainment Target 11

The questions in your examination at the end of Key Stage 3 will test your knowledge and understanding of the National Curriculum in Science. You already know a great deal about this course.

The course is divided up into separate Attainment Targets at different Levels. Your teacher will discuss with you which Levels of Attainment you should concentrate on.

Attainment Target 11 is about *Electricity and Magnetism.*

Level	What you need to know	Do you know it? *(Tick for yes)*	Read about it in Book	Page
4 a	Construct simple electrical circuits.	_____	1	77–82
5 a	Describe simple electrical circuits in words and symbols.	_____	1	76
b	Know how to vary the flow of electricity in a simple circuit and the effects of this.	_____	1	80, 81
6 a	Understand the term voltage and be able to measure the potential difference across a conductor.	_____	1	133
b	Understand how electrostatic charge can be safely discharged.	_____	1	87
c	Recognise and explain electromagnetic effects in familiar devices.	_____	2	150
d	Calculate the cost of electricity consumption in the home from electricity meter readings.	_____	3	155
7 a	Understand the magnetic effect of an electric current and electromagnetic induction.	_____	3	107
b	Understand the chemical effects of an electric current.	_____	3	98, 134
c	Explain familiar electrostatic effects in terms of unbalanced charges.	_____	3	168

Complete the checklist above by ticking **only** the things that you **know**. The book reference numbers will help you to look up the details of the more difficult things. You need to revise anything that you do not know **or** are unsure of. Your teacher will help you to plan this revision.

Examination skills—Knowing Attainment Target 12

The questions in your examination at the end of Key Stage 3 will test your knowledge and understanding of the National Curriculum in Science. You already know a great deal about this course.

The course is divided up into separate Attainment Targets at different Levels. Your teacher will discuss with you which Levels of Attainment you should concentrate on.

Attainment Target 12 is about *The Scientific Aspects of Information Technology including Microelectronics.*

Level	What you need to know	Do you know it? *(Tick for yes)*	Read about it in Book	Page
4 a	Know about the range of uses of microelectronic devices in everyday life.	_____	2	104
b	Use a variety of instruments to measure changes in the environment.	_____	2	10, 107
5 a	Understand the use of switches and relays in simple circuits.	_____	2	105
b	Understand logic gates and their use in decision making and in simple control circuits.	_____	3	112, 113
6 a	Understand the difference between analogue and digital signals and instruments.	_____	2	166
b	Understand the uses of a range of devices for handling information and for communication.	_____	2	108
7 a	Describe and recognise the main features of an information-transmission system.	_____	2	108, 167
b	Describe and use bistable circuits.	_____	3	113
c	Describe and use IT devices to monitor and control experiments.	_____	3	167

 Complete the checklist above by ticking **only** the things that you **know**. The book reference numbers will help you to look up the details of the more difficult things. You need to revise anything that you do not know **or** are unsure of. Your teacher will help you to plan this revision.

Examination skills—Knowing Attainment Target 13

The questions in your examination at the end of Key Stage 3 will test your knowledge and understanding of the National Curriculum in Science. You already know a great deal about this course.

The course is divided up into separate Attainment Targets at different Levels. Your teacher will discuss with you which Levels of Attainment you should concentrate on.

Attainment Target 13 is about *Energy*.

Level	What you need to know	Do you know it? *(Tick for yes)*	Book	Page
4 a	Understand that energy is essential for all types of activity.	_____	1	54
b	Know that there is a range of fuels that provide energy.	_____	2	120
c	Understand that energy can be stored and transferred.	_____	1	56, 58
d	Describe how to use a thermometer to measure temperature.	_____	1	60, 66
e	Describe the changes that take place when familiar substances are heated and cooled.	_____	1	40, 41
5 a	Understand why fuel should be used efficiently and why it should be conserved.	_____ _____	3 2	154 121
b	Understand that the world's energy resources are limited.	_____	2	121
6 a	Describe and recognise energy sources. Understand energy transfers and the idea of conservation of energy.	_____ _____	1 3	56–57 70, 153
b	Understand that energy is conserved but is spread around and becomes less useful.	_____	3	153
c	Explain the features of machines like pulleys and levers that make them useful.	_____	3	80
d	Understand that the Sun is the major energy source for the Earth.	_____	3	71
7 a	Understand energy transfer by convection, conduction	_____	3	72, 73
	and radiation in solids, liquids and gases.	_____	3	74
	Understand methods of controlling these transfers in familiar situations such as insulating the home.	_____	3	154
b	Know that efficiency is a measure of how much energy is transferred in the intended way.	_____	3	158
c	Describe how to judge the methods used to reduce energy consumption in the home.	_____	3	154

Complete the checklist above by ticking **only** the things that you **know**. The book reference numbers will help you to look up the details of the more difficult things. You need to revise anything that you do not know **or** are unsure of. Your teacher will help you to plan this revision.

Examination skills—Knowing Attainment Target 14

The questions in your examination at the end of Key Stage 3 will test your knowledge and understanding of the National Curriculum in Science. You already know a great deal about this course.

The course is divided up into separate Attainment Targets at different Levels. Your teacher will discuss with you which Levels of Attainment you should concentrate on.

Attainment Target 14 is about *Sound and Music.*

Level	What you need to know	Do you know it? *(Tick for yes)*	Book	Page
4 a	Know that it takes time for sound to travel.	_____	3	49
5 a	Know that the pitch of sound depends on the frequency of vibration.	_____	3	46, 149
b	Know how loudness and amplitude are related.	_____	3	149
c	Explain why noise control is important.	_____	3	50
6 a	Know that sound waves transfer energy as they pass through a substance.	_____	3	48
b	Explain how a human ear works.	_____	3	36
	Know the cause of some common hearing defects.	_____	3	37
c	Describe the working of an audio device, like			
	loudspeaker,	_____	3	109
	microphone,	_____	3	165
	telephone.	_____	3	110
7 a	Know that sound can be changed into electrical signals	_____	3	165
	and transmitted over long distances	_____	3	118
	in various ways	_____	3	110, 111
	and changed into sound again.	_____	3	109

Complete the checklist above by ticking **only** the things that you **know**. The book reference numbers will help you to look up the details of the more difficult things. You need to revise anything that you do not know **or** are unsure of. Your teacher will help you to plan this revision.

Examination skills—Knowing Attainment Target 15

The questions in your examination at the end of Key Stage 3 will test your knowledge and understanding of the National Curriculum in Science. You already know a great deal about this course.

The course is divided up into separate Attainment Targets at different Levels. Your teacher will discuss with you which Levels of Attainment you should concentrate on.

Attainment Target 15 is called *Using Light and Electromagnetic Radiation.*

Level	What you need to know	Do you know it? *(Tick for yes)*	Book	Page
4 a	Know that we see objects because light is scattered off them and into our eyes.	____	3	44
b	Know that light travels in straight lines. Explain the size and shape of a shadow.	____	3	44
5 a	Explain how light is reflected.	____	3	42
6 a	Explain how prisms and lenses refract and disperse light.	____	3	45
b	Describe the structure of the human eye.	____	3	34
	Explain how the eye works.	____	3	35
c	Know the cause of some common eye defects and how to correct them.	____	3	146
7 a	Know the wave model of electromagnetic radiation.	____	3	147
b	Know the main types of electromagnetic radiation and some of their uses.	____	3	147
c	Describe the working of an optical device, like camera,	____	3	43
	optical fibre.	____	3	166

 Complete the checklist above by ticking **only** the things that you **know**. The book reference numbers will help you to look up the details of the more difficult things. You need to revise anything that you do not know **or** are unsure of. Your teacher will help you to plan this revision.

Examination skills—Knowing Attainment Target 16

The questions in your examination at the end of Key Stage 3 will test your knowledge and understanding of the National Curriculum in Science. You already know a great deal about this course.

The course is divided up into separate Attainment Targets at different Levels. Your teacher will discuss with you which Levels of Attainment you should concentrate on.

Attainment Target 16 is about *The Earth in Space.*

Level	What you need to know	Do you know it? (Tick for yes)	Book	Page
4 a	Know how the phases of the Moon change.	_____	2	92
b	Know the size and make-up of the solar system.	_____	3	56–57
c	Know that the Sun is a star.	_____	3	56
	Know what a star is.	_____	3	66
5 a	Use a simple model of the solar system to explain the existence of day and night,	_____	3	58
	the change in day length through the year,	_____	3	58
	the seasonal changes,	_____	3	58
	the length of the year,	_____	3	58
	the inclination of the Sun in the sky.	_____	3	58
b	Know the changes in the shape and surface shading of the Moon over a period of time.	_____	2	92
6 a	Describe using scientific words how the Earth, Moon, Sun and planets move relative to one another.	_____	3	57
b	Explain the meanings of the words *galaxy*	_____	2	91
	and *the universe*	_____	3	56
	and know that the positions of the galaxies change over a long time.	_____	3	57
7 a	Be able to argue with evidence that the Earth is not flat.	_____	3	150
b	Know that gravity acts towards the centre of every astronomical body.	_____	3	66

Complete the checklist above by ticking **only** the things that you **know**. The book reference numbers will help you to look up the details of the more difficult things. You need to revise anything that you do not know **or** are unsure of. Your teacher will help you to plan this revision.